COMMITTEE FOR ECONOMIC DEVELOPMENT
RESEARCH STUDY

AGRICULTURE IN AN UNSTABLE ECONOMY

COMMITTEE FOR ECONOMIC DEVELOPMENT
RESEARCH STUDY

Agriculture in an Unstable Economy

BY

THEODORE W. SCHULTZ

Professor of Agricultural Economics
University of Chicago

FIRST EDITION
FOURTH IMPRESSION

McGRAW-HILL BOOK COMPANY, INC.
NEW YORK AND LONDON
1945

FOREWORD

THE interdependence of the different parts of an industrial society is a commonplace of economic thinking. Like many basic and obvious truths, it tends to be ignored in the active economics of daily living. This study on the future of American agriculture confronts us sharply with the significance of this truth.

The farm sector represents one-fifth of our population. It is logical, therefore, that the C.E.D. research program, addressed as it is to the problems of attaining and maintaining high level production and employment, should include a study of agriculture. Nonetheless, it is noteworthy that the C.E.D., an organization of business men, should be giving serious attention to the problems of agriculture and particularly to the impact upon farming of policies and practices in the industrial sector of the economy.

Professor Schultz's study is an analysis of the essential conditions for a healthy, prosperous agriculture. As with so many of our special economic problems, the basic requirement for its rational solution lies in the solution to our key economic problem—high employment and progressively higher production. This book contains much of interest both for the lay reader and the professional economist.

The study is the sixth published in the C.E.D. research program. A list of the research projects, completed and in process, appears on page 276.

THEODORE O. YNTEMA
Research Director

PREFACE

EACH is prone to see agriculture according to his lot; only a few see it as a whole, and fewer still see it as an integral part of an interdependent economy. Not many outside agriculture see it as farmers do, since most people no longer have roots in the soil. This was once a nation of farmers—Washington, Jefferson, and nearly all of their countrymen. Today, our workshops are many, and urbanization has placed its mark upon us. Cities and towns and the occupations that go with them shape the horizon of most Americans.

Farming is fundamentally different from industrial work and business management. Neither business men nor industrial workers gain from their work the experience needed to understand agriculture, and therein lies a major political as well as social problem.

Farm production as a whole is highly stable. Agriculture does not permit rapid changes in output up or down. Farmers do not close down their farms when a depression strikes; they continue to furnish food and other farm products to the nation. They are therefore not "unemployed"; but they do not escape the burden of a depression—as is apparent from the income instability and economic uncertainty that were major factors in "the farm problem" in the twenty years between the wars.

For the housewife too the economic and social conditions of agriculture are only remotely connected to the daily experiences of shopping for food or other products that originate on the farm.

Similarly, farm people—including those who represent or serve them—do not gain from their work within agriculture the knowledge or insight required to understand to what extent they have, for better or for worse, become dependent upon the exchange system and thus upon the performance of the industrial-urban sectors of the economy. Farm leaders, county agents, and workers in the Land-Grant Colleges alike have been so engrossed by the problems *within* agriculture, by the difficulties of a particular crop or a particular farm, that few of them have had time or have been disposed to look at the problems that have their origin in the interrelationships *between* agriculture and the rest of the economy.

This study is devoted to these *between* problems, to the functions of agriculture in the political economy and to the effects of nonfarm activities upon agriculture. Its main purpose is to lay the foundations for a national policy with regard to agriculture.

There are two bridges over which most of the economic traffic between farm and nonfarm people passes. One of these, if it had the capacity to clear the load it is expected to carry, should keep in comparative balance for the two sectors of the economy the utilization of resources and, consequently, their earnings. The other bridge has carried the traffic associated with business fluctuation and its attendant instability. Most of the farm problem during the interwar years arose from the way that traffic was handled on the nonfarm side of the two bridges. In other words, the basic causes for the farm problem—the low earnings of most farm people and the great instability of income from farming—are not *within* agriculture but elsewhere in our economy. In this study these causes and their consequences are examined in the hope that by so doing we may learn how to attain a better balance and greater stability.

The full picture of what needs to be done in our peacetime economy cannot be grasped without this knowledge of the relationship of agriculture to the rest of the economy. But it is not my intention to imply that the reader of this book will know all that needs to be known about American agriculture. The future of agriculture obviously takes in more than economic and political policy. There are other important unsolved difficulties affecting the farmer and the nation. Solving some of these will probably require the devising of new mechanisms, some political, some economic, and some social. Ultimate solutions may have to wait on further scientific knowledge. Depletion and erosion of the soil is one such problem and of critical importance. Many of the difficulties regarding plants and animals arise as scientists try to move forward toward lower production costs and higher returns for farmers. Advances in farm technology do not come easily; costs in time and human effort are large, but, once achieved, the gains are like the strides of a Bunyan.

Only the economic effects of these strides are examined here. However, it is plain that despite the obstacles this technical progress will go forward and that it is urgent that we improve our social and economic machinery if we are to profit by agricultural advances.

Within agriculture there are problems related to production, prices and income about which farmers by their own effort can do a good deal. The work of the U. S. Department of Agriculture and of the Land-Grant Colleges, when it is concerned about economy, focuses largely upon the farmer's productive efficiency. Is it cheaper to use tractors or horses? Would longer-staple cotton be more profitable? Should oats give way to soybeans? Should cattle be fed to a higher finish, hogs to a heavier weight, dairy cows for larger daily output? The ratio of corn prices to hog prices, the peanut-hog ratio, and all other feeding ratios will affect the answers, as will relative price relationships between crops. Improved farm-tenure terms are needed, as well as better use of credit (and of wartime savings) in investments in soil, buildings, machinery, and durable consumer goods; these would improve the efficiency of the farmer and the farm.

These and other measures are within the province of farmers and can be effected by them singly or in concert. They are the *within agriculture* type of problem not dealt with in this study. Important headway has been made in these areas, but too often the pros and cons on these issues are formulated in isolation, too much on the assumption that the solution can be found without reference to what happens elsewhere in the economy. The excess supply of labor in agriculture in peacetime and the instability of the demand for farm products, factors which have their origin primarily in the nonfarming fields, directly and vitally affect many of these *within agriculture* matters.

This study will not tell the reader precisely how to go from where we are to where we may want to go during the next two or three transition years. It does reveal the effects upon farming of the mobilization for war; these necessarily become part of the agricultural setting from now on out. One of the more important policy decisions ahead stems from our wartime program of support prices. To induce high production the government committed itself to support most farm prices at 90 per cent of parity for at least two years after the war. The road we take in making good this commitment will have a direct bearing upon agricultural policy. But even so, the transition is merely an event, an incident, as the war has been, in the more powerful secular drift affecting agriculture and its role in our economy. The reader, accordingly, will not find here a timetable showing the sequence of events likely to follow victory. The twist given agricultural production by the war, the effect upon the financial position of farm people and the efficiency of agriculture, are indicated, and these must be taken into account as we prepare for the longer postwar, with the probable return of the pattern of wide fluctuations in farm-product demand and in earnings from farming.

The habit of identifying agriculture with food leads to much confusion in developing agricultural policies. We now have the knowledge regarding nutrition and food-producing resources to make it possible for us to close the nutritional gap. But policy designed to serve the nutritional requirements of a people is of necessity different from measures to bring balance and stability to agriculture. Programs to correct inadequate diets (whether caused by lack of income or lack of knowledge) cannot be expected to cope with the problems that have come to farm people from the erratic production performance of the industrial-urban community. Some principles that should guide policy-making (in an economic context) as we strive for better nutrition are developed in this book. Since adequate diets are important in the social efficiency of a people, an analysis of the necessary elements of a food policy should not, however, be made subservient to the purposes appropriate for a national policy for agriculture. Food policy must stand on its own merit.

I also want to make clear that I have not examined farm relief except in an incidental way. This country has not yet, for the most part, developed specific measures for agricultural emergencies arising from such natural causes as droughts, floods, hail and storms, or from sudden market gluts caused by trade disturbances or curtailed demand. Nor have policies and principles been adequately developed in another sphere of vital importance to farm people, that of welfare—better health through improved medical services, proper housing, better education, more leisure time, and the like. The extension of social-security benefits—old-age and survivor insurance, unemployment compensation for hired labor in agriculture, and health insurance—belongs in this category. I have not addressed myself to this important sphere except as higher per capita earnings by farm people and more stable incomes from farming would bring with them more security and welfare. Welfare considerations, however, are larger and include more than what I have covered.

I am indebted to my associates: I have benefited from the comments and suggestions of Chester C. Davis and W. I. Myers who went over the entire manuscript. It was David F. Cavers' desire for more elaboration of my proposal for *compensatory payments* that caused me to develop it considerably further than I had done in my paper before the Canadian Political Science and Economics Association. Theodore O. Yntema was quick to see the significance of the broader formulation of agriculture's problem as it emerged in my earlier draft. He also has pointed up several technical issues in connection with Chap. III. D. Gale Johnson, working along beside me on his study on *forward pricing*, frequently compared notes with me. To J. M. Letiche I am indebted for much spade work—the marshaling of available data, the testing of working models, and the careful checking of all figures appearing in the final draft. Sylvia Stone's unique capacity for comprehending the underlying analysis and, with it in hand, painstakingly "tooling" the exposition has added much to the nontechnical clarity of this book. I am also indebted to others—farm leaders, economists with farm organizations, and to my colleagues—for raising points, at times expressing doubts, or asking for further elaboration and thus giving me clues to shortcomings which I otherwise would have missed. Mine is the satisfaction of having gained from their willingness to help and the privilege of standing by what I have put down.

THEODORE W. SCHULTZ.

UNIVERSITY OF CHICAGO,
August, 1945.

CONTENTS

Contents

Contents

Contents

Contents

PART I

Prospective Conditions Affecting Agriculture

I. AGRICULTURE IN WAR AND PEACE

TWICE in the course of three decades American agriculture has been called upon to enlarge its production to fill the demands created by war. Twice American agriculture has responded, expanding its output of food about one-sixth during World War I and double that during this war.[1] At both times the increases added to an agricultural supply that already exceeded peacetime demand and that, following World War I, left a heritage of farm problems that remained unsolved in the twenty-year interlude. During both wars agriculture prospered while war demands lasted. It is well to ask whether the parallelism between the two wars will carry through into another postwar collapse for agriculture.

UNCERTAINTY AHEAD

American farmers are deeply uneasy about their future. Wartime prosperity and the government's assurance of price supports after the war do not dispel fears that peace may bring chronic surpluses of agricultural commodities, depressed price levels, very low farm incomes, and more subsistence farming. Such misgivings are natural since these are the difficulties that plagued farmers after 1919, and the memory of them is still vivid. Will history repeat itself?

Farm people are not alone in their concern about what lies ahead for agriculture. Other groups in society are aware,

---

[1] This is the increase when measured against the 1910–1914 average for World War I and 1935–1939 average for World War II. If 1914 is taken as the base, then food production in 1918 had expanded 11 per cent; and, with 1939 as the base, the 1944 food output had risen 30 per cent.

perhaps more vaguely, that a serious farm problem may again arise when the war is over. Consumers have become keenly conscious of the importance of food to their welfare, partly because of the scarcities caused by the war and partly because of the growing interest in better diet and nutrition. As food again becomes plentiful and as labor-saving technology moves forward in farming, industrial workers might well ask whether they will have to face additional competition for jobs from workers migrating out of agriculture. Several million persons have left the farms during the war, and in the decades to come more millions will seek employment opportunities in non-agricultural occupations. Businessmen are likewise concerned, for an agricultural depression affects adversely a large sector of the American market.

Each of these interests in agriculture is, however, partial. The farm problem will be larger and more complex than the interest of any particular group. It is not only national but international in its compass.

During the prewar years there were many maladjustments within agriculture in the utilization of resources, in the structure of farm prices, and certainly in the level of income of many farm families. All of these difficulties deserve careful study. Yet an examination of each of the numerous particular dislocations, one after another, is not likely to reveal the more fundamental causes that underlie the farm problem. Other parts of the economy must be scrutinized, because most of the economic difficulties likely to beset farmers in the postwar years will not have their origin within agriculture.

A great part of the farm problem is likely to arise through business fluctuations and the unbalanced expansion of the economy. Farm prices and farm incomes are affected by the decisions and policies of workers and households, of business firms, and of government agencies. All of these, however, are matters about which the individual farmer can do little or nothing as he works within the confines of his farm, as he sells his crops and livestock, as he buys machinery, equipment and other producer goods, and commodities and services for family living. It is true that many farmers have joined together in general farm organizations or in commodity groups to provide a channel for dealing with these larger questions affecting them. In the main, farm organizations have given their attention to particular programs that help agriculture. Most of these programs during the thirties were established under the stress of emergencies, with farm relief their main purpose. Only scant attention has been directed to policies and programs necessary to provide the conditions for economic progress. This shortcoming has characterized the special-interest viewpoints not only of agriculture but also of business and labor groups.

A NATIONAL AGRICULTURAL POLICY IS NEEDED

There can be agricultural policies that serve the national interest, that contribute to the development and stability of the economy as a whole, and that place the welfare of farm people on the same footing as the welfare of other groups. The many particular problems *within* agriculture that have received and are receiving attention are not unimportant. Each has probably deserved all the thought and effort that have been given to it. But it is not sufficient to correct the maladjustments *within* agriculture; in fact, it is questionable whether such problems will remain "solved" while significant maladjustments exist *between* agriculture and other parts of the economy.

The emphasis that has been placed upon problems of the *within-agriculture type* is not unduly surprising. First, there is a natural tendency for any group, business and labor and agriculture alike, when it assesses its own situation to consider its problems essentially in isolation. The problems loom large close at hand; their immediacy makes demands for correction. A not inconsiderable second factor is the division of labor that has arisen in our college and university research and thinking about agriculture, and in the Federal

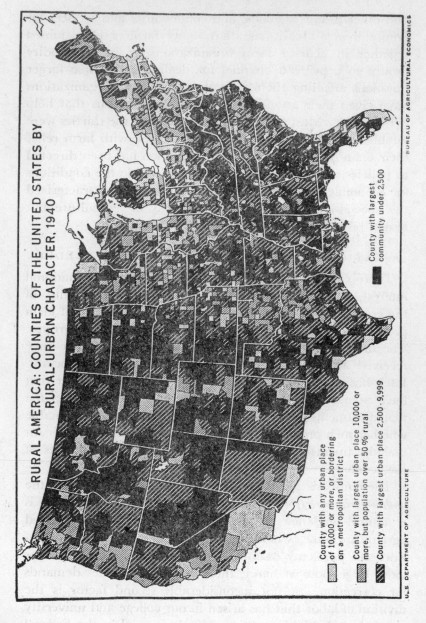

RURAL AMERICA: COUNTIES OF THE UNITED STATES BY
RURAL-URBAN CHARACTER, 1940

County with any urban place
of 10,000 or more, or bordering
on a metropolitan district

County with largest urban place 10,000 or
more, but population over 50% rural

County with largest urban place 2,500 - 9,999

County with largest
community under 2,500

BUREAU OF AGRICULTURAL ECONOMICS

U. S. DEPARTMENT OF AGRICULTURE

government which further "compartmentalizes" ideas, policies, and programs. The mandates that established the U.S. Department of Agriculture and the authority that is vested in its various agencies carefully restrict the activities of the department to matters within agriculture.[1] Finally, the emergencies that came as a consequence of the great depression necessarily centered public attention on relief and rescue programs which were in the main highly particularistic in nature.

In this study we shall attend primarily to the *between*, and only secondarily to the *within*, problems affecting agriculture. The *overcrowded and underproductive employment* in agriculture is a problem that has its origin largely in our developing economy. It is inherent in the forces shaping the supply and demand for farm products. The *instability of the income from farming* stems chiefly from business fluctuations. To understand this one must understand our business economy. To remedy it one must turn to fiscal-monetary policy and related measures. The *pricing of farm products* to facilitate the best use of agricultural resources and to channel farm products to consumers—not too largely into storage bins—has become both a national and an international problem.

THE POSTWAR AGRICULTURAL OUTLOOK

To orient our explorations we shall need at least a preliminary idea as to the agricultural situation likely to confront this country after the war. The basis for the following projections will be given in some detail in subsequent chapters.

How has the mobilization for World War II affected American agriculture? Production has been expanded:

---

[1] It is to the credit of the professional personnel within the U.S. Department of Agriculture, especially those in the social sciences, that they are seeking to understand and analyze agriculture, not in isolation, but as a part of the political economy. The Association of Land-Grant Colleges and Universities issued a report, *Postwar Agricultural Policy*, October, 1944, which definitely takes the larger view. See a review of this report by Theodore W. Schultz in the *Journal of Land and Public Utility Economics*, May, 1945.

food by about one-third, and all of agricultural production by one-fourth.[1]   About 30 million acres have been added to our harvested land.   Production of livestock has been increased more than crops.   The granaries that were over-flowing with food and feed when the war started have been emptied.   (Cotton is the exception, for the excessive stocks of cotton have not been liquidated.)   A land boom has been induced by high farm product prices and large farm incomes. The farm population has dropped about 5 million as a conse-quence of the mobilization for war.   The improvement in the capital position of farm people has been an important development; for the first time in three decades, farm people rate A1 in their capital position, in terms of the intangible assets they own and in the equity they have in their property.

In the outlook for the years immediately following the war, we find important similarities and also differences between the changes that are in prospect and those that followed World War I.   The outlook definitely has a pessimistic undertone.

Barring a pronounced inflation, the postwar agricultural outlook adds up to this: Within one or at the most two years after the war, farm prices are likely to recede from the price ceilings that have held them in check, and many of them are likely to break through the price floors set by the government. Although the drop will not be so precipitous or so great as that following World War I, it is likely to be sufficient to cause a widespread, serious depression in agriculture.   The gist of this outlook is something as follows:

1. Agriculture will stay in full production after the war, regardless of the performance of business or the level of for-eign trade.   While agriculture can be induced to expand its production, as it has during World War I and World War II, it is essentially a one-way street.   We have learned that it is

[1] This expansion occurred from 1939 to 1944.   The statistics that follow in this chapter are for the most part summary figures drawn from subsequent chapters. Accordingly, the various sources will be identified later in this study.

not only costly and difficult but virtually impossible to bring about a contraction in total agricultural output during the course of a few years. The aggregate output of farm products in the United States is not likely to be reduced appreciably after this war except as unfavorable weather happens to reduce yields. The import of this is obvious: We shall have a larger volume of farm products than we had before the war —for agricultural output as a whole, nearly one-fourth more than we had in 1939.[1]

2. In the face of this large supply of farm products, the demand for them is likely to drop sharply as soon as war rehabilitation and relief are over and our granaries have been restocked. Even if we attain and maintain full employment at home and relatively free and open trade with other countries, the demand for American farm products will fall far below the levels of 1944. Considerable contraction is certain to come as a consequence of our Allies' returning to their more normal sources of supply.

3. Besides the general additional supply, chronic agricultural surpluses in special commodities are likely to put in their appearance within two to five years after the war—in fats and oils, wheat, cotton, rice, coffee, and sugar—unless strong corrective measures are taken to bring supply and demand into balance. All these commodities enter world markets. Sugar and fats and oils will become much scarcer before they become abundant once more. Cotton, however, has stayed in a surplus position throughout the war. Large stocks of wheat are already putting in their appearance.

[1] During the past three years we have fed to livestock and chickens a billion bushels of wheat and most of the corn accumulated prior to the war. Imports from Canada have been large. Large amounts of fertilizer have also been used, and the weather has been favorable. Each of these factors has contributed somewhat to the expansion in agricultural production. As granaries are refilled and less favorable weather occurs, output of livestock products will be reduced accordingly. Meanwhile, however, farmers are continuing to improve their practices and techniques, and as new farm machinery and equipment become available they will do much "retooling" and thus further increase their productivity.

4. Despite the commitments authorized by Congress to support the market prices of farm products for at least two years after the war, farm prices may drop sharply in dollars and cents[1] and are very likely to decline markedly relative to other prices as we make the transition to a peacetime economy. Under existing legislation, the government is not prepared to make its program of support prices effective for the period covered by the commitment. There are, therefore, no convincing reasons for believing that farm prices will settle or be maintained at a level higher, relative to other prices, than they were before the war. Even at that level the enlarged agricultural production may not clear the markets.

5. The terms of exchange available to farm people (the ratio of prices received to prices paid by farmers) are likely to drop by one-fourth to one-third from the levels of 1944. Translated into parity, this means a drop from a parity of about 115 to a parity somewhere between 80 and 90.

6. The proportion of the working population engaged in farming gives promise of being smaller after the war than it was in 1939. It has been reduced from 20 to 15 per cent as a consequence of the mobilization for war. This reduction could be a real gain for agriculture; if the people who have left do not return, the relative earnings per worker engaged in farming would be much better than under the prewar distribution of the nation's labor force. Some, and perhaps much, of the gain that has been made in lessening the excess supply of labor in agriculture is likely to be lost, since many persons will probably return to agriculture after the war.

CONDITIONS NECESSARY FOR ECONOMIC PROGRESS IN AGRICULTURE

There is a high probability, therefore, that the postwar period will find American agriculture substantially over-

[1] The decline in absolute terms will depend largely upon the kind and the extent of the inflation that the postwar brings to parts of industry.

extended—a condition that will be one of the many heritages of the war, but that was in the making in any event. This poses a general question: How may agriculture attain a more balanced relationship to other parts of the economy? The maladjustments and dislocations resulting from the war make this question urgent. But the imbalance of agriculture is a problem of long standing. During most of the years between the two wars agriculture (except for a few favorable régions) was chronically depressed. In a developing industrial economy there are basic forces at work reshaping the supply and demand for farm products, pushing supply ahead of demand and thus setting the stage for low earnings for most people engaged in agriculture. The war has accelerated this process.

It is essential, therefore, that we take the more comprehensive view and examine the causes for the imbalance, whether their origin is in the mobilization for war or in modern industrialization.[1] What basic conditions are necessary for the economic progress of agriculture? Two primary problems have arisen in modern agriculture, namely, the overcrowded and underproductive employment in agriculture and the instability of farm income. These two problems are the focal issues of this study. They are basic to an understanding of the effects that a modern, urban-industrial society has upon agriculture. The excess labor in agriculture appears to be closely associated with long-run industrial development; the instability of farm income appears to have its origin primarily in the fluctuations of modern business.

[1] We shall use the terms "industrialization," "industrial," and "industry," unless otherwise indicated in the text, as including both secondary and tertiary industries, that is, all nonagricultural productive activities, all goods and services other than farm products. See the first paragraph of Chap. V for a brief explanation of the concepts "secondary and tertiary" industries.

II. THE AGRICULTURAL SETTING

AGRICULTURE and industry are of different temperaments; one is slow and sluggish in its movements and the other sensitive and erratic. The quick rises and falls in industrial output are well known, but a factor in our economy that is little recognized is that the *production effort* in farming and the resulting output of food, feed, and fiber seldom change substantially from one year to another (when we take agricultural production as a whole). Even during the unprecedented droughts of 1934 and 1936 agricultural production did not fall off 10 per cent.[1] Nor do bumper crops bring large bulges in total output. In considering the future of American agriculture, awareness of this behavior is essential.[2]

Cotton growers have continued to grow cotton during the war and they will be at it after the war, producing in the

[1] In this context we gauge production partly by the amount produced (crops) and partly by the amount marketed (livestock) and not by strictly current agricultural production. We do this because in the case of livestock the amount marketed is taken as production. In a drought year as severe as 1934 cattle inventories especially are reduced, and this keeps the supply going to market higher than it otherwise would be. Here we have, however, one of the many "self-compensating" features inherent in the aggregate supply of farm products available for consumers. The important fact, however, is that the *production effort* in farming is highly constant from one year to another regardless of business conditions.

[2] The figures below show the year-to-year fluctuations in agricultural production.

VOLUME OF AGRICULTURAL PRODUCTION OF THE UNITED STATES, 1920–1944
(1935–1939 = 100)

Year	1920	1921	1922	1923	1924	1925	1926	1927	1928	1929	1930	1931	1932
Index	92	83	91	94	98	97	100	98	102	99	98	102	96

Year	1933	1934	1935	1936	1937	1938	1939	1940	1941	1942	1943	1944	
Index	96	93	91	94	106	103	106	110	113	124	129	133	

SOURCE: *Farm Income Situation*, U.S. Department of Agriculture, Bureau of Agricultural Economics, December, 1944.

main too much low-grade, short-staple cotton. Wheat farmers have stayed at wheat and Midwest farmers have been loyal to corn and livestock. Responding to the war market, they have expanded acreages and livestock somewhat, drawing on soil reserves and accumulated feed supply. A few farmers, of course, alter their production considerably from one year to another, but most of them, of necessity, go on milking about the same number of cows and feeding about the same number of cattle, hogs, and sheep—because they produce and have available about the same amount of feed one year after another. Approximately the same number of acres on each farm are suitable each year for growing particular crops.

Although the agricultural production of the United States may be roughly 25 per cent larger when peace comes than it was before the war, most farmers will be following about the same crop rotations and will have essentially the same live-stock combination that they had at the close of the thirties.[1] When the postwar demand for farm products shrinks, farmers as a whole are not likely to reduce their production effort. They will not abandon either farms or acreages; instead, they will stay in full production.[2]

AGRICULTURE AND INDUSTRY DO NOT
STAY IN STEP

Even with the bumper crops resulting from the unusually favorable weather and with the large inventory of feed that

---

[1] Exceptions may be noted. The production of hemp is essentially a new war industry. The added peanut acreage has introduced new rotations and in some areas a considerable departure from prewar farming. The expansion of soybeans in the corn belt also represents a pronounced change in crops on many farms. There are other examples, but these more radical departures from former production patterns are the exceptions.

[2] Increasingly, we find that the supply of agricultural commodities as a whole has in the short run a "one-way" flexibility: higher prices induce an expansion; lower prices, however, do not bring about a comparable contraction. But changes in relative prices within agriculture usually induce shifts in the use of resources quickly and effectively when agricultural prices as a whole are stable.

was on hand when the war started and could be converted quickly into animal products, it is remarkable that an increase of 33 per cent over the 1935–1939 level was attained in agriculture by 1944.[1] Few persons realize that it took five years to effect that increase. In the same period industrial production rose 135 per cent, as seen in the following figures:

COMPARISON OF WAR-INDUCED EXPANSION IN AGRICULTURE AND INDUSTRY[1]
(1935–1939 average production = 100)

	1944 Production Index
Agricultural production:	
All crops	125
All livestock and livestock products	139
Total	133
Industrial production:	
Durable manufacturing	353
Nondurable manufacturing	171
Mineral	140
Total	235

[1] From *Farm Income Situation*, U.S. Department of Agriculture, Bureau of Agricultural Economics, December, 1944, and *Federal Reserve Bulletin* (February, 1945).

Many of the more serious economic difficulties that confront agriculture are born out of this difference in the pace of agriculture and industry. The plowman's tread does not allow running for a stretch and then walking, or even stopping altogether. Agriculture has a steady gait, while other producers in the economy sometimes run and at other times simply stand still. Farmers, in the main, stay in full production regardless of the effects of business fluctuations upon the demand for farm products and in spite of governmental efforts to reduce output.[2] This assures consumers of a large and steady supply of food and other farm products, but it means great instability in farm prices and farm income.

[1] The expansion is equal to one-fourth when it is based on 1939. The one-fourth is the better measure of the increase that has occurred, but since many of our statistics are based on 1935–1939, it is necessary to use this latter base in some comparisons.

[2] Some crops and livestock were reduced but others were increased during the adjustment programs of the thirties.

The Agricultural Setting

Differences in Attitudes

Because farmers seldom alter considerably the rate at which they produce and because industry often changes its rate of output, it is not surprising that farmers have attitudes different from businessmen about the main obstacles facing them as producers.

Farmers are not haunted, as are men in industry, by the possibility of idle plant and idle men. Not that farm income is unaffected by business conditions—far from it—but farmers are not unemployed during a depression. They stay at their jobs; in fact, they often work harder as prices decline. Their principal economic devil is the fluctuation of farm prices. They fear, and with justification, that farm prices will drop sharply again after the war.[1]

In seeking a postwar agricultural policy, we need, therefore, to ask: "Should agriculture modify its gait?" If so, should it be the aim of national policy to help agriculture reduce its output quickly when curtailed industrial output occasions a drop in the demand for farm products? And, conversely, increase its output when industry expands? Or would it be better to help industry change its gait? Put this way, the choice should not be difficult. It is obvious that the steady performance of agriculture is a major national asset, while the erratic rate of production in industry is a serious liability.

WAR-INDUCED CHANGES IN AGRICULTURE

How a war affects the agricultural economy is best seen through the relative changes that occur in production, prices, and income.

---

[1] This drop in farm prices is not likely to be restricted to a few farm products whose output was increased as a consequence of the war. Farmers are constantly vulnerable to erratic changes in farm prices, sometimes because of variations in farm production, more often because of unstable industrial activity. War magnifies the fluctuations of farm prices, as the experience of World War I and its aftermath demonstrated. When farm products become dear, they usually fetch too much. Thus, when farm prices go high, they go too high, and induce land speculation and an overextension of credit resulting in many

Effects of War Demands

The short-run consequences of a marked increase in the demand for farm products are characteristically as follows: (*a*) relatively small change in farm output, (*b*) a fairly marked change in farm prices, and (*c*) a pronounced change in farm income—as the following figures for World Wars I and II indicate:

	1919 Increase during World War I (1910–1914 = 100)	1944 Increase during World War II (1935–1939 = 100)
Agricultural production.........	110	133
Farm prices[1]...................	215	182
Net farm income[2].............	264	282

SOURCE: *Agricultural Outlook Charts*, U.S. Department of Agriculture, Bureau of Agricultural Economics, November, 1944.

[1] Prices received by farmers.

[2] Net farm income per person engaged in agriculture.

When the abnormal demand for the produce of American farms contracts, as it did following World War I, production is not curtailed appreciably, farm prices drop sharply, and net income plunges most of all.

The main reasons for this behavior of farm output, prices, and income are fairly obvious:

In Production. There usually is no appreciable amount of slack within agriculture; resources are, as a rule, fairly fully employed, and it is difficult technically to bring additional resources into use in less than two or three years. Accordingly, when an enlarged demand lifts farm prices, the output response is both slow and small.

In Prices. Farm prices, in the main, are determined in what are still essentially competitive markets which have a

---

farmers assuming high fixed costs; when they drop, they usually go too low. Fluctuating farm prices breed uncertainty and disorder within agriculture.

strong speculative undertone. These markets quickly reflect the drift in expectations—whether it is bullish or bearish. In addition, when the demand increases, farm prices are pushed up proportionately more than retail prices, because the "cost" margins between farmers and consumers are relatively fixed. As demand contracts, the reverse in farm prices is equally steep.

In Income. Net farm income is, of course, a compound of prices and output minus expenses, and since variable expenses are usually small on most farms, net farm incomes fluctuate greatly.

AGRICULTURAL PRODUCTION, PRICES, AND INCOME, UNITED STATES, 1910-44

INDEX NUMBERS (1910-14=100)

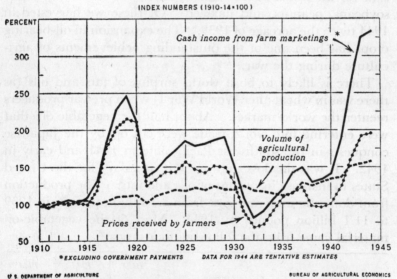

* EXCLUDING GOVERNMENT PAYMENTS   DATA FOR 1944 ARE TENTATIVE ESTIMATES

U S DEPARTMENT OF AGRICULTURE   BUREAU OF AGRICULTURAL ECONOMICS

Wartime Shifts in Production: Crops

The additional production of food during World War II has been primarily in livestock rather than in crops, in sharp contrast to World War I, when in the "battle for wheat" the emphasis was much more on crops. We were slow in increasing the acreages of feed and food crops, partly because we had large reserves of both corn and wheat during the early part of the war. Not until there had been heavy feeding of wheat and marked inroads on feed stores, as livestock numbers expanded, were acreages of major feed and food crops lifted.

Corn, wheat, and cotton are the big three among American crops. Corn for harvest rose from 86 million acres in 1941 to 94 million in 1943, and to 97 million in 1944; wheat actually dropped from somewhat over 53 million acres in 1939 to 49 million in 1942, and then jumped to 59 million in 1944; cotton, however, dropped from about 24 million acres in 1939 to about 20 million in 1944.[1]

The major wartime changes in output have occurred in some of the minor crops, notably in the oil-bearing group—soybeans, peanuts, and flaxseed. Of these we harvested in 1944 twice the acreage of 1939. The expansion in oil-bearing crops has been one of the outstanding achievements of agriculture during the war.

There is likely to be a world surplus of fats and oils (as there was in wheat after World War I) when prewar producers reenter the world market. About half the vegetable oils that were entering into world trade were cut off by the Japanese conquests in the southwest Pacific late in 1941 and early in 1942. It was this loss that made it necessary for the United States to increase its output of oils and fats. The production from domestic materials rose from 8.2 billion pounds in 1939 to 11.1 billion pounds by 1944. Most of the vegetable-oil material came from the following four crops:[2]

	1939	1943	1944
Soybeans (million bushels)	90	193	193
Flaxseed (million bushels)	20	52	24
Cottonseed (million tons)	4.9	4.7	4.9
Peanuts (billion pounds)	1.2	2.2	2.2

[1] *Crops and Markets*, U.S. Department of Agriculture, Washington, D.C., January, 1945.

[2] *Ibid.*, p. 2.

The Agricultural Setting

WARTIME INCREASES IN UNITED STATES CROP ACREAGE
1945 GOALS AND 1944 ACTUAL AS PERCENTAGE OF 1935-39 AVERAGE

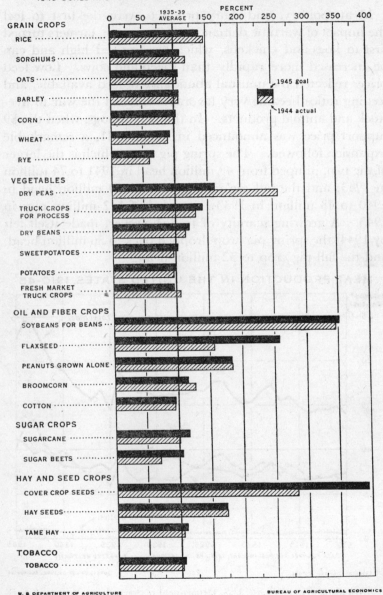

U. S. DEPARTMENT OF AGRICULTURE   BUREAU OF AGRICULTURAL ECONOMICS

· 17 ·

Wartime Shifts in Production: Livestock

Meat, poultry, and dairy products were the first to feel the impact of wartime demands. In response, farmers turned first to hogs and chickens, which were priced high and can be increased more rapidly than sheep and cows. Low feed prices reflected the unusual abundance of feed available, and feeding ratios became very favorable early in the war to livestock and animal products. In the case of hogs, when the $9 support price was announced in April, 1941, a remarkable expansion followed. The spring pig crop, which is the larger of the two, jumped from 49 million head in 1941 to 74 million in 1943; and the fall pig crop rose from 30 million head in 1940 to 48 million in 1943—a record of 122 million pigs in 1943. A growing scarcity of feed, however, made itself felt by 1944; the spring pig crop dropped back to 56 million head, and the fall pig crop to 32 million head.[1]

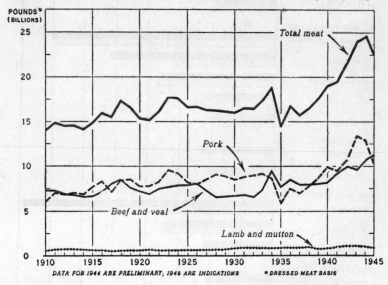

MEAT PRODUCTION IN THE UNITED STATES, 1910-45

DATA FOR 1944 ARE PRELIMINARY; 1945 ARE INDICATIONS • DRESSED MEAT BASIS

U. S. DEPARTMENT OF AGRICULTURE   BUREAU OF AGRICULTURAL ECONOMICS

[1] *Agricultural Outlook Charts*, U.S. Department of Agriculture, Bureau of Agricultural Economics, November, 1944, p. 74.

World War II has changed the production pattern of livestock products much more than did World War I, as the following comparisons indicate:

	World War I Production in 1918 (1910–1914 = 100)	World War II Production[1] in 1944 (1935–1939 = 100)
Meats (dressed weight):		
Pork (excluding lard)....................	124	175
Beef and veal...........................	122	135
Lamb and mutton.......................	74	112
Total meats..........................	121	152
Poultry products:		
Eggs...................................	99	155
Chickens (dressed weight)................	99	143
Turkeys (dressed weight).................	...	145
Dairy products:		
Total milk for human consumption.........	106	113
Cheese................................	...	150
Condensed and evaporated milk	...	161
Fats and oils:		
Lard..................................	116	189
Butter................................	88	85

[1] *National Food Situation*, U.S. Department of Agriculture, Bureau of Agricultural Economics, October, 1944, p. 17.

Pork and lard production increased the most, with peaks in 1944 fully 75 per cent above prewar. During World War I the main increase in livestock was also in hogs, but the rate of expansion was about a third of that attained in World War II. Feed supplies have been the determining factor. During the other war feed supplies were short. At the beginning of this war the corn and wheat bins in the ever-normal granary were full, and a series of large crops following 1939 contributed appreciably to the feed supply.

It does not take long to go from eggs to hens. Chickens and eggs have been increased a half, with eggs going from 3.2 billion dozen in 1939 to 5.1 in 1944, and chickens used for meat rising from about 2.0 to 3.5 billion pounds. The production of beef and veal has increased more than a third, although farmers have added 12 million head to their inventories of cattle other than milk cows.[1] The production of sheep and lambs has not changed much.

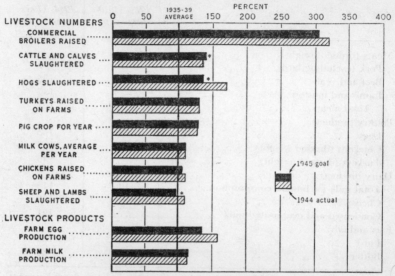

WARTIME INCREASES IN UNITED STATES LIVESTOCK NUMBERS
1945 GOALS AND 1944 ACTUAL AS PERCENTAGE OF 1935-39 AVERAGE

*ESTIMATED NUMBER SLAUGHTERED IF LIVESTOCK POPULATION GOAL IS ATTAINED

U. S DEPARTMENT OF AGRICULTURE   BUREAU OF AGRICULTURAL ECONOMICS

Milk production increased from 1939 to 1942 as the number of milk cows and the production per cow rose, but since then, although the number of cows has continued to rise, the pro-

[1] This accumulation of cattle inventories may become a difficult transition problem. During World War I cattle (other than milk cows) on farms rose from 39.6 million head in 1914 to 50.6 million head in 1919. Inventories were cut down after the war at a great loss to farmers and to the nation, since the extra meat could have been used well during the war. When World War II started in 1939, cattle on farms (other than milk cows) stood at 41.4 million head, and on January 1, 1944, at 54.6 million, an increase of over 12 million head. Preliminary figures put January 1, 1945, numbers at 51.9 million head. Most of this added inventory will again come to market after the war as was the case following 1919. (*Crops and Markets*, U.S. Department of Agriculture, Washington, D.C., January, 1945.)

duction per cow has declined enough to check the rise in the amount of milk produced.

Changes in Consumption

Up to the end of 1944 a deliberate policy of avoiding the accumulation of stocks was pursued in the government's wartime management of the food supply. This "bare-shelf"

PRODUCTION OF FOOD AND PRODUCTION PLUS NET IMPORTS OF ALL FOOD PRODUCTS, UNITED STATES, 1909-43

INDEX NUMBERS (1935-39=100)

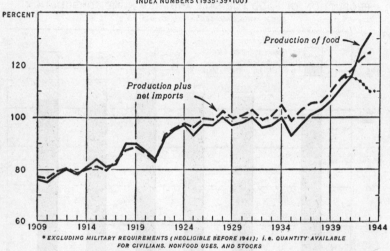

* EXCLUDING MILITARY REQUIREMENTS (NEOLIGIBLE BEFORE 1941): i. e. QUANTITY AVAILABLE FOR CIVILIANS, NONFOOD USES, AND STOCKS

U. S. DEPARTMENT OF AGRICULTURE   BUREAU OF AGRICULTURAL ECONOMICS

policy has been seriously vulnerable on two counts: it meant unpreparedness for (a) a long war and (b) a short crop. Had the war been won in the summer of 1944, this policy would have escaped both of these contingencies. After we had consumed all too much of the very large production of 1943 and 1944, additional requirements for food, especially for Europe, appeared, at the very time that our production of meat and fat (mostly pork and lard) had passed their peak.

World War II accordingly did not necessitate major

· **21** ·

changes in the kinds or amounts of food that Americans consumed up to 1945. In nutritive values, diets in the United States through 1944, taken as a whole, actually improved. The amounts consumed per capita had not changed appreciably, and rationing improved the distribution somewhat.

The increase in food production from 1939 to 1944 was sufficient to take care of the additional noncivilian require-

MILITARY AND LEND-LEASE PURCHASES COMPARED WITH TOTAL PRODUCTION OF FOOD FOR SALE AND FARM HOME CONSUMPTION

INDEX NUMBERS (1935-39=100)

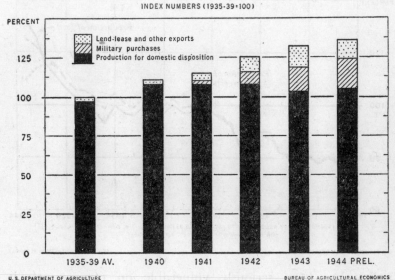

U. S. DEPARTMENT OF AGRICULTURE   BUREAU OF AGRICULTURAL ECONOMICS

ments, namely, supplies for the armed forces and lend-lease shipments to other of the United Nations. Food rationing, accordingly, was undertaken not so much to curtail consumption as to hold it in check and promote more equitable distribution. Larger incomes coupled with a greater desire for food[1] made for a larger demand; food rationing curbed this increase.[2] The amount of food energy consumed has

---

[1] Arising in large part from wartime pressures on the individual.

[2] On a per capita basis the civilian consumption of meats was 15 per **cent**

stayed virtually constant, with a small rise in proteins and fats and a slight fall in carbohydrates. The per capita intake of food minerals and most vitamins has increased appreciably except for ascorbic acid and vitamin A. The

---

larger in 1944 than it was on the average during 1935–1939, wholly as a result of the very marked increase in production of pork. The smaller pig crops of 1944 reduced the production of pork in 1945. On a per capita basis, the civilian consumption of eggs and chickens has risen 18 to 33 per cent respectively when we compare 1944 with the 1935–1939 average. The main decreases have been in dairy products, especially in cheese and butter, and in sugar. The following table from the Bureau of Agricultural Economics, *National Food Situation*, October, 1944, gives the apparent civilian consumption of major foods per capita, 1935–1939 average and 1944.

CONSUMPTION OF MAJOR FOODS

	Average 1935–1939, lb.	1944, lb.	1944 in percentage of 1935–1939
Meats (dressed weight):			
Beef and veal...................	62.8	63	100
Lamb and mutton...............	6.7	6	90
Pork (excluding lard)............	56.1	74	132
Total meat...................	125.6	143	114
Poultry products:			
Eggs..........................	37.3	43.4	116
Chickens (dressed weight).........	17.9	22.7	127
Turkeys (dressed weight).........	2.6	3.2	123
Dairy products:			
Total milk.....................	801.3	777	97
Cheese.......................	5.5	5.1	93
Condensed and evaporated........	16.7	15.1	90
Fats and oils:			
Butter........................	16.7	12.0	72
Lard..........................	11.0	14.0	127
Shortening....................	11.7	9.2	79
Margarine.....................	2.3	3.2	139
Fruits, fresh and processed..........	163.5	165.4	101
Vegetables, including potatoes........	429.5	428.8	100
Sugar.........................	96.5	84.0	87
Grains........................	209.9	222.3	106

Bureau of Agricultural Economics in *National Food Situation*, February, 1944, gives the following changes:

1943 APPARENT CIVILIAN CONSUMPTION PER CAPITA
(1935–1939 = 100)

	Index		Index
Food energy	102	Iron	113
Protein	109	Vitamin A value	97
Fats	106	Ascorbic acid (vitamin C)	99
Carbohydrates	98	Thiamine (vitamin B₁)	136
Calcium	114	Riboflavin	117
Phosphorus	109	Niacin	117

Empty Granaries

The feed and food granaries of the United States were full to overflowing when the war started, with storage space at a premium. In the main wheat-growing sections, wheat filled not only the country elevators but many old school buildings and churches as well. There was not enough space for the new crop on top of stocks, which in 1941 and 1942 exceeded 600,000,000 bushels. The Commodity Credit Corporation dotted railroad sidings with steel bins to store a half-billion bushels of corn in addition to that which farmers usually carried forward. Oats and barley stocks were also large.

The new ever-normal granary was full indeed, and had it not been for the war, the whole storage program of the Commodity Credit Corporation would probably have smashed itself on the same rock that sank the old Federal Farm Board. As it turned out, the advent of war converted these very large inventories of feed and food into valuable assets.

The food and feed granary has been emptied by wartime demands.[1] Starting with 1945 and on through the early postwar period, it will be necessary to depend upon current

[1] In the three years 1942 to 1944, 1,084 million bushels of U.S. wheat were fed. (In addition a large amount of wheat was imported for feed.) U.S. wheat stocks dropped from 632 million bushels on June 30, 1941, to 315 million bushels on June 30, 1944.

production. Storage programs can contribute importantly to stabilizing agricultural production, especially that of livestock. But it should be evident from prewar experience that merely accumulating crops is not an adequate storage policy. Two problems will confront us after the war:

1. *At what rate should the food and feed granaries be refilled?*
2. *What changes are necessary in the basic legislation establishing the rules under which the Commodity Credit Corporation operates the farm storage program?*

Both these problems will be considered and proposals offered in Chap. X.

Obsolete and Depleted Farm Machinery and Equipment

The war gave sharp impetus to the need and the demand for farm machinery. Before the war, a few farm regions, where incomes had been fairly high, had replaced many horses and horse-drawn equipment and obsolete tractors with new, modern machinery. Conversion had been greatest in the Northeast, in the corn belt, and in the western cotton areas. In the northern Great Plains, droughts and low income had made new machinery an impossibility, and in the older cotton areas farmers had not even made normal replacements. The areas that had not converted have been pinched acutely during the war by the shortage of new farm machinery.

The wartime labor shortage has made farmers realize as never before the extent to which modern machinery may be substituted for labor in crop production, and increasingly in livestock production. The fact that farm machinery can reduce production costs, not only on large farms and those situated on rather level land but also on other types of farms, has now been demonstrated.

With the war came the big swell in farm incomes. Had the manufacture and sales of new farm machinery and equipment been doubled in 1943 and 1944, all orders would still not have been filled. Instead of expanding output, however, it was deemed necessary to curtail the manufacture of farm machinery in 1942 to 80 per cent and in 1943 to 40 per cent of the 1940 level. Nor has the 1944 and 1945 supply been anywhere near adequate.[1] The backlog of farm needs for tractors, trucks, and automobiles, for power-drawn field equipment (especially for the more complex units such as corn pickers, combines, and certain hay-handling machinery), and for milking machines and stationary equipment using electrical power may represent well over two years' normal purchases.

After the war a strong factor hastening the use of mechanical equipment will be the return to farms of veterans who have had experience with machinery while in the service. This will accelerate the adoption of farm machinery most in the areas having the least mechanization.

Certain aspects of farm mechanization are of special concern:

1. Because of the importance of maintaining and strengthening the competitive position of the *family-type farm*, new farm machinery should be available to fit the technical

[1] The 1944 and 1945 production of important farm equipment for domestic use has been as follows: (based on *The Agricultural Situation*, U.S. Department of Agriculture, Bureau of Agricultural Economics, February, 1945, p. 13).

Equipment	Per cent of 1940 output	
	1944[a]	1945[b]
Tractors for farm use............................	85	70
Tillage, planting, cultivating, fertilizing, spraying equipment.....................................	90	100
Harvesting and haying equipment................	155	145
Wagons and nonmotor trucks....................	100	90
Dairy, poultry, barn equipment..................	120	115
Pumps..	100	100

[a] Actual production in year beginning July 1, 1943.
[b] Scheduled production in year beginning July 1, 1944.

requirements of family-operated farms. Smaller machinery units are needed to serve more adequately the small farms situated on rolling and hilly lands. The farm machinery and equipment industry is undergoing developments which may bring about further modification in designs to meet the requirements of small farms, as well as lower the price of farm machinery. It is all to the good that such adaptations are now being made.

2. At the close of World War I many farmers were caught in the land boom and their wartime earnings were dissipated in the purchase of land at excessively high prices. This saddled much of agriculture with high fixed costs and weakened its financial condition. Many farmers were forced into bankruptcy. To what extent will it be possible to induce farmers to use at least some of their wartime earnings after this war to buy modern, efficient machinery and equipment, and thereby set the stage for lowering their cost of production? Two to five billion dollars diverted from the land market to the purchase of farm machinery and equipment soon after the war would make a big dent in the funds that might otherwise contribute to land inflation and at the same time would retool agriculture to do a better production job in years to come.

3. Some farmers in areas having little or no experience with modern machinery are in danger of buying in haste and regretting later. Many are likely to buy the wrong types of machines, and some will buy altogether too much for the farming unit that they operate.

A War-induced Land Boom

With wartime farm incomes two and a half times as large as prewar; with farm prices twice as high and likely to stay high for a short time; with government payments to farmers being continued; with high support-price commitments by Federal legislation; with sharply reduced supplies of the lumber, hardware, and other building materials, machinery, equipment, and fencing materials which might absorb some of the added earnings of farmers; and with the desire of many farmers to establish their sons at farming when they return from the armed forces—*another land boom is in the making*.

Memory of the tragic aftermath of the 1918–1919 land boom and appropriate public measures might check rising land prices. Memories, however, are often short, and some individuals are sure the mistake last time was in not "getting out" soon enough, an error they promise themselves to avoid this time.

A farm-land boom does not spread itself evenly over the country. Some areas are swept by the flame while others escape. High farm incomes in areas where land contributes much to the productivity of the farm are the fuel that feeds the fire.[1] The best lands of the corn belt will boom while those in the New England area remain quiet. The price of the highly productive tobacco land of Kentucky rises dramatically, along with the better cattle-grazing lands of the inter-mountain states which have enjoyed high cattle prices and good grazing seasons. The black Mississippi delta values boom while the red Piedmont land more nearly escapes. In the drought-ridden 100th meridian states, insurance companies and other landholders still have many farms to sell, and land prices there have not risen as they did following World War. I. Nevertheless, a very active market has arisen where there was none before.

Speculation in land can do untold harm. The 1919–1920 boom played havoc with hundreds of thousands of farm families in the succeeding decade. Most farmers are highly vulnerable to wide swings in land values. When land prices drop, the decline does not merely eliminate what savings the family on a mortgaged farm may have put into the land, but it may "liquidate" both the farm business and home, although

[1] Land values have increased most where incomes have risen most and where farms owned by nonoperating landlords may be leased readily to operating farmers.

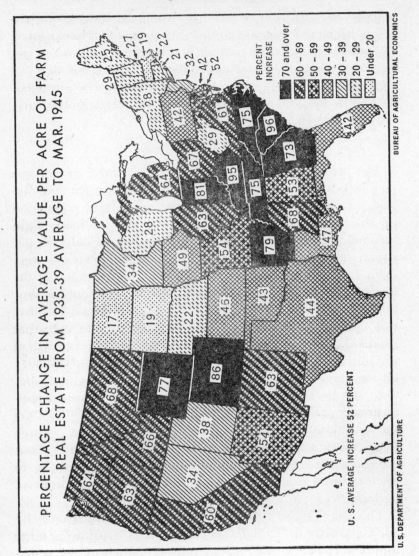

PERCENTAGE CHANGE IN AVERAGE VALUE PER ACRE OF FARM
REAL ESTATE FROM 1935-39 AVERAGE TO MAR. 1945

PERCENT
INCREASE

70 and over
60 – 69
50 – 59
40 – 49
30 – 39
20 – 29
Under 20

U. S. AVERAGE INCREASE 52 PERCENT

U.S. DEPARTMENT OF AGRICULTURE

BUREAU OF AGRICULTURAL ECONOMICS

usually not until the farmer has exhausted himself and the soil of his farm in years of futile effort to stave off bankruptcy.

Shall we stand aside and let another farm-land boom put its curse upon American agriculture, on the thesis that the right to buy and sell farm land can in no way be abridged? This question will certainly have to be faced in the early months after the war.

Farm Population Down

The per capita income of farm people, relative to nonfarm people, is affected significantly by the size of the farm population. During the interwar years the pressure of population in agriculture made food cheap—but it also made farm incomes per head low. In the worsening of agriculture's per capita income position the main contributing factors were (a) a large natural increase in the farm population, (b) the loss of substantial market outlets abroad with only a slow growth of the domestic demand for farm products to offset this (caused in no small part by the low level of industrial production during most of this period), and (c) the growth of the supply of farm products following advances in technology on the farm. The principal corrective, very slow and sluggish, has been the movement of people from farms to non-farm occupations. During the two decades of 1920 to 1939 the net migration from farms was 10 million persons. Large as this movement was, it was far from sufficient to bring about an equilibrium in the distribution of resources, that is, to offer incomes from farming comparable to those outside of agriculture.

The war changed this intergroup income ratio markedly by adding greatly to the demand for food and by drawing large numbers of people out of agriculture. Much of the added demand is temporary, however, and will disappear as war conditions recede. The decrease of the farm population by 5 million persons (1940–1944) is on a different footing. The farm population, which had not dropped below 30 million

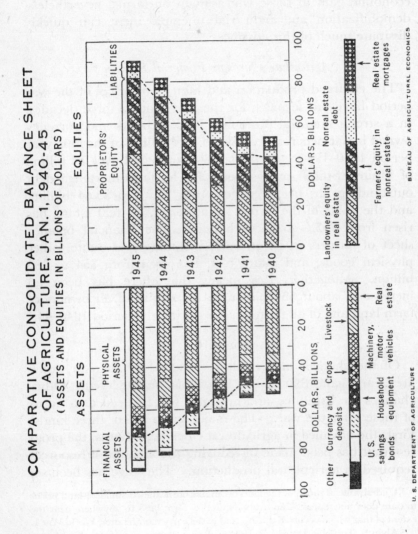

COMPARATIVE CONSOLIDATED BALANCE SHEET
OF AGRICULTURE, JAN. 1, 1940-45
(ASSETS AND EQUITIES IN BILLIONS OF DOLLARS)

EQUITIES

LIABILITIES

PROPRIETORS' EQUITY

1945
1944
1943
1942
1941
1940

DOLLARS, BILLIONS

Landowners' equity in real estate

Farmers' equity in nonreal estate

Nonreal estate debt

Real estate mortgages

BUREAU OF AGRICULTURAL ECONOMICS

ASSETS

FINANCIAL ASSETS

PHYSICAL ASSETS

DOLLARS, BILLIONS

Other

Currency and deposits

U. S. savings bonds

Household equipment

Crops

Machinery, motor vehicles

Livestock

Real estate

U. S. DEPARTMENT OF AGRICULTURE

between World Wars I and II, has declined to about 25 million. This decrease in the farm population brings a real economic gain to those who remain on farms; nevertheless, demobilization and industrial unemployment can quickly dissipate much of this advance.

Agriculture's Stronger Financial Position

The enlarged production and high farm prices of the war period have put farmers, for the first time in three decades, in a strong financial position. Bank deposits and currency owned by farmers rose from $4 to $9.7 billion in the four-year period 1940–1944. Farmers have purchased over $2 billion of United States savings bonds. The farm-mortgage debt outstanding has been reduced from $6.59 to $5.64 billion, and the value of the farmer's main asset, his real estate, has risen from $33.6 to $45.6 billion.[1] The financial balance sheet of farmers in its entirety, including real estate, other physical goods, and intangibles, has risen from $54 to $83 billion. Altogether, this means that there has been an increase of about $30 billion in the equity of all owners of farm land and of all farm tenants during the period 1940–44.[2]

Summary

Of the changes in agriculture induced by the war, some are clearly gains that should, if possible, be preserved. Other changes are liabilities, and measures will be needed to rid us of these after the war. The major gains are of three kinds: First, the advance in agricultural efficiency; that is, the progress that has been made in reducing the amount of resources required in agricultural production. The stage has been set

[1] Undesirable as much of the land boom has been, the rise in farm-land prices to date does not represent an overvaluation of farm land to anywhere near the extent of that which occurred during, and in the early months after, World War I.

[2] Alvin S. Tostlebe, Donald C. Horton, Roy J. Burroughs, Harald C. Larsen, Lawrence A. Jones, and Albert R. Johnston, *The Impact of the War on the Financial Structure of Agriculture*, U.S. Department of Agriculture, Bureau of Agricultural Economics, Washington, D.C., September, 1944.

for a very considerable "retooling" in agriculture. New farm machinery and equipment will mean reduced labor requirements. The second, and by all odds the most important, gain for agriculture, is the migration of people from rural areas and from farms, induced by the wartime shortage of labor in other parts of the economy. This movement has gone a long way to redress the maldistribution of the labor force adverse to agriculture that had developed prior to the war. A third major gain is the marked improvement in the financial position of farmers. This may, however, be either an asset or a liability, depending on how the additional liquid assets are employed. If wartime earnings are used to reduce debts, to buy farm machinery and equipment, to build and improve farm homes, and for education and related expenditures that will increase the mobility of the farm population, they will bring important real gains. A repetition of our earlier experience, pouring wartime earnings into farm land, will turn this gain into a burden.

Postwar liabilities for agriculture loom, first, in the fact that the pattern of production will be geared to wartime demands. A serious surplus is likely to occur in fats and oils, comparable to the wheat surplus following World War I. The present wheat acreage will also be too large unless we are prepared to price wheat into our economy not only as food but also as feed. The oversupply in cotton, much of it short-staple and poor in quality, has, if anything, been worsened by the steps taken during the war. It is apparent that the war will also have brought about a considerable lack of balance within the livestock industry. Inventories of cattle for meat have become excessively large and will be marketed after the peak of the wartime demand has been spent. Hogs and chickens are already being adjusted downward. In contrast, an expanded market for milk products, anticipated if high-level employment is attained, could not be fully supplied for some time. Nevertheless, the necessary changes in production patterns, in crops and in livestock, are not unduly large compared to the requirements of the transition from war to peace in many branches of industry.

The second and most critical adjustment confronting agriculture after the war is in prices. The war has not so much upset the relationship among the prices of farm products as it has changed the relationship of farm prices to other prices in the economy. The demand has been such that farm prices have virtually doubled, despite wartime price controls. This extraordinary demand is likely to disappear as soon as relief requirements are met. Meanwhile, agricultural production as a whole has increased a fourth under the stimulus of high prices and organized drives to meet production goals. Most of this production will continue after the war. The burden of falling farm prices in all likelihood will be great. The government program of support prices is not well conceived to facilitate the adjustments in farm prices that will be required during the postwar period.[1]

PREWAR MALADJUSTMENTS CARRIED FORWARD

Once peace is reestablished, the old prewar farm problems will again be with us. As food becomes plentiful and cheap, we are likely to find ourselves concerned about particular surpluses, wastage of soil, bad farm tenure, deep poverty in the South, erratic and hazardous climate in the Plains states, serious imbalance in the cotton and wheat economies, over-population and low incomes in nearly all farming areas—

---

[1] It should be noted that in this treatment several effects of the war on agriculture have not been analyzed. Important among these is the conservation of soil productivity. This has been omitted chiefly because it is not at all clear what the aggregate results have been. In the corn belt the expansion of both soybeans and corn has put considerable additional pressure on soil resources and undoubtedly many farms have been depleted somewhat further as a consequence. The big increase in peanuts picked, instead of hogged off, in the South has taken a large toll in soil productivity. On the other hand, in many farming areas, especially in the South, the greater scarcity of labor and its higher relative cost have put a premium on adjustments in farming practices that facilitate soil conservation. More extensive farming of the type that gives positive results in terms of conserving soils has been accelerated.

all of the old vexing issues that claimed the energies of farm leaders and others during the twenties and thirties. The more important of these are considered briefly below.

Wheat for Feed as Well as Food

In the interim between World Wars I and II no adequate solution was found for the surplus problem confronting wheat producers. Barriers to world trade curtailed consumption; pools and storage programs to support wheat prices gave relief only while stocks were being accumulated; acreage-restriction programs did not succeed in reducing wheat production; and wheat prices in the United States were tied to an obsolete 1910-1914 parity which worked badly when it worked at all.[1] When the war started, after more than two decades of various farm programs and large public expenditures on behalf of wheat, no satisfactory solution had been arrived at.

Reducing wheat acreage to 50 million or less from the 59 million acres of 1944 is not the answer. This nation has many more than 50 million acres that have a high comparative value in growing wheat. (Some land devoted to wheat production would undoubtedly produce more if it were put into grass, a feed crop, or into fallow[2] than it does in wheat. Such adjustments, however, would come nowhere near the whole measure of the problem.) The agricultural resources—land, machinery, managerial skill, and the efforts of the farm families concerned—specialized to grow wheat represent a capacity much larger than the acreage and production considered appropriate in the late thirties.

The nub of the wheat problem does not lie in the volume produced. It lies in the price. The advances made in wheat-growing technology have cut costs, and the lowering of fixed costs with the decline in land values and taxes during

[1] *Cf.* pp. 179–180 and 257–258 for a discussion of parity prices.

[2] It has been estimated that in the ten Great Plains states about 2 million fewer acres were fallowed for the 1945 crop than for the 1943 crop.

the twenties and thirties (a land boom may cancel these, however) has substantially improved the competitive position of wheat growers.

The answer to the postwar wheat situation will be found chiefly in the decisions on these questions:

1. Are we willing (*a*) to enlarge the market for wheat by using it both for feed and food, and not for food so exclusively

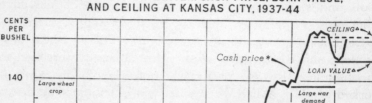

WHEAT, NO. 2 HARD WINTER: CASH PRICE, LOAN VALUE, AND CEILING AT KANSAS CITY, 1937-44

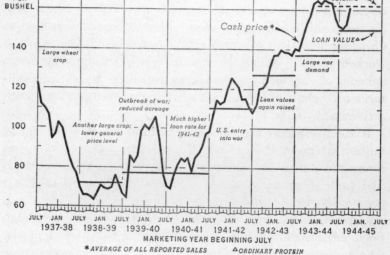

*AVERAGE OF ALL REPORTED SALES   △ORDINARY PROTEIN

U S DEPARTMENT OF AGRICULTURE   BUREAU OF AGRICULTURAL ECONOMICS

as we were prone to do prior to the war? and (*b*) to accomplish this by pricing wheat so that it may flow into both feed and food channels?[1]

2. Are we prepared to reenter foreign markets actively on the supposition that we have a comparative advantage in this product in world commerce because of the advance that has been made in our wheat-producing technology and, if

[1] When wheat is priced at not more than 10 per cent above corn prices, it is possible to use much wheat as feed.

we are, will international trade arrangements permit us to do so?

3. Or will we try once more to solve the wheat problem by programs designed to curtail acreage[1] and by price measures wedded to a 1910–1914 parity formula?

Cotton Is Out of Gear

The cogwheels of cost and price in the cotton economy are not in mesh with other parts of the national and international economy.   Government efforts to help cotton, largely through price support and acreage control, have in many respects worsened its competitive position.   We have been pricing cotton out of both the foreign and domestic markets.   First, the fact that cotton is, and has long been, out of gear in relationship to the productive resources of the South has been ignored.   Cotton is often an exploitative crop, hard on the soil, and in many areas its cultivation has caused much soil wastage, a cost to the Southern economy which escapes in considerable part the private year-to-year ledger of farmers. Secondly, American cotton is no longer meshed into the cost and price structure of other countries.   By our actions, we have divorced our cotton from the world economy.   Third, we have accumulated stocks of cotton wholly out of proportion to the number of bales required for carry-over purposes. The CCC loans on cotton have overvalued the poorer grades and shorter staples; as a consequence, the huge carry-over is largely low-grade, short-staple cotton.   Fourth, through our efforts to curtail the number of acres devoted to cotton, the production pattern has been essentially frozen.   Land in certain areas that should have been devoted to other uses has remained in cotton, while other areas that should have increased the acreage devoted to cotton (for example, many

[1] Conservation of soil resources is related to acreage and must be considered. In the ten Plains states about 7 million acres were returned to grass from 1933 to 1944.

parts of the Mississippi Delta) have been held in check, resulting in some inefficient uses of resources.

The cotton problem is difficult to solve not only because of its complexity but because of the nature of the obstacles that block the path. The first major step is to relate cotton again to the rest of the cost-price structure of the United States and the world. The political and social institutions that have evolved around cotton present serious barriers to this objective. Cotton has become, in our partially administered farm economy, singularly a "political crop," price and production determinations being made with an eye to short-term political considerations and not with reference to rational use of agricultural resources. Looming large among the obstacles is the parity-price concept, the 1910–1914 parity, to which the production, storage, and price legislation of cotton are tied.

War did not correct any of the fundamental dislocations in the cotton economy. Cotton and cottonseed prices doubled, but 20-cent cotton did not put cotton in shape. The strong wartime demand for food and feed crops provided real opportunities for correcting some of the dislocations in cotton, but these opportunities were not utilized to the full. In spite of an extraordinary carry-over, ranging between 10 and 12 million bales, production was very largely maintained although more of the land and labor used for cotton might have been better employed to produce much-needed food and feed.

The following production and carry-over data suggest how little the war demand has benefited the surplus cotton problem:

	1939	1943	1944
Price received by farmers (cents per pound).....	9	20	20.4
Acres harvested (million).....................	23.8	21.7	20.1
Production (million bales)....................	11.8	11.5	12.0
Carry-over (million bales)....................	13.0	10.5	10.6

SOURCES: *Crops and Markets*, and *Agricultural Outlook Charts*, both from U.S. Department of Agriculture, Washington, D.C., January, 1945, and November, 1944.

What kind of price and production policies will this country pursue in cotton after the war? When the mills of Europe, and those of Japan, again produce for peacetime civilian consumption, there will be a considerable outlet for some of the accumulated low grades and short staples. This demand, however, will not put United States cotton on a road that will take it out of its difficulties. Nor will storage programs or AAA benefit payments do the task. A price policy tied to an historical base of 1910–1914 and an AAA production program also based on historical production patterns are likely to accentuate further the economic dislocations within cotton.

The future holds no promise of simplifying this problem. The introduction of a mechanical cotton picker may herald a revolution in cotton production as sweeping and significant in its social and economic implications as that which followed the development of the reaper for cereal crops.

The conversion of the cotton South is undoubtedly the most important as well as the most difficult problem in agriculture that will confront the United States. While it is comparatively easy to point out measures that will prove harmful, positive steps that are at all feasible are not so apparent. The heart of the problem is not cotton but an excess supply of labor and the resulting low income per head; so low that it condemns millions of people, especially Negroes, to poverty wholly incompatible with America's resources and capacity to produce.

It is worth noting that no such poverty was evident before the war among peasant farmers in western European countries. The resources of the cotton South are gravely overtaxed by the pressure of people against the land. Repricing cotton in line with its value, by itself, would be only one minor step in a well-conceived program of conversion for this major region.

Erratic Weather and Income about the 100th Meridian

Erratic weather and the consequent uncertainty of crops in the Plains states, in large parts of the Dakotas, Nebraska, Kansas, Oklahoma, the panhandle of Texas, and sections of

Montana and Colorado,[1] is the key to many of the difficulties of agriculture in this large area. The land itself is productive: the area provides all our sorghum, much of our wheat and barley, large quantities of oats, hay, grass, and considerable corn and cotton. Some of the feed produced in the region is shipped to other sections, but most of it is fed where it is produced, and it supports a very considerable livestock industry of hogs, chickens, and cattle, and some sheep and milk cows.

Against its liabilities, symbolized by the dust bowl, droughts, and grasshoppers, the area has certain agricultural advantages. Most of the land is well adapted to modern power-drawn farm machinery; the climate, especially in the middle and northern parts, favors the storage of grain; the output per man is high; its network of highways and railroads provides fairly adequate transportation; and there are many towns that render various necessary services. Farmers in this area are capable and venturesome.

In spite of these advantages, agriculture in this region has not yet found an answer to the problem of erratic weather. What type of farm economy is best adapted to this climatic hazard? The layman is prone to think of the 100th meridian section as not having enough rainfall, but that is only part of the story. Climate is the product of several elements, and in this region each of these elements is highly variable. The interaction of tropical and polar air masses results in excessively high and low temperatures, with 100°F heat often occurring in the summer, while cold registering −40°F is common in the winter. Hail, frosts, and hot winds are all severe. Along with these, the rainfall varies exceedingly. Taken together, these factors make for a climate more hazardous from an agricultural point of view than that in any other large farming area in this country.

As fate would have it, the vicissitudes of climate are not the

---

[1] The ten Plains states, which include in addition to those given in the text New Mexico and Wyoming, contain about 40 per cent of the nation's cropland and make up 37 per cent of the land area of the United States.

only ones this region has to endure.   Farm-price fluctuations have compounded the economic effect of crop fluctuations, with the prosperity of good years made more intense by high prices and the poverty of bad years made worse by low prices. There was a series of rainy seasons, roughly from 1910 to 1920, which was also a period of rising farm prices, with very high prices prevailing during World War I.   Then came adverse weather, with a series of droughts starting with 1931 and reaching an apex in the droughts of 1934 and 1936, even as farm prices were pulled down by the great depression.   Since 1939, there have been good crops and once more war prices. Erratic weather and erratic prices have thus dictated the economic history of this region; and the two have synchronized in such a way in recent decades as to accentuate their effects.

How may the resources of this region be harnessed, in spite of climatic hazards, to permit a stable and prosperous agriculture?   There is no easy answer.   The small parcels of land sponsored by the Homestead Acts proved a serious misfit in this area.   And the early expectations from dry-land farming were too optimistic.

A basic problem is to find some way of embedding the "cost" of the weather risk and uncertainty into the land itself.

Lack of knowledge of the course of weather, the eternal optimism of most farmers, the long swings between a series of bad years and a run of good years, coupled with the economic inability of many families once situated in the region to reorganize their operations or relocate, account for much of the poor fit between what has been tried and what may prove satisfactory.   All told, there is too little weather history to ascertain the main features of the climate.   How often are droughts of the severity and compass of 1934 and 1936 likely to occur?   Available experience and records are too recent and too few to provide a dependable historical basis from which to generalize.

To what extent is crop insurance an answer—a way of placing upon the land the cost of carrying the risk and uncertainty of yields? Might the feed supply be made more dependable, making possible a more stable livestock economy? Can this be accomplished by a bold use of storage techniques? What is the place of larger farms, grazing associations, governmental purchases, and control of land? Chapter X will offer an answer to these questions.

Farm Prices Fluctuate Too Much

The concern that farmers have about the erratic character of farm prices was discussed briefly at the outset of this chapter. Farm prices change more frequently and fluctuate more widely than any other major set of producer prices. Constantly changing prices have their cost, usually resulting in waste and costly economic maladjustments. How frequently farm prices should change should be determined primarily by the changes that occur from time to time in the demand and supply of farm products, and by the production and consumption effects of changes in farm prices. The production consequences that flow from changes in farm prices can be labeled "positive" or "negative." There are those which induce farmers to alter their production plans and those which chiefly give rise to economic uncertainty. In practice, we want as much of the first and as little of the second as possible. We want to maximize those price changes which are necessary to keep farm production in line with changes in the demand and cost of food, and to minimize those which contribute to economic uncertainty in farming.[1]

Farm prices in the past, altogether too erratic, have not only burdened agriculture with much unnecessary price uncertainty, but their instability has impaired appreciably the positive function of prices, namely, to guide and direct production. In the area of farm-product pricing, postwar policy makers will be faced by this major question: *How can the erratic elements in farm prices be eliminated in order to improve*

[1] See Theodore W. Schultz, *Redirecting Farm Policy*, The Macmillan Company, New York, 1943, pp. 45–46.

the capacity of farm prices to guide farmers in the use to which they put their resources?

Higher Income per Person Needed

Each of the problems already discussed is a part of a much larger difficulty that confronts agriculture. The wheat, cotton, erratic-weather, and price problems have become critical because the patient has been in a low state of general health. Agriculture's economic pulse has been poor for a long time, the causes organic and deep-seated. Diagnosis points to a fundamental disease of long standing, a bad case of excess resources in agriculture. To put it simply, this means that *the expenditure of human effort in agriculture has earned too little relative to what human effort earns in other parts of the economy. This is the real disparity.* Prices are merely one evidence of the dislocation. The drive for parity prices by farmers has been in the main an effort to redress the relative earning power between agriculture and the rest of society. Support for parity prices comes in considerable part from those who see the fundamental need for "equality for agriculture."[1]

In Part I we have described the prospective conditions that are likely to prevail in agriculture; in other words, the setting of the postwar agricultural problem. The causes of the low level of farm incomes and of the extreme fluctuations to which they are subject are diagnosed in the chapters of Part II, which follows.

[1] *Ibid.*, pp. 11–19.

PART II

Fundamentals of the Agricultural Problem in an
Expanding and Fluctuating Economy

III. UNEQUAL GROWTH OF THE SUPPLY AND DEMAND FOR FARM PRODUCTS[1]

RATES OF EXPANSION

ALTHOUGH available statistics are not well designed to measure the relative growth of the demand and supply of farm products, what data there are all point to a slowing down in the growth of demand and an acceleration of the supply. The main forces responsible for this pattern of development are (*a*) a slackening in the increase of the population, (*b*) the effect of the low income-elasticity of farm products as people become richer, and (*c*) the technical revolution in progress in agricultural production.

These forces are secular, making themselves felt in the long pull, not only in the American economy but in other countries as well. They may be hidden temporarily by war or by trade fluctuations. But they are forces that already had their head prior to World War I; they moved on persistently during the interwar years; and they have not been checked by what has happened during World War II. On the contrary, they have gained momentum and their effect will be sharply in evidence after the war. It is the task of the economic system

---

[1] The writer has presented some of the main features of the analysis developed in this chapter in a paper read before the Twentieth Institute of the Norman Wait Harris Foundation of the University of Chicago on Sept. 8, 1944, "Food and Agriculture in a Developing Economy." See *Food for the World*, University of Chicago Press, Chicago, 1945, edited by Theodore W. Schultz.

to reconcile forces and counterforces affecting the supply and demand for these and other products. The equilibrating mechanism of our economy apparently has not had sufficient capacity, however, to cope adequately with the agricultural situation.

A developing economy places strains and stresses upon the institutions and mechanisms that bear the burden of adapting it to advances in technology, improvements in the skills of people, accumulation of capital, changes in tastes, and changes in population. To achieve what is, in fact, a moving equilibrium requires adaptation, recombination, and change, and these, as a rule, do not occur easily and smoothly. Consequently, disequilibria occur in the structure of prices, in income, and in the capacity to produce and consume. The resulting maladjustments are, in one sense, a measure of the severity of the strain; in another sense, they indicate the extent to which the economic system fails to cope with the underlying forces.

Three sets of circumstances are possible in the rate of growth in the demand and the supply of farm products:[1] (*a*) an equal increase in both demand and supply;[2] (*b*) an unequal expansion, in which demand pushes hard against supply; (*c*) an unequal growth, in which supply outdistances demand. The first situation would be interesting to explore, but since it introduces no adjustment difficulties, it places no burden upon the equilibrating mechanism. The second circumstance, with

[1] Such growth, as already indicated, comes as a consequence of improvements in the skills of workers, advances in technology, accumulation of capital, extension in market, improvements in the organization of economic activity, and other causes. It is possible to have differing developments both as to time and as to place, and also as to the causal forces at work. It is therefore necessary to state the particular type of development that is under consideration.

[2] To illustrate: If the per capita demand for farm products during the course of a decade were to expand so that 20 per cent more was being purchased by consumers at the same relative price, and if, during the same period, the per capita supply increased so that 20 per cent more farm products were being produced and sold by farmers at the same relative price—then the demand and supply would have increased at the same rate.

demand for farm products pushing hard against the supply, (the state of affairs now present in China and India), in the early 1800's seemed destined to prevail universally and worried Malthus, Ricardo, and their contemporaries. The third condition, where the supply of farm products increases so fast that it presses hard against the demand, is the one that has in fact occurred. It is the one to which this study is directed, for it seems to describe most nearly the contemporary experiences of the United States, Canada, Western Europe, Australia, New Zealand, and of several countries in South America.[1]

It is convenient to analyze the difficulties that confront agriculture in a modern economy, first, in terms of the long run, which we shall call the "secular view," exploring those developments that usually come gradually, requiring a decade or more to manifest themselves; and second, in terms of the short run, which we shall call the "cyclical view," dealing with fluctuations that come and go quickly. In this and in

---

[1] Professor Frank W. Notestein has classified population into three general types—Incipient Decline, Transitional Growth, and High Growth Potential. In his valuable paper, "Population—the Long View," he says: "Populations in which fertility has fallen below the replacement level or those in which it is near and rapidly approaching that level may be characterized as those of 'incipient decline,' our first demographic type. Other populations are in an earlier stage of demographic evolution. Among them birth and death rates are still high and growth is rapid, but the decline of the birth rate is well established. These we may characterize as in the stage of 'transitional growth,' the second type. Still other populations have scarcely begun their demographic transition. Mortality is high and variable and is the chief determinant of growth, while fertility is high and thus far has shown no evidence of a downward trend. In these populations rapid growth is to be expected just as soon as technical developments make possible a decline in mortality. We may characterize this type as that of 'high growth potential.'" (See *Food for the World*, edited by Theodore W. Schultz, p. 41.) Unequal rates of growth in the demand and supply of food, with supply exceeding demand, are typical of Notestein's first group (populations of "incipient decline"), and in large part also of his second group, "transitional growth," but are not applicable to his third group, "high growth potential." Populations in his third group fit more nearly into the Malthusian formulation. They are, however, in most instances isolated, trade and marketwise; they fall outside the orbit of the primary markets serving American agriculture. The United States itself falls into the first group.

the next two chapters we shall examine primarily the secular developments, and then go on to a treatment of the business cycle and agriculture. This division permits us to separate the main, persistent forces that cause underemployment in agriculture, with the attendant low per capita earnings,[1] from the forces that bring about marked *instability of income from farming*.

Type I. Equal Rates of Growth[2]

When the demand for farm products increases as fast as its supply, presumably there would not arise a "farm problem" caused by too many resources in agriculture. Nor would it create a scarcity "food problem." The amount of food consumed per capita might be low or high, but it would not decrease; on the other hand, diets would not necessarily improve. The capacity of the economy to adjust and adapt would not undergo test, however, since no transfer of resources into or out of agriculture would be necessary to correct major differences in rates of growth, and to reestablish an equilibrium in the allocation of resources between agriculture and the nonagricultural sectors of the economy.[3]

[1] Underemployment is underproductive employment, resulting in lower earnings per person than could be obtained elsewhere. In agriculture the combination of resources involves too much labor and often too little capital. Thus, farm labor does not produce as efficiently as it could in other lines of work and its earnings are low relative to earnings of nonfarm workers. Farm people often work longer and harder than nonfarm people, yet they usually earn much less per person.

[2] One of the implicit assumptions underlying each of these three conditions is that resources have not been transferred either into or out of agriculture. These models are especially useful to show the direction and the extent of the transfer of resources that would be necessary to approach an equilibrium.

[3] We do well to guard against a superficial inference that an equal rate of growth in the supply of and demand for food is desirable. This type of development carries no assurance whatever that diets will be improved or that the distribution of food will be such as to serve best the general welfare of people. Equal rates of growth would check, perhaps block, economic progress. The one inference permissible, as indicated, is that no burden is placed by this type of development upon the capacity of the economy to transfer resources necessary to approach an equilibrium—because equilibrium exists without such transfer.

Type II.   Unequal Rates of Growth with the Demand for Farm Products in the Forefront

This situation is caused by overpopulation and a shortage of land.   From it arises the specter of not enough food, an inevitable condition according to the classicists.   John Stuart Mill put the analysis underlying a development of this type succinctly:[1]

Agricultural skill and knowledge are of slow growth, and still slower diffusion.   Inventions and discoveries, too, occur only occasionally, while the increase of population and capital are continuous agencies.   It therefore seldom happens that improvement, even during a short time, has so much the start of population and capital as actually to lower rent, or raise the rate of profits.   There are many countries in which the growth of population and capital is not rapid, but in these agricultural improvement is less active still. Population almost everywhere treads close on the heels of agricultural improvement, and effaces its effects as fast as they are produced. . . . Agricultural improvement may thus be considered to be not so much a counterforce conflicting with increase of population, as a partial relaxation of the bonds which confine that increase.[2]

[1] Overpopulation relative to the supply of land is still one of the main causes of poverty in much of the world, certainly in India and China.   At the time of Malthus the British population was doubling itself in a half century.   The question that troubled Malthus was simply this: Could the island produce enough extra food to feed this rapidly multiplying population?   J. R. Hicks, in commenting upon the difference of the fate of England and Ireland in avoiding the peril of a serious want of food, adds: "As the problem appeared to the Malthusians, shortage of agricultural land was an insuperable obstacle; when once the population of any country had reached the point where shortage of land becomes acute, the people would be bound to suffer from poverty, poverty which could only be remedied by the population becoming smaller." (*The Social Framework*, Oxford University Press, 1942, pp. 55–56.)

The implications of the growth of the demand for food pressing hard against the "niggardliness of Nature" for rent payments, the cost of food, and economic progress are well-known contributions of the older economists.

[2] John Stuart Mill, *Principles of Political Economy*, Book IV, Chap. III, Sec. 5, pp. 721 and 722.   Mill goes on to say (pp. 723, 724): "The economical progress of a society constituted of landlords, capitalists, and labourers tends to the progressive enrichment of the landlord class; while the cost of the labourer's

Type III. Unequal Rates of Growth with Supply of Farm Products Ahead of Demand

When this development occurs, a *farm problem* is likely to arise. Farm products become plentiful and cheap, and land values and rent payments fall. The equilibrating mechanism is faced with a transfer problem, that is, the task of moving an excess supply of resources out of agriculture.[1] Instead of hungry mouths begging for food, agricultural surpluses go begging for a market.[2]

Type III development typifies the United States. It is a far cry from the situation regarding food and agriculture which brought forth Malthus's gloomy predictions. It would be useful to trace economic history in the 150 years since Malthus wrote to discover what has happened that has so profoundly changed the economic pattern. The import of the change, however, has not gone unnoticed.[3]

subsistence tends on the whole to increase, and profits to fall. Agricultural improvements are a counteracting force to the two last effects; but the first, though a case is conceivable in which it would be temporarily checked, is ultimately in a high degree promoted by those improvements; and the increase of population tends to transfer all the benefits derived from agricultural improvements to the landlords alone."

[1] Among the necessary conditions for this situation is the low price elasticity of the demand and the fact that advances in technology affecting the supply are not costless.

[2] John Stuart Mill, in the original text (1848) of his *Principles*, anticipated the possibility of the food supply gaining on the demand when he wrote, "[Agriculture] . . . so far as present foresight can extend, does not seem to be susceptible to improved processes to so great a degree as some branches of manufacture; but inventions may be in reserve for the future which may invert this relation." (Book IV, Chap. II.) This passage unfortunately was omitted in the 5th edition (1862) at the very time when important advances were being made in agricultural technology.

[3] We shall note only a few: Alva Myrdal, *Family and Nation*, Harper & Brothers, New York, 1942; Alvin H. Hansen, "Economic Progress in a Declining Population," *The American Economic Review*, Vol. 29 (1939); Joseph S. Davis, "The Specter of Dearth of Food: History's Answer to Sir William Crookes," *On Agricultural Policy*, Stanford University Press, Stanford University, Calif., 1939; Edwin Cannon, "The Need for Simpler Economics," *Economic Journal*, Vol. XLIII (1933).

CAUSES FOR THE SLOWING DOWN OF
GROWTH OF DEMAND

The rate of expansion of the demand for farm products[1] depends upon changes in population, income, and consumers' taste. What path each of these forces is likely to take in the United States after the war will be considered in turn. Before doing so, however, it may prove helpful to trace the general consequences of changes in these forces by means of two examples. In the economy of which American agriculture is an integral part, the prospect is that increases in population during the next several decades will be a factor of dwindling importance, while a further rise in income is likely to be a major development. As this occurs, we shall need to know much more than we do now about how people will want to spend additional income in satisfying their wants for farm

---

[1] Up to this point, for the most part, we have taken food to represent the production of agriculture. This procedure has made it possible to maintain a link with the work of the older economists. Since our purpose, however, is to ascertain the changes likely to occur (during the next several decades) in the claims that the economy as a whole is likely to make on agricultural resources, it is necessary to shift to a more comprehensive formulation. The concept of food excludes a number of important commodities produced by agriculture; moreover, food usually refers to products and services at the point of consumption rather than to farm products at the point at which they leave agriculture. Obviously, agriculture supplies a number of major products, such as cotton, wool, jute, some wood products, tobacco, and feed, which are used as industrial raw materials and satisfy wants other than food. Also, it is obvious that at the point at which food is purchased by consumers many nonfarm services have been added to the food (after it has left the farm). These nonfarm services are the result of resource inputs other than land, labor, and capital in agriculture. (These nonfarm services probably do not create any additional demand for farm products as a whole.) They do not represent claims on agricultural resources. Accordingly, we shall use the term "farm products" as including all agricultural produce, whether of crop or livestock origin, whether ultimately used for food or for nonfood purposes. "Farm products," as used in this study, are the products as and when they are sold by farmers. Farm products thus defined give us a point of focus in the pricing process at which supply-and-demand forces make their claims for the allocation of resources in agriculture. When we refer to food, it will be in the conventional context, namely, to goods and services used as food by consumers at the point when they are taken over by consumers.

products.[1] The task that this presents is one of ascertaining the income elasticity of farm products. Income elasticity measures the relation between changes in income and changes in the use of income. It is the ratio between the relative increase in the consumption of a product and the relative increase in income, with other factors remaining constant. For example, when a family acquires 10 per cent more income and expends the additional income in such a way that the outlay of the family for a particular product increases 10 per cent, the ratio is 1:1. Accordingly, the income elasticity for this particular product for this particular family is unity (1.0), on the assumption that taste and relative prices have remained constant. If, however, with a 10 per cent increase in income the additional outlay for the product is less than 10 per cent, the income elasticity is less than unity and accordingly is referred to as "inelastic" or "low in elasticity." Conversely, if the rate of outlay for the product is greater than the rate of increase in income, the income elasticity of the product is high.[2]

Two simple examples will illustrate the interplay of the forces shaping the demand for farm products. The assumptions are selected with an eye to the United States—first, to

---

[1] Students of population have added appreciably to our knowledge in their field. Not only have assumptions and procedures been developed, but research has progressed so that we now have available reasonable estimates of what to expect in population in western countries during the next two or three decades. Research to ascertain the changes in expenditure of income has not advanced so far.

[2] The above definition is formulated in terms of changes in income and changes in the expenditure for a product in retail stores. Available statistics do not permit an accurate estimate of the income elasticity of a product in terms of the changes in quantity consumed associated with changes in income. An increase in expenditure for food does not necessarily imply an equivalent increase in demand for farm resources. As family incomes rise, a part of the additional expenditure on food will be for more service, such as home delivery of milk, better packaging, higher "quality" and perhaps a change from low-price to high-price stores. Accordingly, it is necessary to warn the reader that the income elasticities derived from expenditure data overstate the real change in demand for farm products as they leave the farm.

the war period, roughly 1940 to the end of the war; and, second, to the first postwar decade after the transition has been completed. Yet, it should be stressed that the consequences are the results of the assumptions selected and that they are not a prediction of what will happen.[1]

Example 1. The population of the United States, 131,456,-000 on Jan. 1, 1940, rose to 139,126,000 as of January, 1945, an increase of nearly 6 per cent. The rise in real national income in this period, when converted to a per capita basis, represents an increase in the neighborhood of 40 per cent. If these changes had occurred under peacetime conditions, with all the population in civilian pursuits and with goods and services available to civilians, what effect would they have had upon the demand for farm products?[2] Let us assume an income elasticity for farm products of .25. Then the demand presumably would have increased 6 per cent on account of population growth, and 10 per cent on account of rise in per capita income, an aggregate of 16 per cent.[3] If, meanwhile, the output of farm products had expanded only 16 per cent, the additional production would have found buyers at the same relative prices that prevailed at the beginning of the period. Agricultural production, however, increased about 25 per cent during the war years. The inference is plain: had the extraordinary wartime rise in incomes and the 6 per cent increase in population taken place under peacetime conditions, they would not have created enough additional demand for farm products to absorb the production of agriculture of 1943 or 1944 at prices anywhere near those that have prevailed or even at prices as low rela-

[1] In both examples we shall assume that the production and consumption of farm products are in equilibrium at the beginning of each period and, further, that relative prices remain constant.

[2] These estimates are given in somewhat greater detail in the section on income. The income elasticity for farm products is based on the analysis presented later in this chapter.

[3] More accurately, 16.6 per cent since the two percentage increases are superimposed.

tively as they were just prior to the war,[1] unless the export demand had increased very considerably.[2]

Example 2. In this example the assumptions are chosen with a view to postwar conditions, specifically in the first decade after transition has been effected. We assume for this decade: (*a*) a 5 per cent increase in population,[3] (*b*) a 20 per cent increase in income per head,[4] and (*c*) an income

---

[1] Prices received by farmers in 1939 stood at a parity of 76 (with 1910-1914 = 100) compared to 118 in 1943. This means, of course, that farm prices rose sharply relative to other prices. Why did they do this, in view of the large additional supply and the low income elasticity of farm products? The answer lies primarily in the greatly expanded demand for food for noncivilian requirements: during 1935–1939, 97.4 per cent of the total food disappearance went to civilians, while in 1944 only 80.4 per cent of the total was available to them. (The forecast for 1945 is even lower, namely, 77.3 per cent for civilian uses.) Military, including military relief feeding, took 12.8 per cent; War Food Administration purchases (mostly for lend-lease) took 5.5 per cent; and exports accounted for 1.3 per cent of the total food disappearance in 1944. *Cf. The National Food Situation*, U.S. Department of Agriculture, Bureau of Agricultural Economics, April–May, 1945, p. 8.

[2] If the income elasticity of farm products were as high as .5, the additional demand from the 40 per cent increase in income would have been 20 per cent in the example above, and this plus the 6 per cent increase on the account of population would have given a total expansion of 26 per cent, or an increase in the demand no less than that assumed for supply. This makes evident the critical importance of the particular conditions affecting income elasticity of farm products.

What a development of this kind would do to income from farming depends upon the price elasticity of the demand. Elasticity of less than unity would have adverse effects, for the less the elasticity, the greater the loss in income from farming.

[3] The war-induced increase in births (mostly in 1942 and 1943) has pulled the figures for war years above expectations. It is here assumed that after the war the prewar trend will reassert itself.

[4] This is a conservative estimate of the rate of increase in per capita income if full employment is attained and maintained. An annual rate of increase between 3 and 4 per cent appears to be more compatible with the probable advances in technology, accumulations of capital, and improvements in skills of people. A rate of increase in income as high as 4 per cent per year (which would exceed 4 per cent in secondary and tertiary industries because of the low income elasticity of farm products) would be a powerful force in bringing about the essentials of a moving equilibrium between agriculture and nonagricultural fields of economic activity, as we shall show later in this study.

elasticity for farm products of .25.[1]   What effects would these changes have on the growth of the demand for farm products? With these conditions prevailing, the additional demand would total 10 per cent.   If, as might well be, agricultural production were to expand about 20 per cent during the decade,[2] the resulting large oversupply of farm products would require a very substantial movement of resources out of agriculture if the farm sector is not to suffer exceedingly low earnings per person.[3]

The demand for American farm products is derived in large part from populations whose rate of growth is already small and has been diminishing. Within the immediate market range of American agriculture there is not likely to be any considerable increase in population during the next several decades. Furthermore, those nations whose rate of population growth is still large—for example, the USSR, Brazil, the Danubian countries—are not likely to import farm products to satisfy their rising domestic demand, but instead are likely to introduce improvements in farm technology to increase their own agricultural production. Thus, population increases in such countries are not likely to provide additional demand for farm products produced in the United States. Nations with populations still having a high growth potential, for example, China and India, lie mostly outside the market of American agriculture, and for that matter outside the market of most of the agriculture of Western countries.

While population growth has declined in importance in affecting demand, the behavior of people in satisfying their wants as they become richer assumes greater importance. Incomes per capita may rise substantially—provided Western nations have the ability to take advantage of the expanding

[1] The critical reader should be warned that this figure is probably too high relative to Example 1, since it appears that as per capita incomes rise, the income elasticity of farm products tends to fall.

[2] An increase of this magnitude seems likely if farm prices are maintained at the levels at which the support prices are established by present legislation.

[3] On the assumption, which seems reasonable, that the price elasticity of the demand is substantially less than unity.

productivity of the economy. How this additional income is spent becomes a primary determinant of the growth of the demand for farm products in a developing economy of the type that exists here. The income elasticity of farm products, therefore, needs to be made the keystone of any systematic analysis of the growth of the demand for farm products. Lesser determinants are the changes in taste, advances in the knowledge of nutrition (which affect taste and also increase the efficiency of food), public measures to facilitate better diets, changes in the number and composition of the population, and changes in the extent of the market.[1]

Before going further it is necessary to provide the empirical evidence for the assumptions selected and employed in the two preceding examples. During the decade 1950 to 1960, will the population of the United States increase by 5 per cent? Will income per capita rise by 20 per cent? Is income elasticity for food more or less than the .25 assumed? How may progress in nutrition affect the demand for food?

Population

The nightmare of overpopulation that oppressed Malthus and his contemporaries no longer troubles our minds. The rate of population growth in the United States has been dropping rapidly since 1870.[2]

Decade	Per Cent Increase in U.S. Population
1870–1880	26.0
1880–1890	25.5
1890–1900	20.7
1900–1910	21.2
1910–1920	16.2
1920–1930	14.8
1930–1940	7.0
1940–1945 (5 years)	5.7

[1] See a discussion of this formulation by Theodore W. Schultz in "Two Conditions Necessary for Economic Progress in Agriculture," *Canadian Journal of Economics and Political Science*, Vol. X, No. 3 (1944), pp. 305–306.

[2] National Resources Committee, *The Problem of a Changing Population*

The anticipated increases in population during the decade 1950 to 1960 have been estimated as follows:

	Per Cent
United States[1]	5.4
Europe (exclusive of USSR)[2]	1.4
USSR[2]	12.3

The pattern of population growth has a second important effect upon agriculture. The net reproduction rates in industrial-urban areas are decidedly lower than those in farming and rural areas. Notestein and his associates call attention to this difference in the projected growth of the population in northern and western Europe, which is industrialized, as against eastern Europe, which is still largely agricultural. The *National Resources Report* indicates that a similar development has been under way in the United States. As a consequence of these rural-urban differences in net reproduction rates, the population increase still occur-

---

Washington, May, 1938, Table 1, p. 21; and *The Statistical Abstract of the United States, 1942*, p. 9. The 1940–1945 period is based on estimates released by the Bureau of the Census, giving the population as of Jan. 1, 1945, as 139,126,000.

[1] W. S. Thompson and P. K. Whelpton, *Estimates of Future Population of the United States 1940–2000*, Washington, D.C., 1943, Table F1, p. 29, have prepared estimates of the population of the United States based on several sets of assumptions. With medium fertility and mortality and no immigration, their estimate of the population of the United States for 1950 is 143.9 million and for 1960, 151.6 million, which is an increase of 5.4 per cent for the decade 1950–1960. From 1940 through 1945 the population of the United States has increased at an average rate of almost 1.1 per cent a year, which is substantially higher than that of the preceding decade.

[2] Frank W. Notestein, Irene B. Taeuber, Dudley Kirk, Ansley J. Coale, Louise K. Kiser, in *The Future Population of Europe and the Soviet Union* (League of Nations Publication, New York, 1944), show that the population of Europe (exclusive of the USSR) in 1939 was 399 million; and that the projected population for 1950 is estimated at 415 million, an increase of 4 per cent; and for 1960, at 421 million, an increase for the decade 1950–1960 of 1.4 per cent (Table 1, p. 45). The projected population for the USSR rises from 174 million in 1940 to 203 million by 1950, and to 228 million by 1960 (Table 2, p. 56). For estimates of population for the year 2000, see Notestein's paper, "Population—the Long View," in *Food for the World*, edited by Theodore W. Schultz.

ring in the United States and like countries has a kind of perverse effect on agriculture. While it adds somewhat to the demand for farm products, it also further burdens agriculture by adding very considerably to the excess supply of labor resources in agriculture. For the next two or three decades the increase in farm population will in all likelihood aggravate the farm problem, already peculiarly vulnerable to overpopulation relative to economic opportunity.[1]

Income

With the return of prosperity, induced by the war, has come a wave of optimism bringing in its wake a widespread belief that the wartime gains in income will be maintained and that the additional purchasing power will, among other things, provide an adequate market for farm products. The low income elasticity of farm products certainly does not support this expectation, even if the gains in income are held.

Any attempt to ascertain the prospective growth of incomes is on a distinctly different footing from the attempt to project changes in population. Changes in income are more erratic, less determined by a few slowly changing factors, and much more sensitive to the general instability of the economy than are changes in population. Headway has been made in measuring income but little has been done to stake out its prospective growth. A casual indication is provided by the record of the immediate past: income per capita rose rapidly for several decades prior to World War I, showed no decisive drift during the interwar years, and advanced markedly during World War II.

Kuznets found that "Over the thirty years 1909–1938 aggregate payments, excluding entrepreneurial savings, in

[1] League of Nations, European Conference on Rural Life, *Population and Agriculture with Special Reference to Agriculture Overpopulation*, 1939; Contributions by the International Institute of Agriculture, Doc. 1; European Conference on Rural Life Publications No. 3, Geneva, 1939

1929 prices, rose substantially. But since population and the number gainfully occupied also grew rapidly, aggregate payments per capita and per person gainfully occupied rose only moderately (about 11 and 7 per cent respectively)."[1] Colin Clark[2] shows incomes growing rapidly in the decades

[1] Simon Kuznets, *National Income and Its Composition, 1919–1938*, National Bureau of Economic Research, New York, 1941, Vol. I, Table 11, p. 158. Kuznets gives the aggregate income payments to individuals in 1929 prices, excluding entrepreneurial savings, for 1919–1923 as $533 per capita; for 1924–1928, as $626; for 1929–1933, as $598; and for 1934–1938, as $581. Obviously, these figures do not indicate any pronounced upward drift for the interwar period.

[2] *The Conditions of Economic Progress*, Macmillan & Co., Ltd., London, 1940. The following data are from the table facing p. 148. It is important to note

NATIONAL INCOME PRODUCED PER HEAD OF WORKING POPULATION
(In work and unemployed on basis of 48-hour week)

Year	United States	Great Britain	Sweden	Germany	Australia
1870	730	546	197	460 (1876)	
1880	813	687	209	522	551
1890	958	750	243	575	652
1900	1161	865⎱ 901⎰	325	618	645
1910	1211	953 (1912)	459 (1912)	688 (1911–13)	
1915	1263	966 (1913)	486	704 (1913)	742
1920	1258	....	651	....	754
1925	1465	1077	600	579	1051
1930	1407	1107	704	659	868
1932	910	932	650	557	972
1935	1253	1145	768	693	1169
1937	1485	1275	....	828	1212

Year	Canada	New Zealand	France	Japan
1870	....	....	410	
1880	....	....	469	
1890	....	....	551	72
1900	1130	880	630	72
1910	1061	....	629	99
1915	....	....	...	106
1920	1409	....	512	153
1925	1342	1271	701	248
1930	1296	1132	670	295
1932	1028	1167	667	319
1935	1260	1406	641 (1934)	345
1937	....	1702	....	337 (1936)

prior to World War I, followed by erratic changes with very slow growth during the interwar period, both for the United States and Great Britain. The income per head of working population increased 50 per cent in the United States from 1880 to 1910 (going from $813 to $1211). The increase in Great Britain was somewhat less rapid, rising from $687 to $953 (1880–1912). The Swedish experience differs, with marked growth during the earlier period and with a considerable rise during the interwar years.

It is impossible to measure precisely changes in real income that occur in wartime. A conservative estimate is that the national product, measured in 1939 dollars, increased from $71.6 billion in 1939 to $105.9 billion in the first half of 1943,[1] an increase of virtually 50 per cent. Adjusted to a per capita basis,[2] this is a rise of nearly 40 per cent. (This is the figure that we used in Example 1.) Can this gain in income be maintained after the war? Obviously not, unless production and employment are at high levels. Provided resources are

---

that the income produced per head of working population is not directly related to income produced per capita, and that the slowing down of the rate of upward movement in any country may be caused by an increase in unemployment, by a decline in productivity per worker per hour, or by a combination of the two. It is evident in the case of the United States and Great Britain that the whole flattening of the curve may be attributed to the increasing unemployment and the reduction in the hours of work, but with productivity per worker per hour continuing to increase.

[1] Simon Kuznets, *National Product War and Prewar*, "Our Economy in War Series," Occasional Paper 17, National Bureau of Economic Research, New York, February, 1944. Income is in terms of 1939 final product prices and is based on Kuznets' assumption "a," the least favorable of the three, regarding relative efficiency of resources in munitions and war construction. See Appendix Table 12, p. 52.

[2] In this calculation we have taken the $71.6 billion net national product and divided by 131,456,000 (the U.S. population as of Jan. 1, 1940) giving a per capita income of $545; and $105.9 billion by 139,126,000 (the population estimated for Jan. 1, 1945) resulting in a per capita figure of $761, an increase of 39.3 per cent. Note that Kuznets' figure of $105.9 billion is taken as a war peak and applied to population as of January, 1945.

efficiently and fully employed, further gains in income may be had in subsequent decades from advances in technology, greater efficiency in the working population, further growth in labor force, and from other sources, amounting to 3 to 4 per cent per annum.[1]

Income Elasticity

As incomes increase, the distribution of consumer expenditures among different items changes: the proportion of the income spent on the necessaries, such as food, decreases, while that spent on luxuries and put into savings increases. This is known as "Engel's law," based on the study that he published in 1888. This formulation of the expenditures of people as they become richer was an important first step. Yet it is a long way from providing an answer to the question, what is the income elasticity of farm products?

In an expanding economy, with incomes rising and with technology in agriculture improving, it makes a great difference whether the income elasticity of farm products is less than .5 or substantially more, and whether it is falling slowly or rapidly. In other words, we need to know the position and also the drift of the income elasticity of farm products.

In this study we shall focus upon the income elasticity of farm products taken as a whole and not upon the differences among farm products. It is well known that the income elasticity of some fruits, vegetables, meats, and dairy products is comparatively high relative to that of most farm products, while potatoes, wheat and rye (for bread), and grain for cereals have not only a low, but in some cases actually a negative income elasticity. Some farm products used for industrial purposes may well develop a high elasticity against income. All these differences are important in understanding the economic forces playing upon a particular farm product.

[1] In our Example 2 we assumed a growth in income of only 2 per cent per year, which would be far from the essentials of full employment of all resources.

Nevertheless, there is such a broad band of effective substitution in the use of agricultural resources in producing alternative farm products that much real insight can be had

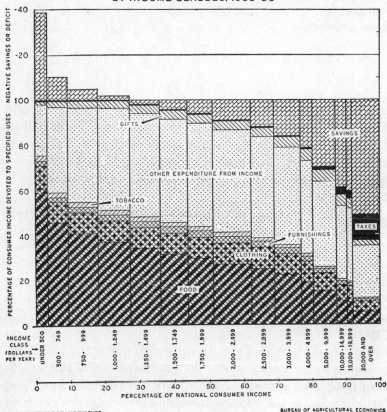

ALLOCATION OF CONSUMER INCOME TO SAVINGS, GIFTS, PERSONAL TAXES, EXPENDITURES FOR CONSUMERS' GOODS DERIVED FROM AGRICULTURAL PRODUCTS, AND OTHER EXPENDITURES, BY INCOME CLASSES, 1935-36

U. S. DEPARTMENT OF AGRICULTURE   BUREAU OF AGRICULTURAL ECONOMICS

regarding agriculture from the over-all approach followed here.

Again, it is necessary to stress that we are concerned with the claims that the demand resulting from larger incomes may make on agricultural resources. It is the demand for the products as they leave agriculture, and not at a later stage, in which we are interested. This distinction is particularly relevant at this point because it appears that the income elasticity of food, clothing, and of other goods made from farm products is higher than the income elasticity of farm products. The reason is that, as incomes rise, most consumers desire more services incorporated and attached to farm products.

EXPENDITURES FOR FARM PRODUCTS

1870–1910

The economic development from the Civil War to World War I offers some instructive data for gauging the effects of rises in income on the demand for farm products, inasmuch as real incomes per capita (in terms of 1929–1934 prices) rose from \$311 in 1870 to \$574 in 1910, a rise of virtually 85 per cent.

In Table I we have a very rough measure of the proportion of the income of American people that went into farm products during each census year from 1870 to 1910. This table rests on the assumption that farm incomes adjusted for agricultural exports and imports are an approximate measure of the "expenditure" of Americans for farm products. In 1870, with a per capita income in real terms of \$311, 34 per cent was "spent" for farm products. In 1910, when the per capita income had risen to \$574, the proportion "spent" for farm products fell to 19 per cent. As a consequence of this significant decline of almost one half in the proportion "spent" on farm products, the per capita dollar expenditures on farm products were only slightly greater in 1910 than in 1870, though real per capita income had risen 85 per cent. In comparing 1870 and 1910, we find that although prices generally declined (they dropped sharply from 1870 to 1896, after which they rose substantially), the relative position of the price of farm products to that of all commodities did not

TABLE I
UNITED STATES NATIONAL INCOME AND "EXPENDITURE" ON FARM PRODUCTS ADJUSTED FOR AGRICULTURAL EXPORTS AND IMPORTS, PER CAPITA, 1870–1910

Year	(1) National Income per capita, current prices[a]	(2) "Domestic expenditures" on farm products per capita, current prices[b]	(3) Proportion (2) is of (1), per cent[c]	(4) National income per capita in real terms, 1925–1934 prices[d]	(5) "Domestic expenditures" on farm products per capita, in real terms, 1925–1934 prices[e]
1870	$180	$61	34	$311	$106
1880	160	52	32	358	115
1890	206	45	22	431	95
1900	254	44	17	528	90
1910	341	66	19	574	109

[a] *Cf.* Colin Clark, *The Conditions of Economic Progress*, Macmillan & Company, Ltd., London, 1940, pp. 78–79. Based on W. I. King, *Wealth and Income of the People of the United States*, The Macmillan Company, New York, 1915, p. 129. The only adjustment is the inclusion of the annual value of rents from dwelling houses. The population figures are from the *Statistical Abstract of the United States, 1942*, p. 11.

[b] Based on farm income minus the value of agricultural exports plus the value of agricultural imports minus the value of imports of crude rubber and raw silk. Value of agricultural exports and imports at the port overvalues these somewhat relative to farm income, which is determined by farm prices. However, since neither exports nor imports bulked large or changed considerably relative to the total farm income, no appreciable error is introduced by this overvaluation. Frederick Strauss and Louis H. Bean, *Gross Farm Income and Indices of Farm Products and Prices in the United States, 1869–1937*, U.S. Department of Agriculture, Technical Bulletin 703, Table 7, p. 23; and U.S. Department of Commerce, *Statistical Abstract of the United States, 1942*, p. 548.

[c] The per cent that column 2 is of column 1.

[d] From the same source as column 1, converted from money income to real terms by use of a retail price index for 1925–1934. *Cf.* Colin Clark, *op. cit.*, p. 78.

[e] Obtained by multiplying columns 3 and 4.

change markedly (farm prices rose somewhat, relatively).[1] Leaving changes in taste aside, the inference is that the very marked rise in real per capita income was accompanied by a marked decline in the proportion of that income that was

[1] All commodity prices dropped from an index of 135 in 1870 to 103 in 1910. The index for the price of foods dropped from 139 to 101, and farm products from 112 to 104, during the same period. Accordingly, farm prices rose somewhat relative to nonagricultural commodities at wholesale in the United States during the period 1870–1910. See W. F. Warren and F. A. Pearson, "Index Numbers of Wholesale Prices in the U.S., 1786–1931," *Prices* (New York, 1933), Table III, p. 26.

"spent" for farm products. Thus, it would appear that the elasticity of expenditure for farm products with respect to income was in the neighborhood of zero; certainly at best it had a very low positive value.[1]

1922 to 1939

For a later period than 1870 to 1910, it is less easy to gauge the effects of rises in income on the demand for farm products. However, from the apparent relationship between national income and "expenditure" for farm products from 1922 to

TABLE II

UNITED STATES NATIONAL INCOME AND "EXPENDITURES" ON FARM PRODUCTS ADJUSTED FOR AGRICULTURAL EXPORTS AND IMPORTS, PER CAPITA, 1922 TO 1939

	(1)	(2)	(3)	(4)	(5)
Year	*National income per capita, current prices*[a]	*"Domestic expenditures" on farm products per capita, current prices*[b]	*Proportion (2) is of (1), per cent*	*National income per capita in real terms, 1929 prices*[c]	*"Domestic expenditures" on farm products in real terms, 1929 prices*[d]
1922	$522	$ 84	16.1	$553	89
1925	656	101	15.4	644	99
1929	716	96	13.4	716	96
1934	392	50	12.8	491	63
1937	547	75	13.7	625	86
1939	552	64	11.6	673	78

[a] Computed from: Simon Kuznets, *National Income and Its Composition, 1919–1938*, National Bureau of Economic Research, New York, 1941, Vol. I, p. 139. Simon Kuznets, *National Product War and Prewar*, Appendix Table 7, p. 46. *Statistical Abstract of the United States, 1942*, p. 11.

[b] Frederick Strauss and Louis H. Bean, *Gross Farm Income and Indices of Farm Products and Prices in the United States, 1869–1937*, Table 7, p. 23. *Statistical Abstract of the United States, 1940*, p. 668. *Statistical Abstract of the United States, 1942*, pp. 11, 548, 745.

[c] Simon Kuznets, *National Income and Its Composition, 1919–1938*, Vol. I, p. 153. Simon Kuznets, *National Product War and Prewar*, Appendix Table 7, p. 46. *Statistical Abstract of the United States, 1942*, pp. 11, 372.

[d] (3) multiplied by (4).

[1] What we have is an increase of 85 per cent in real income accompanied by a 3 per cent increase in "expenditures" for farm products. If other factors had remained constant, this would have been an income elasticity for farm products of .03.

1939 (see Table II), we may guess that for this period also the income elasticity of farm products was very low.[1]

Thus the apparent relationship between income and "expenditure" for farm products (indicated in Tables I and II) suggests the same conclusion.

Gauging Present Elasticity

There are, however, several reasons for taking these tentative historical results as representing the lower limits of income elasticity of farm products. To stake out the range within which the income elasticity of farm products may fall, we take consumer expenditures for food as establishing the upper limit.[2]

Allen and Bowley,[3] in 1935, summarized the results of a number of family-expenditure studies. In no case did they find the income elasticity of the demand for food, at the average expenditure level, to be as high as 1. In ten of their

---

[1] Between World Wars I and II, incomes fluctuated widely, as is evident from Table II. But here, again, the proportion of the national per capita income presumably "spent" for farm products declined, dropping from about 16 per cent in 1922 to 11.6 per cent in 1939. The per capita income, in terms of 1929 prices, rose about 30 per cent from 1922 to 1929, and the amount "spent" for farm products, also in 1929 prices, rose about 8 per cent. Since prices that farmers received increased fully 20 per cent from 1922 to 1929, and since all commodity prices at wholesale dropped slightly, the 8 per cent rise in the amount "spent" for farm products was larger on account of the changes in the relative position of farm to other prices than it would have been had prices remained constant. For the entire period, from 1922 to 1939, the per capita income (in 1929 prices) rose about one-fifth, yet the amount "spent" for farm products (in 1929 prices) dropped from $89 to $78, a decline of nearly 13 per cent. Farm prices, however, dropped about 28 per cent from 1922–1939, while all commodities at wholesale declined about 20 per cent.

[2] Consumer expenditures on food leave out all the nonfood farm products and include all the nonfarm factors that have been incorporated in food when consumers make their purchases. We shall show later that the income elasticity of the demand for the nonfarm services that become attached to the farm products when they are purchased by consumers as food is greater than the income elasticity of the net demand for farm products without such services.

[3] R. G. D. Allen and A. L. Bowley, *Family Expenditures, A Study of Its Variations,* London, 1935, Table A, pp. 32–33.

budget studies, food fell between .8 and .9;[1] in eight studies, between .5 and .7;[2] and in three, between .3 and .45.[3]   Clark,[4] using United States data of nonfarm families, reports, "The average income elasticity of demand for food for the community as a whole is only .38, although it is clearly higher in the lower ranges of income."[5]   For incomes from $0 to $3,000, the elasticity of food as calculated by Clark was .80, and for incomes $3,000 and larger it was .14.[6]   The 1935–1936 Consumer Purchase Study in the United States was undoubtedly the most comprehensive ever attempted.   Kaplan,[7] drawing on this study, found that the expenditure elasticity of food, at the mean, was as follows: for wage-earner families, Chicago, .636; wage-earner families, Denver, .633; salaried business families, Chicago, .347; and for salaried business families, Denver, .461.   Kaplan points out, however, that the expenditures for food in the higher income families include more services: " . . . the percentage spent for food declines but gradually for incomes between $1,500 and $5,000.   With increasing income, the food bill takes on expenses of eating out and entertaining, as well as the introduction of delicacies into the food budget."[8]   Gold and Enlow[9] give the elasticity of

[1] *Ibid.*, Liverpool, 1929, workers, .9; Belgium, 1928–1929, workers, .8; Germany, 1927–1928, workers, .8, and salaried employees, .8; Oslo, 1912–1913, all classes, .8; Oslo and Bergen, 1918–1919, all classes, .9; Finland, 1920–1921, workers, .8; Czechoslovakia, 1927, workers, .85, and 1929, workers, .8; and United States, 1918, all classes, .8.

[2] *Ibid.*, London School of Economics, 1932, all classes, .5; Amsterdam, 1923–1924, all classes, .5; Germany, 1927–1928, officials, .7; Basle, 1912, all classes, .7, and 1921, all classes, .6; Czechoslovakia, 1927, officials, .7, and 1929, officials, .7; and United States, 1928–1929, farmers, 0.7.

[3] *Ibid.*, Copenhagen, 1922, all classes, .3; Denmark, 1922, all classes, .3; Poland, 1929, workers, .45.

[4] Colin Clark, *The Conditions of Economic Progress*, pp. 436–439.   Clark's calculations are based on data appearing in M. Leven, H. Moulton, C. Warburton, *America's Capacity to Consume*, Brookings Institution, Washington, D.C., 1934.

[5] *Ibid.*, p. 438.

[6] *Ibid.*, p. 437.

[7] A. D. H. Kaplan, "Expenditure Patterns of Urban Families," *Journal of American Statistical Association*, Vol. 33 (1938), pp. 97, 98.

[8] *Ibid.*, p. 85.

[9] Norman L. Gold and Maxime Enlow, "The Demand for Food by Low

expenditure for food for the population as a whole (based on the Consumer Purchase Study of 1935–1936), as follows:

Income Class	Elasticity of Expenditure
Under $500	.5
$ 500–$1,000	.5
1,000– 1,500	.4
1,500– 2,000	.4
2,000– 3,000	.4

In 1929, with per capita incomes somewhat higher, the elasticity of food expenditure may have been even slightly lower than the 1935–1936 figures. With incomes as high as those of 1943 and 1944 (probably 40 per cent above the levels of 1939 on the per capita real basis), the elasticity of expenditure for food may have fallen to less than .4. We now turn to a brief exploration of the area between the lower and upper limits.[1]

Income Families," *Quarterly Journal of Economics*, Vol. LVII (1943), Table 1, p. 602.

[1] We have refrained from including in this study an exhaustive review of the literature on the elasticity of expenditure for food. Nor does it seem appropriate to include the several analyses that we have made in focusing various studies to the problem at hand. One such additional computation does, however, deserve attention at this point; it is based on data in Hildegarde Kneeland, *Consumer Expenditures in the United States, Estimates for 1935–1936*, National Resources Committee, Washington, D.C., 1939, Table 18, p. 6.

Income range per capita	Expenditure range per capita	Elasticity of expenditures with respect to income	
$465–$ 560	$142–$156	.4826[a]	.5064[b]
560– 674	156– 171	.4722	.4962
674– 830	171– 189	.4546	.4821
830–1,038	189– 201	.2533	.2764

---

[a] Elasticity $= \dfrac{\Delta E/E_1}{\Delta Y/Y_1}$ [b] Elasticity $= \dfrac{\Delta E/(E_1 + E_2)}{\Delta Y/(Y_1 + Y_2)}$

ΔE = increment in expenditure per capita in the expenditure range.
E_1 = expenditure per capita of lower expenditure range.
E_2 = expenditure per capita of the higher expenditure range.
ΔY = increment in income per capita in income range.
Y_1 = income per capita of the lower income range.
Y_2 = income per capita of the higher income range.

From the preceding analysis it may be presumed (very tentatively indeed) that the income elasticity of farm products lies somewhere between .4 (based on expenditures for food, from the Consumer Purchase Studies) and about .1 (based on expenditures for farm products, from the rough historical data prior to World War I). To take the mid-point, namely, .25, is a crude way of ascertaining the approximate point.

Until more exhaustive studies have been made,[1] we must draw upon qualitative analysis, turning principally on the supposition that people as they become richer increase their expenditures proportionately more for the nonfarm services in food than for the farm products in food. (For example, people eat more meals in restaurants and other public establishments as their incomes rise.)

Certain commodities tend to stay fairly constant in their physical composition as farm products, but may change substantially in value at the point at which consumers buy them, reflecting the amount and kind of nonfarm services added in processing, handling, delivering, and serving these products as food. Examining the expenditures for such products, we can obtain another approximation of the income elasticity of food products at the farm level. Cheese is a good example. Whether cheese is prepared as common Cheddar or whether it is eventually made into a highly refined Blue cheese, the raw materials do not vary greatly, nor, consequently, do the claims made on agricultural resources. In Table III, a number of commodities of this type have been selected, and their elasticities have been ascertained, both for physical consumption (quantity) and for value of consumption (quantity plus quality) against income. In each case the elasticity of physical consumption is less, and considerably less, than the elasticity of the value of consumption of the product. For the products listed, the average

[1] Such a study is being projected by Professor Jacob Marschak, Director of the Cowles Commission for Economic Research, University of Chicago, and Theodore W. Schultz.

TABLE III

THE ELASTICITY OF PHYSICAL CONSUMPTION AND THE ELASTICITY OF THE VALUE
OF CONSUMPTION WITH RESPECT TO INCOME OF UNITED STATES NONRELIEF
NONFARM FAMILIES, MARCH–NOVEMBER, 1936

Family income range	Commodity	Elasticity of physical consumption	Elasticity of the value of consumption
$1,233–$1,707	Tomato juice......	1.6311	1.8579
	Cheese...........	0.4654	0.5902
	Milk	0.3587	0.4138
	Butter	0.3072	0.3681
	Bananas..........	0.2952	0.3220
	Eggs.............	0.1625	0.3080
	Canned tomatoes..	−0.0128	0.1038
	Beans............	−0.4180	−0.2890
$1,707–$2,396	Tomato juice......	1.2740	1.3763
	Cheese...........	0.3538	0.4070
	Milk.............	0.2611	0.3146
	Butter...........	0.2094	0.2675
	Bananas..........	0.1803	0.2098
	Eggs.............	0.1457	0.2834
	Canned tomatoes..	−0.9046	0.0000
	Beans............	−0.5587	−0.4645

SOURCES: Data used are from: *Consumer Purchases of Certain Foods, U.S. Non-relief Non-farm Families, March–November, 1936*, U.S. Department of Agriculture, Washington, D.C., Division of Marketing and Marketing Agreements, March, 1940. The income figures were derived by calculating the average income per family in the income levels $1,000–$1,500, $1,500–$2,000, $2,000–$3,000 respectively. *Cf.* National Resources Planning Board, *Family Expenditures in the United States, Statistical Tables and Appendixes*, Washington, D.C., June, 1941, p. 29.

The elasticity formula used is

$$\frac{\Delta x}{\Delta y} \frac{y}{x}$$

where Δx = the increment in the average *physical* consumption of all families in the first case, and the increment in the *value* of average consumption per family in the second, Δy = the increment in the mean of the income range.

y = the mean in the lower-income range.
x = the mean of the physical consumption of all families in the lower-income range in the first case, and the mean of the value of average consumption per family in the lower-income range in the second.

difference for the lower-income range ($1,233–$1,707) appears to be nearly 25 per cent, that is, the elasticity based on physical consumption is about a fourth less than it is when based on value of consumption.

A new index[1] of consumption, prepared by the Bureau of Agricultural Economics, U.S. Department of Agriculture, attempts to establish the relationship between changes in income and physical consumption (again, however, in terms of retail sales). For the period 1929–1942 the elasticity of per capita consumption of food (physical volume) with respect to real per capita income was approximately .21.[2] These various bits of information do suggest that the rough procedure of taking the mid-point, namely, .25, may not be very far wrong. At least it is not inconsistent with the evidence at hand.

One additional observation needs to be made: whatever the income elasticity of farm products is at a given level of incomes, there is a strong likelihood that as incomes rise further, this elasticity will become even less.[3]

NUTRITION AND EXPENDITURES ON FOOD[4]

Progress in nutrition also affects the demand for food. With incomes and prices given, advances in applied nutrition

[1] The new index of per capita consumption, both total and by groups, differs from the earlier index in that it is constructed from "retail weights" of foods consumed. Allowances are made for farm-to-retail-market losses and processing losses. One additional difference: the earlier index was weighted by BLS retail prices in cities, whereas the new index is weighted by a series of prices which presumably reflect retail prices in rural areas as well as in cities.

[2] For income payments the U.S. Department of Commerce series has been used; it has been divided by total population. This per capita figure has been adjusted by wholesale commodity price index (1926 = 100). (*Federal Reserve Bulletin*, June, 1944, p. 593.)

[3] It is necessary to emphasize again the fact that all the assumptions appearing in this chapter are focused on long-run developments and thus cannot be applied to consequences growing out of short-run fluctuations. Obviously, changes in population do not throw any appreciable light on the instability of farm incomes, nor does the income elasticity when it is as low as that of farm products. The problem of instability of income from farming arises primarily out of short-run fluctuations in the nonagricultural sectors of the economy.

[4] This section was first prepared by Theodore W. Schultz as part of a paper, "Food Supply and Nutrition in a Developing Economy," read before the American Home Economics Association, June, 1944, published in the *Journal of Home Economics*, Vol. 36 (1944), pp. 405–408.

make themselves felt in the economic sphere in two significant ways: (*a*) by changing the taste of consumers, and (*b*) by increasing the efficiency of food. The first of these may either increase or decrease the demand for food; the second, however, definitely points to a curtailment in demand. Nutrition as a movement has expressed itself thus far chiefly in measures, private and public, to close the nutritional gap. This movement has added to the demand for food.

Much depends, accordingly, on how nutrition is put to use. It is not in any sense predetermined what nutrition *as knowledge* and *as a movement* will do to the demand for farm products. Education may bring people to place a higher value on food, relative to other goods and services; even with incomes remaining constant, they would then choose to spend more of their incomes for food. Such changes in the values underlying consumers' choices are fundamental, and they are not likely to occur rapidly. The common belief is that more complete knowledge regarding nutrition will induce people to consume more of the expensive foods, costlier in terms of land, labor, and other resources required to produce them. Much of the planned promotion in behalf of better nutrition in the interwar years was of this nature. It fitted in well with people's taste and food habits, and it also supplemented the wish of public policy makers to enlarge the market for farm products.

Other than education, certain public measures to improve diets are indirect; for example, measures that lessen the inequality of incomes among families. Food consumption being more expansible in the lower-income groups, a more equal distribution of income would increase the demand. Progress of this kind, however, is likely to be very slow and gradual; even under favorable conditions, it is not likely to add appreciably to the demand for farm products during the course of a decade or two.

There are, however, direct steps to aid consumers to attain better diets which would have a considerable bearing on the demand for food. Governments will undoubtedly do much in this sphere if agricultural surpluses persist. Food-stamp plans, food grants and aids, in-factory feeding, school-lunch programs, are some of the measures for doing this task.

Closing the Nutritional Gap

Many families in the United States do not have an adequate diet, that is, adequate in terms of nutrition. Before the war, despite the large supply of food and the ease with which more food might have been produced, many Americans were short on some essential nutrients in their food. A recent report summarizes the deficiencies, pointing out that in 1936 "fewer than a fifth of the families in this country had diets that met the National Research Council's recommendations for all of the seven nutrients considered (protein, calcium, iron, vitamin A value, ascorbic acid, thiamine, and riboflavin)."[1] By 1942 there had occurred a general dietary improvement as families benefited from higher incomes and advances in nutrition education. In the case of riboflavin, in 1936 three-fourths of all families had diets that fell below the National Research Council's recommendations; in 1942 about one-half were below this mark. In calcium, thiamine, and ascorbic acid, whereas in 1936 only one-half were up to the recommendations of the National Research Council, by 1942 the proportion had risen to two-thirds for calcium, three-fourths for thiamine, and to nine-tenths for ascorbic acid. There were also marked dietary improvements in vitamin A value, iron, and protein.

Another way to measure this nutritional gap is in terms of the additional acres of crops and numbers of livestock that would be needed to supply enough food for a specified diet. To do this it is necessary to start with some assumptions with regard to the cost of the diet and the distribution of food among consumers. A diet that would meet the nutritional

[1] "Family Food Consumption in the United States," U.S. Department of Agriculture, Washington, D.C., *Miscellaneous Publication 550*, 1944, pp. 34–35.

standards established by the National Research Council at moderate cost and with consumption evenly distributed would have required no more acreage of crops and slaughter of livestock to supply the 1942 population than was produced in 1941.[1] To supply a low-cost diet to all low-income families, a moderate-cost diet to families with moderate incomes, and a liberal diet to all high-income families, assuming consumption of food to be evenly distributed among families within each group, would have required no more food, feed, and livestock than a diet at moderate cost.[2] These estimates, however, understate the amount of food that would be required to supply to all families diets of a level that would meet the nutritional levels recommended by the National Research Council, because of the assumptions made regarding distribution.

A more realistic procedure would entail estimating the additional amount of food required, with the national income and the price of food at specified levels, to bring all inadequate diets up to some minimum level, the social and economic conditions of the differing portions of the population remaining as they are. How large is the nutritional gap when formulated thus? The relevant data now available are too fragmentary to give a conclusive answer. The following is intended merely as a very rough approximation: With the national income at the 1944 level and with farm prices at 90 per cent of parity (very high incomes and relatively low farm prices), not more than 10 per cent more food would

[1] O. V. Wells, "Estimates of Quantities of Food Necessary to Provide Certain Specific Diets and Crop Acreages and Number of Livestock Required for Indicated Production," Statement before Committee Investigating National Defense Migration, House of Representatives, February 13, 1942 (U.S. Department of Agriculture, Washington, D.C.). For this diet 321 million acres would have been required to supply the population of 133,900,000 while the 1941 acreage of food and feed was 324 million. All livestock production in 1941, except sheep and lambs and milk, ran higher than the amount specified.

[2] *Ibid.*, *cf.* Table 3. O. V. Wells's estimate indicates 319 million acres for food and feed for this diet compared to 321 million acres for the diet at moderate cost distributed evenly among families.

need to be added as a supplement to what consumers would buy, to meet nutritional standards. The 10 per cent figure is on the large and safe side; the figure very likely would be somewhat less than that. The amount required to supplement diets would, however, rise as incomes fell and also as farm prices rose.

Leaving the nutritional gap aside or supposing it has been closed, the increasing efficiency in use of food, resulting from advances in knowledge of nutrition, is likely to reduce the demand for food. Many ways are being disclosed for improving diets at less cost—cost in terms of the land, labor, and other resources it takes to produce food. The special effort to economize on resources during the war offers insight as to what may be expected. In this respect, advances in nutrition are a kind of technological progress, enlarging the range of satisfactions for people in the area of available food products, and making apparent how better diets may be obtained at less cost. As this development takes place it will not, as is commonly supposed, create additional demand for food; on the contrary, by making it possible to substitute cheaper nutrients for more expensive ones (for example, some fats and proteins from vegetables for some of those from animal sources), advances in nutrition are likely to save on food producing resources.

CAUSES FOR THE FAST GROWTH OF THE SUPPLY

The rate at which the supply of farm products expands depends upon advances in technology, improvements in the skills of farm people, investment (or disinvestment) in agriculture, this last including the development of land resources and changes in producer preferences. Changes in relative prices notwithstanding, some of these forces affecting the output of farm products are likely to continue to increase the supply. The foremost is technology.

Technology

A revolution in agricultural production, the counterpart of the technological advance in industry, is going on about us.

There are, however, two major differences between industry and agriculture with regard to technology. First, the basic and applied research in the sciences that contributes to the advances in agricultural technology is not done by the firm (farm) but by public agencies, namely, the state agricultural experiment stations and the U.S. Department of Agriculture. In industry most of this research is done by the firm and, since it is costly, only large corporations can afford to engage in it. In agriculture, by contrast, the necessary research has been not only institutionalized but socialized. The small family-type farm is obviously in no position to finance, organize, and conduct the highly complicated, costly studies entailed in agricultural chemistry, plant and animal breeding, feeding, agronomy, and the many other applied sciences that enter into farm technology. It is, therefore, appropriate that the cost be borne by society as a whole, through the agency of the government.[1] Since the research is done by public agencies, the results are and should be available to any and all producers.[2] Any discoveries improving the technology, therefore, do not become the property of a particular group of farmers. The new knowledge is made common knowledge; in fact, much effort and the expenditure of considerable public funds are involved in disseminating such new knowledge to farm people through the federal-state agricultural extension services.

The competitive structure of agriculture is highly conducive to the introduction of new technology. This constitutes the second major difference between agriculture and industry insofar as technological advances are concerned. Much

[1] The expenditures of the Federal and state governments on agricultural researches in the United States appeared to have exceeded $40 million annually prior to the war.

[2] There are signs that some university organizations are attempting to take advantage of their new researches to obtain revenue through the sale of the patents. Patents in themselves are a necessary protection to assure that the discoveries will not be misappropriated and misused. To use the patent, however, also as a source of revenue, especially in the agricultural processing and merchandising field with its imperfections in competition, raises problems in social policy.

plant and equipment may be made obsolete by the new technology, but the introduction of the new technique will not be postponed to maintain the capital value of such obsolete investments. Competition makes it necessary for farmers as producers to adopt the new technology or find themselves at a disadvantage relative to other farmers who do so. The spread of advances in technology in agriculture has back of it the impelling force of competition, with hundreds of thousands of small firms in a highly competitive relationship, one to another, in production.[1] This situation is in sharp contrast to the upper reaches of industry where most research is carried on, and where the number of firms in competition with each other is commonly very small, sufficiently so to give rise to those imperfections in competition that permit the firm to decide whether to adopt the new technique or postpone doing so.

A forward surge in farm technology is on, still *in its early stages*. It will take decades for the already known improvements in farm practices and techniques to be transmitted from the more advanced to the more backward farming areas; from the wheat and corn belts to the backward parts of the Appalachians and the South; and from countries like Canada, Australia, and the United States, countries that are far in the lead in farm technology, to those now using primitive and inefficient tools and machinery, crops and livestock techniques.

The United States entered the war with about 6 million farms. By 1944 the number of farms had shrunk perhaps

[1] It is commonly thought that the public appropriations for agricultural research benefit farm people primarily. This is far from true; the gains from these researches are quickly transmitted to those who buy and use farm products in lower prices, and new and better commodities; farmers benefit, when they do, in their capacity as consumers. They do not, as a rule, benefit as producers because of the sluggishness that characterizes the transfer of resources out of agriculture, except that those who first introduce the new technique benefit until the price of the product falls as a result of the expanded output. Advances in technology in agriculture have been an important factor depressing farm prices and, accordingly, rewards to agricultural resources, below their equilibrium value.

one-tenth, the farm population had declined one-sixth, and the labor supply had lost much in quality though not greatly in quantity. Nevertheless, agricultural production had been increased fully one-fourth. It has been estimated that by 1950, 4 million of our farms could readily produce a third more than did the entire 6 million prior to the war.[1]

Farm technology now in the offing indicates that if farm prices are maintained so that they average parity,[2] improved crop and livestock practices already established may well bring a further increase in agricultural production of as much as 20 per cent during the first decade after the war.

Mechanization affects production in diverse ways. Mechanical power and equipment is primarily labor-saving; it also sends a larger share of the product to market; and it increases crop yields, through farmers doing their field work more effectively. When mechanical power is substituted for draft animals, the hay, pasture, and feed grains used to feed horses and mules are released to produce milk, pork, beef, eggs, and other animal products. This substitution increases the proportion of the farm output that enters market channels. The importance of such substitution of machines for draft animals is apparent from the fact that a further decline of only 2 million in the number of horses and mules would release 6.5 million acres of cropland for other uses—enough feed to produce 5.5 billion pounds more milk.[1]

---

[1] Based on unpublished data by Sherman E. Johnson of the Bureau of Agricultural Economics, U.S. Department of Agriculture.

[2] This estimate will strike some readers as "very high." It should be noted, however, that it is based on the assumption that farm prices are "supported" at 100 per cent of parity (as parity is defined by law). Alternative price assumptions are considered below.

Among these practices we include an increase in the use of fertilizers and lime, improved varieties of crops, including pasture, and those erosion-control measures which quickly increase crop yields. On the livestock side, better feeding and care and breeding improvements give immediate promise of increased efficiencies.

Improved practices and new techniques thus have two salient features: (*a*) they are labor-saving, for they tend to reduce the marginal productivity of labor in agriculture (they replace labor, thus making it more plentiful and cheaper); and (*b*) they increase, by contrast, the marginal productivity of certain types of capital—such as power-driven machinery and equipment, hybrid seeds, and new breeds of animals. Returns from capital inputs of this type are therefore high in spite of the general excess of resources in agriculture. With the technological changes in progress, and with the widespread capital rationing both internal (self-induced) and external (imposed), many areas in agriculture are starving for new capital. The marginal efficiency of capital in much of agriculture is higher than going rates of interest,[1] even with liberal allowance for risk and uncertainty. The flow of new capital into agriculture is in many instances blocked by the excess supply of labor resources.

To illustrate this point, consider the important Piedmont area covering the upper one-third of South Carolina and Georgia (except for the Blue Ridge) and central eastern Alabama. Its farms average less than 100 acres in size, with cotton and corn the main crops; erosion is widespread. In 1939 about three-fifths of the farms in this area produced less than $600 worth of products. But in spite of soil depletion, erosion, and low earnings, if as much capital were invested as is in a typical Iowa farm, management and labor returns to family workers would be adequate to support a fairly high level of living and the returns for the capital invested might

[1] See D. Gale Johnson, "Contribution of Price Policy to the Income and Resource Problems in Agriculture," *Journal of Farm Economics*, Vol. 26, November, 1944. Johnson finds that in 1939 the returns on capital in the Middle Atlantic, East North Central, South Atlantic, and East South Central regions averaged about 12 per cent, and annual returns to workers in agriculture about $390. Unpublished data of Johnson's show the returns on capital in Georgia to have been about 19 per cent, while in a state like Iowa, favored in that there is relatively less capital rationing and also less of an excess supply of labor, returns on capital may have been about 10 per cent in 1939.

well exceed the returns obtainable on most Iowa farms. A farm technology is available for the Piedmont that will conserve soil resources and earn two to three times as much as is possible with present technology. To make the shift to the better technology requires not 80 to 100 acres, but a farming unit of 300 to 500 acres, and instead of $200 to $500 of capital (above the value of the land), some $5,000 to $15,000 appears to be essential. The main obstacles are (*a*) excess population crowded into the Piedmont and (*b*) capital institutions geared to the old farm technology.

New Land Development

The general market situation for farm products after the war may not warrant the development of more land, but, even so, some new land is likely to be put to agricultural uses. The amount of new land developed in the next decade will be determined only in part by farm-product prices. The principal nonprice factor in land development is political in nature. Many communities are sufficiently influential to induce the state, and often also the Federal government, to appropriate funds for irrigation, drainage, or clearing of land in which the community is interested. The high wartime prices of farm products have stimulated a considerable amount of new land development, and more projects seem sure to be undertaken as soon as labor and materials are available. After the war some farm land will also be abandoned. A net increase of 20 million acres in cropland by 1950 (from 1942 levels) is not an unreasonable expectation.[1]

What Supply Is Possible and Likely?

The U.S. Department of Agriculture, in cooperation with the land-grant colleges, in a report, *Our Food Potential*,[2] asks the

---

[1] *Farming Opportunities Outlook, Problems and Policies*, Report of Interbureau Committee on Post-war Agricultural Programs, U.S. Department of Agriculture, Washington, D.C., December, 1944. (A preliminary draft.) This report deals in detail with prospects for new land developments.

[2] *Our Food Potential*, U.S. Department of Agriculture, Washington, D.C. (in

question: How much food could the United States produce on the assumption that the war were to continue ten years and if the need for food were so compelling that the largest possible production had to be attained? The conclusion reached is that it would be practicable in such a situation for the United States to supply nearly 2¼ times as much food nutriments as were supplied in 1943. In 1935–1939 we produced enough food for 130 million people, and in 1943 enough for 170 million people, according to this report. We could supply food for 380 million people in the course of a decade if we consider the quantity supplied to the average United States civilian in 1943 as the measure for one person.[1]

Obviously, these are estimates intended to measure the maximum range of our capacity to supply food. There is no implication in the report that it is either desirable or necessary to attempt to attain this amount of additional production. The figures, however, suggest that American agriculture has much more elasticity on the supply side, given a few years of time, than is commonly supposed.

In appraising what volume farmers are likely to produce after the war, some assumptions about farm prices are necessary. With the new technology, labor force, land developments, capital, and skills that are at hand and in prospect, there are good reasons for believing that the agricultural production in the United States will, in the first decade after the war, take the following course:

cooperation with the land-grant colleges), January, 1944. (A preliminary draft.)

[1] The report goes on to show that in two years, with only normal rates of technological improvements, additional food (enough for 30 million people) could be produced. Within ten years the potential supply could be increased through better farming practices so that 50 million more people could be taken care of; 40 million more could be taken care of through land development; 30 million through the prevention of waste; and, lastly, 60 million more through shifting to immediate human consumption some foods now used to feed livestock. These steps would add to the 1943 supply enough food for 210 million people, making a total food potential adequate for 380 million people within ten years.

1. With farm prices *averaging* at least parity (as **parity** is now defined by law),[1] an increase in agricultural production of as much as 20 per cent over the wartime level (1942–1945 average) may be expected.

2. With farm prices *averaging* 90 to 95 per cent of parity, agricultural production may be expected to rise about 15 per cent above the average production of 1942–1945.

3. With farm prices *averaging* 85 to 90 per cent of parity, the increase may still exceed 10 per cent during the first decade after the war.

4. Even with farm prices as low as 75 per cent of parity, some increase in agricultural production may be expected, possibly as little as 5 per cent but more likely nearer 10 per cent.

The significant thing in this expected response of agricultural production to various levels of relative prices is the propensity of the supply to increase in spite of falling relative prices—a rough measure of the strength of the forces that are at work reshaping the supply. Lower farm prices, even as low as 75 per cent of the legal parity (as defined in established farm legislation), are not likely to reduce agricultural production.[2]

MAJOR AGRICULTURAL CONSEQUENCES

What are the consequences of this unequal growth of the demand and supply of farm products with the supply so definitely in the vanguard? The nature of the underlying forces is clear. The demand is growing slowly because the

[1] Parity prices as defined by existing legislation mean farm prices relative to prices paid by farmers the same as during the base period which, for the bulk of farm products, is 1910–1914.

[2] Farm prices as low as 75 per cent of parity (average for all farm products) would probably produce sufficient returns for a few branches of agriculture to provide rewards to the factors used in production comparable to returns for like factors employed in nonagricultural production at full employment. However, for most of American agriculture it would mean (if it occurred during the first decade after the war) a very low level of earnings—far below a level consistent with an equilibrium distribution of the labor force.

rate of growth of the populations that provide a market for American agriculture is dropping and may soon cease to increase altogether, and because the income elasticity of farm products of these populations is very low. The supply, however, grows faster than demand because of the big strides that farm technology is making, the ever-abundant supply of labor in agriculture, and the advances in its skills, additions to capital, and the development of new land.

The major economic consequences, if the equilibrating mechanism does not have the capacity constantly to transfer a very considerable quantity of resources out of agriculture, are not difficult to ascertain. They are listed here, leaving for later an examination of the problems they present and the elements of appropriate policy.[1]

1. We would expect a chronic disequilibrium adverse to agriculture to occur and to persist, except during wars, for a short period during business booms, and for the intervals whenever governments accumulate large inventories of farm products.

2. We would expect agriculture to be burdened constantly with an excess supply of labor even when business is expanding and when there are brisk job opportunities in nonagricultural industries. The burden of equilibrating the excess supply of resources in agriculture falls primarily on the labor force, because the improvements in farm technology are largely labor-saving in their effects. Labor, furthermore, constitutes the bulk of the resources employed in agriculture and workers are transferable. To equate the forces and counter-forces affecting the supply and demand of farm products, what is constantly required is a redistribution of the labor force with relatively fewer workers engaged in agriculture as the economy develops. Slowly, but always belatedly, this is happening.

3. We would expect migration out of agriculture to increase

[1] In this listing the present writer follows closely his essay, "Food and Agriculture in a Developing Economy," *Food for the World.*

· 82 ·

as farm prices fell (certainly when they fell relative to other product prices) and to slow down, even if it did not stop altogether, as farm prices rose. Here, however, our expectations have not been borne out by experience, as is seen in the review of labor distribution in the next chapter.

4. We would expect farm products to be cheaper, as a consequence of the chronic disequilibrium caused by the differing rates of growth of the demand and supply of food, than they would be if the excess supply of labor in agriculture were a minimum. Raising the price of farm products by governmental action does not remedy this situation since it does not get at the underlying causes.

5. We would expect international trade to fail, in fact to be unable, to keep incomes per head from declining in certain agricultural countries. International trade enlarges the capacity of an economy to equilibrate the forces affecting the demand and supply of farm products. This feature of international trade is commonly stressed by students in the field. But what is not recognized, or at least has been left unsaid, is the fact that international trade does not and cannot keep incomes per head from declining in agricultural countries with a developing economy of the type we have described. The difficulty arises from the fact that some countries are not in a position to move labor resources out of agriculture. Any trading country is likely to have its per capita income reduced by the forces reshaping the supply and demand for farm products if (*a*) it is primarily agricultural, (*b*) it is dependent on farm products for its exports, (*c*) it is producing farm products the supply of which is affected by the introduction of labor-saving farm technology, and (*d*) it does not have the capacity to industrialize and thus absorb the excess supply of labor developing in agriculture.[1] Trade offers other types of gains, but it is no remedy for this difficulty, which is rooted

[1] See Theodore W. Schultz, "Two Conditions Necessary for Economic Progress in Agriculture," *The Canadian Journal of Economics and Political Science*, Vol. X, No. 3 (1944), pp. 305–306.

in the nature of the country's resources. The effect on incomes is decidedly adverse unless some of the people migrate, thus transferring labor to countries that have the resources required for industrialization.[1]

A country with a large industrial potential, however, can correct the excess supply of labor in the farm sector by internal migration. Although the United States is very fortunate in this respect, we have not kept our house in order, as is apparent from the low earnings in much of our agriculture, especially in the South. Russia is also fortunate; so are such industrial countries of western Europe as Great Britain, Germany, and Belgium. Some of the countries that have more recently become important in agricultural trade are also favorably situated, for example, Canada, Australia, Brazil, and to a lesser extent, Argentina. But what about Cuba, old Poland, and the Danubian countries, for example? In the Danubian area most of the population continues in farming, even though advances in farm technology affecting the main products of these countries have reduced labor requirements by one-third, perhaps even by one-half. The opportunities to industrialize, however, have been all too restricted, and additional capital is needed to facilitate some industrialization. Where is the excess supply of labor in agriculture to go? Freer trade will give these producers access to the world markets and therein lies a gain, but trade does not and cannot keep the relative level of incomes per worker in such countries from going down. This is one of the significant consequences of the changing structure of demand as people become richer; it is one of the far-reaching consequences of the advances in technology now going forward in agriculture.

[1] Industrialization is used here in a generic sense, namely, to include growth in any and all fields producing goods and services other than farm products.

IV. DISTRIBUTION OF THE LABOR
FORCE AND EARNINGS

THE low earnings of people engaged in farming are a surface manifestation of a more fundamental dislocation. Apart from war years and the effects of cyclical fluctuations, the rates of growth of the supply and demand for farm products have been so unequal as to cause most parts of agriculture to be chronically depressed. As the output outdistances the demand, agriculture finds itself with an excess supply of resources consisting primarily of labor. Low earnings for farm people result from this excess.

The burden of equilibrating the excess supply of resources in agriculture falls mainly upon the labor force. First, labor is quantitatively the major part—upward of seven-tenths—of the resources employed in farming in the United States.[1] Second, the improvements in farm technology have been largely laborsaving in their effects. Advances in farm technology have made capital resources, such as power-driven farm machinery and equipment, highly productive. Thus, in spite of the excess supply of labor in agriculture, these new types of capital have been increased. Third, labor is more readily transferable than other resources. The rate of disinvestment in land is usually very slow. Rents under these conditions may drop and the capitalized value of land may decline relatively; yet most of the land stays in production because the new technology has increased its productivity. Many of the advances in farm technology have been of such

[1] Assuming that the total value product of agriculture is allocated to the several factors in accordance with the marginal principle. The actual calculations are at best very rough in view of many difficulties in data and procedures.

a kind that they not only have held land in use but have actually drawn additional land, low in productivity, into cultivation.

Consequently, we should expect a redistribution of the labor force with relatively fewer workers engaged in agriculture. The statistics on this point are conclusive. The proportion of the labor force engaged in agriculture has been dropping,

FARM PRODUCTION, FARM EMPLOYMENT, FARM LABOR PRODUCTIVITY, AND TOTAL POPULATION, UNITED STATES, 1870-1940

INDEX NUMBERS (1870=100)

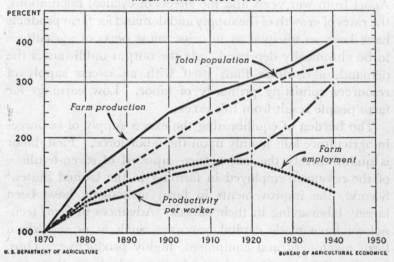

U. S. DEPARTMENT OF AGRICULTURE   BUREAU OF AGRICULTURAL ECONOMICS.

not only in the United States and the older industrial countries in Europe, but also in the more largely agricultural countries and in parts of the Orient. The universality of this decline is striking. It has been going on for decades. It suggests that there are powerful and persistent forces at work with no signs that these forces have run their course. On the contrary, there are reasons for believing that a decade or two hence the proportion of the labor force that will be needed to produce farm products will be considerably below present figures.

TABLE IV
ESTIMATED PROPORTION OF WORKING POPULATION ENGAGED IN AGRICULTURE IN TEN COUNTRIES

Country	1890 or 1891, per cent	1900 or 1901, per cent	1910 or 1911, per cent	1920 or 1921, per cent	1930 or 1931, per cent	1939 or 1940, per cent	1944, per cent
Great Britain[a]	10.2	8.4	8.0	7.1	6.4	5.7[i]	
United States	41.9[c]	36.8[c]	31.2[c]	26.1[c]	21.6[k]	19.9[k]	15.0[m]
Germany[a]	33.3[f]	27.0[g]	....	....	20.4[i]	17.9[n]	
Canada[b]	45.5	40.2	34.3	32.8	28.8	25.2[i]	22.0[l]
Switzerland[a]	37.7[e]	31.5	27.3	26.6	22.2	20.8[n]	
Australia[a]	31.1	32.8	30.1	25.7	24.4[i]	20.4[o]	
France[a]		33.1	....	28.6	24.5		
Sweden[a]	53.5	49.8	44.6	40.6	36.0	31.9[n]	
Italy[a]	....	59.4	55.4	56.1	46.8	20.4[n]	
Japan[a]	71.8[d]		61.5[h]	53.5	50.3		
			59.5[p]	53.1	44.8	40.4	

[a] Colin Clark, *The Conditions of Economic Progress*, The Macmillan Company, New York, 1940, pp. 185–201. Mr. Clark's figures are for primary industries and include agriculture, forestry, and fishing. In some cases they are a proportion of people living on farms to the total population.

[b] George V. Haythorne and Leonard C. Marsh, *Land and Labor*, Oxford University Press, Toronto, for McGill University, 1941, p. 35.

[c] P. K. Whelpton, "Occupational Groups in the United States, 1820–1920," *Journal of American Statistical Association*, Vol. 21, September, 1926, p. 340.

[d] For 1897.

[e] For 1888.

[f] For 1895.

[g] For 1907.

[h] For 1912.

[i] For 1933.

[j] For 1937.

[k] *U.S. Census*, 1940, Vol. III, Part 1, p. 25.

[l] Preliminary estimates from the Dominion Bureau of Statistics, Agricultural Branch.

[m] Based on a total employed civilian labor force of 50.6 million, of which 7.6 million were employed on farms.

[n] *The Statesman's Yearbook, 1943.* People engaged in agriculture as percentage of total population. Figure for Italy is for 1936.

[o] Estimate from *Official Year Book of the Commonwealth of Australia, 1941.*

[p] *Nogyo Nenkan, 1941*, p. 27. Agricultural families as per cent of total families.

A NATIONAL POLICY GOAL BASED ON EARNINGS

Since it is desirable from the point of view of the economy as a whole to encourage rather than to discourage advances in labor-saving technology for agriculture, and since farm people for many years to come are likely to have a very considerable natural increase in their numbers, and inasmuch as the growth of demand is likely to be less for farm products than it is for goods and services of other producers—*the primary adjustment that is necessary to approach an equilibrium involves the migration of many people out of agriculture into other fields of endeavor. We have here a transfer problem, a redistribution of the working population, to relieve agriculture of the excess supply of labor engaged in, and dependent upon, farming for its income.*

That the farm problem is exceedingly complex is evident from the many types of difficulties that arose during the inter-war years. The question is therefore often put: Where does one start in formulating a national policy with regard to agriculture? Between the two wars, the main focus fell upon low farm prices attributed to loss of markets and to excessive output. Crop control was initiated to hold production of basic crops in check. Efforts to ameliorate the farm problem also involved better use of land, storage, soil conservation, subsidies, foreign trade, new uses for farm products, better nutrition, credit, marketing arrangements, and farm management. When properly viewed, each of these contributes to understanding farm problems. With so many approaches at hand, however, it is all the more essential to discover the more fundamental elements in the farm problem to make sure that attacks on these many fronts are consistent and necessary.

We have set forth in the preceding chapter, in considerable detail, the forces at work aggravating the maldistribution of the nation's labor forces—that is, continually diminishing the number of workers needed on the farms. The crucial question in policy formulation is: Should these forces be checked or counterbalanced? It is not desirable, in the main, to check these forces associated with a developing economy, since they are essentially positive in their contribution. If they are not to be checked, how can they be counterbalanced? It is necessary to improve the capacity of the economy to equalize earnings by helping people move out of farming. *A national agricultural policy, therefore, should have as its primary goal the attainment of a better equilibrium in the distribution of the labor force.*

Distribution of the Labor Force and Earnings

Prices and Migration

We might expect prices to be the spark plug in this area as elsewhere in the economy, and migration out of agriculture to accelerate as farm prices and earnings fell. But this is not what has happened. The movement of workers in and out of agriculture has been inconsistent with our economic rationale as to what people do (in the short run) in adjusting to changes in relative prices of products. At this point we shall merely put the question and discuss the causes and implications of their behavior later. Why do farm people leave agriculture when farm prices rise, and why do many of them return when farm prices fall?[1] We need also to ask ourselves why farmers generally express concern about farm wages being too high when farm incomes are high and rising, and why they are disposed to view farm wages as being too low when farm incomes are low and falling.[2]

[1] The same question may be put with regard to changes in farm prices relative to other commodity prices.

[2] It is necessary to hold in mind constantly that most of the labor force engaged in farming is self-employed, largely as operators and family workers on family farms. The number of hired farm workers in 1943, and their proportion in total farm employment, was as follows:

	Annual average number of hired workers	Per cent hired workers were of total farm employment
United States	2,406,000	23.4
New England	82,000	32.9
Middle Atlantic	203,000	32.8
East North Central	266,000	18.9
West North Central	286,000	17.8
South Atlantic	463,000	23.7
East South Central	261,000	15.8
West South Central	430,000	24.5
Mountain	142,000	32.3
Pacific	273,000	47.2

SOURCE: Louis J. Ducoff, *Wages of Agricultural Labor in the United States*, U.S. Department of Agriculture, Bureau of Agricultural Economics, September, 1944, p. 28.

From the figures below it is evident that as farm prices fell the net migration of people from farms declined; net migration rose as farm prices rose. During 1932, when farm prices were actually the lowest they had been in thirty years, there

FARM EMPLOYMENT IN THE UNITED STATES, 1910-42

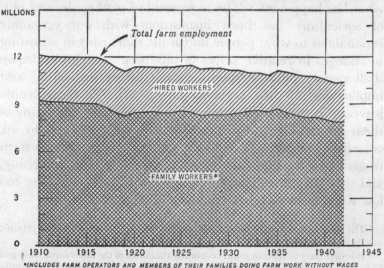

*INCLUDES FARM OPERATORS AND MEMBERS OF THEIR FAMILIES DOING FARM WORK WITHOUT WAGES

U. S. DEPARTMENT OF AGRICULTURE   BUREAU OF AGRICULTURAL ECONOMICS

was in fact a net movement of people to farms, temporarily reversing the preceding forty-year trend. The index of prices received by farmers dropped in 1932 to 61 from its 1925–1929

Period	Prices received by farmers (1935–1939 = 100)	Net migration from farms (numbers)
1925–1929	139	2,965,000
1930–1934	83	976,000
1935–1939	100	2,772,000
1940–1944	143	5,000,000[a]

[a] Figures for 1944 have not been released. From January, 1940, to January, 1944, a net loss of 4,660,000 persons occurred in the farm population—including all individuals who either moved away from farms or who are living in places that are no longer farms because all agricultural operations have ceased. This figure does not include the net loss to the armed forces, estimated at 1,650,-000 men who were living on farms at the time they enlisted or were inducted. The total figure had undoubtedly risen to well over 5,000,000 by Jan. 1, 1945.

average of 139; that year the net migration to farms reached 325,000 persons. The remarkable migration out of agriculture since 1940 took place even as farm prices rose—as farm prices doubled and the income of agriculture per person virtually trebled. This seemingly paradoxical behavior indicates difficulties that will be encountered in facilitating the movement of labor out of agriculture.

EXCESS SUPPLY OF LABOR IN AGRICULTURE

The overlarge supply of labor in agriculture increased considerably during the interwar years, especially after 1930. This escaped the notice of the general public chiefly because it is not so visible as is industrial unemployment. Excess labor in agriculture expresses itself primarily in much underproductive employment; this is harder to detect and measure than industrial unemployment. Some headway has been made—through the Census—in counting and classifying the unemployed, and some headway has been made in social legislation to aid workers unable to find work. But no technique has as yet been developed for counting the excess labor in agriculture, nor has legislation been framed to aid such workers. It is not an easy thing to do.

One would have supposed that while programs were being developed to help subsistence and low-income farmers, it should have been evident that agriculture was burdened with excess labor. But even those who contributed to these schemes of assistance—though aware of differential birth rates between the agricultural and industrial sectors of our society, the migratory pattern that had prevailed for several decades, and the differences in economic opportunities among regions and occupations—did not have anything like a full realization of the man power forced into uneconomic uses in farming. It has taken the mobilization for war to show us how great an excess of man power was attempting to derive a living from farming.

The excess labor in agriculture is concealed in part by what would be comparable to a spread-work policy in industry. Labor is not left unemployed, but farm workers generally, both self-employed and hired, are at a greater disadvantage, with consequent lowered earnings. The nature of farm work is such that the surplus labor does not show up in a shorter day, or in fewer work days per year. The overlarge supply of labor does, however, lower both the physical and value productivity per worker. In the main, it reduces the value both of hired and of family labor, decreasing the earnings of both. Family workers, including farm operators, constitute about three-fourths of all workers in agriculture, and there is much effective substitution between nonhired and hired labor.

Why does agriculture absorb this excess labor force and in so doing reduce its per capita earnings? Why doesn't the labor in agriculture become unemployed, as it does in industry? As we have seen, farm production and employment continue at a steady, even gait, regardless of boom or depression. This certainly is not because farmers have less self-interest in the returns they receive for their effort than do other entrepreneurs. The explanation may be found first in the competitive structure of agriculture, and second in its high proportion of fixed costs.

The competitive structure of agriculture forces resources to stay employed, which is not the case in much of industry. Farms being small and numerous, a farmer acting alone cannot affect the price either of the products he sells or the factors he buys. He gains nothing through curtailing production by letting part of his farm lie idle. A like situation prevails in any industry in which the firms are small and numerous, the labor is self-employed, and that which is hired is unorganized. Production is maintained simply because prices, wages, and profits do not become obstacles to production.

Production costs on most farms are in large part fixed costs that go on regardless of the amount the farm produces. Fixed labor costs are of course the most important expense. Farmers, with few exceptions, cannot dismiss their labor during a depression; to do so would usually mean dismissing themselves and members of their families. (When farm prices fall, theoretically they could leave agriculture and find industrial jobs, but as we have seen, unemployment in industry forces them to stay on the farm.) Nor is labor the farmer's only fixed cost: mortgage payments, taxes, and installments on farm equipment must be met, no matter whether the farmer receives low or high prices for his product.

Thus he has no alternative but to keep his farm in full production. When the demand for farm products contracts, it is not within the power of the farmer to make output the variable and treat his selling price and "wage" as constants. With farm-product supply remaining roughly constant, a contraction in the demand causes farm prices to fall unless the government intervenes.

There can be no doubt that society as a whole gains from the steady production effort of agriculture, though agriculture becomes the recipient of earnings both low and highly unstable. Society also gains from the fact that agriculture continues to absorb labor when industry is stagnant, thereby keeping more people in employment, each doing something of some value. It reduces the numbers on relief; it also makes food cheap. But it seriously lowers the per capita earnings of farm people.

It is apparent, therefore, that the test for ascertaining the amount of excess labor in agriculture lies in per capita earnings. What we want to know is how the earnings of workers in farming compare with earnings in other industries, for work which farm people are prepared to do. Stated thus, the test depends on the value productivity of workers, assuming that the worker receives the amount he contributes to total production. In this way the weighing of labor requirements in agriculture is linked to the larger task of attaining a general equilibrium in the distribution of resources between agriculture and other industries. For the twenty-year span, 1920–1939, earnings per worker in agriculture were declining relative to earnings in industry. This decline is, in itself, sufficient proof that the excess of labor in agriculture was increasing.

Movement of People Induced by the War

Some idea of the excess number of people that had been crowded into agriculture (chiefly by the poor performance of other parts of the economy) may be had from the developments that have taken place since the start of the war. The Bureaus of Census and Agricultural Economics have jointly released estimates showing the following changes in the farm population from April, 1940, to April, 1944:[1]

Farm population (all figures in thousands)	April, 1940	April, 1944	Change 1940 to 1944	
			Number	Per cent
In private households:				
Head employed in farm occupations...	21,720	18,330	−3,390	−15.6
Head employed in nonfarm occupations	4,200	5,350	1,150	27.4
Head not in labor force[a]............	4,430	1,900	−2,530	−57.1
Not in private households.............	200	290	90	45.0
Total farm population..............	30,550	25,870	−4,680	−15.3

[a] Figures include persons in households with head in public emergency work or seeking work and persons with employment status of head not reported.

Even more revealing of the war's effects on the farm population are the following figures showing the actual net departures from farms during the four-year period.[2]

4 Years (Jan. 1, 1940, to Jan. 1, 1944)	Millions of Persons
Net migration from farms[a]............................	4.66
Net loss to armed forces..............................	1.65
Other net withdrawals[b]...............................	2.00
Total...	8.31

[a] Net number of individuals who either moved away from farms or who are living at places that are no longer farms because all agricultural operations have ceased.

[b] An estimate of net withdrawals from on-farm labor supply through shifts into other occupations without change in residence.

[1] "Estimates of Farm Population and Farm Households: April, 1944, and April, 1940," U.S. Department of Commerce and U.S. Department of Agriculture, Census–Bureau of Agricultural Economics Series 1, Jan. 14, 1945.

[2] Based mainly upon *Farm Population Estimates, January, 1944*, U.S. Department of Agriculture, Bureau of Agricultural Economics, November, 1944,

In spite of the extraordinary movement of people out of agriculture during these four years, agricultural production increased markedly. The acreage harvested rose from 330 to 347 million; the output of livestock, from an index of 112 to 138; and total agricultural production expanded from an index of 110 to 129.

Many Farm People Still Have Few or No Opportunities in Farming

This movement of people from farms has not as yet spent itself. If a high level of industrial production and employment is achieved after the war, there are reasons to believe that agriculture will still have several million persons who will migrate to other occupations. This is the over-all situation, even though there have been acute labor shortages on some farms and during the war many farm people found it necessary to work exceedingly long hours, even to the point of endangering their health. Many old people who normally would have retired have stayed at work, and others who already had withdrawn from active work returned to farming. Many young people took up farm work earlier than usual and many women entered the agricultural labor force.[1] Yet a number of reasons suggest that the labor supply in agriculture continues to be too large when we consider agriculture as a whole.

1. The movement of labor out of agriculture since 1940 has been so rapid that there has not been sufficient time

[1] Ducoff, Hagood, and Taeuber estimated that there were 200,000 persons under fourteen in farm employment in April, 1940, compared to 500,000 in April, 1943. By October, 1943, the figure had reached 1,200,000. They estimated that 1,978,000 females, fourteen years old and over, were working during October, 1943, compared to 458,000 in April, 1940. Much of this increase is seasonal in character because April is a low point in farm work compared to the fall. The same comparisons for April, 1940, and April, 1943, suggest an increase of 528,000. ["Effects of the War on the Agricultural Working Force and on the Rural-farm Population," *Social Forces*, Vol. 21, No. 4 (May, 1943).]

to permit farmers to recombine their resources, a process that is necessary in order to economize on labor.[1]   Agriculture had become adjusted to the large supply of labor that was at hand.   To operate suddenly with much less labor requires a considerable recombination of factors and in many cases it means increasing the size of the farm, which is not accomplished easily or quickly.

2. Labor-saving equipment and machinery have not been available in sufficient amounts.   The acute shortage of new farm machinery has greatly retarded the adjustment of farms to the growing scarcities of farm labor.   Had all the machinery been available that farmers were prepared to buy during the war years, the release of additional large numbers of farm workers would have been possible.   There is no point in trying to guess how many persons would have been freed. It is sufficient to note the direction of the change and the fact that it would have released a considerable number.

3. The migration of workers out of agriculture has been hindered considerably by social arrangements, customs, and

[1] Early in 1945 the writer had the opportunity to study at first hand many farms in the Piedmont, Black Belt, and the southeast peanut areas of Alabama. The extent of the adjustments that the reduced labor supply has entailed is illustrated by the following three farming units in this region:

Case 1.   Twenty-nine families were living on this farm when the war started. In February, 1945, there were only eleven families.   To do the farm work with his present equipment and techniques, the operator needed urgently at least four more families.   Yet with eleven families the farm was oversupplied with labor on the basis of at least two important criteria: (*a*) Wages were still only about $1 per day plus some noncash considerations, and (*b*) even with its superior management, the present combination of resources of this farming unit could not offer more than a relatively low level of living if the farm carries more than four families.

Case 2.   In 1940 this farm had on it fifty-three families; by March, 1945, it was down to twenty-five families.   Asked how many families he would have on this farm ten years hence, the operator replied, "Not more than ten but we will have to do a basic job of reorganizing."

Case 3.   The FSA farm owner of an 80-acre farm, with 60 acres of cropland, had four sons who left the farm to enter the armed forces.   The father and mother made some crop changes and provided themselves with a secondhand tractor; they then farmed the 80 acres alone.

laws (especially those associated with the race problem in the South), and by Federal and state agency rulings and requirements which in many agricultural areas keep farm people from economic opportunities otherwise open to them.

4. The special consideration given farm workers in draft deferments, especially during 1943, relieved acute labor shortages that were developing in many dairy and other commercial farming areas; but it also has had the effect of holding workers on farms and inducing some to seek farm employment who otherwise either would have taken employment off the farm or would have entered the armed services.

5. While earnings in agriculture have increased substantially in the war period, relative to earnings of workers in industry, agricultural earnings are still far out of line. This imbalance is corroborated by the fact that many people have continued to leave the farm, of their own accord, because the opportunities in farming are not as attractive as those open to them in other industries. The changes in earnings in the two sectors of our economy, from 1940 to 1944, are shown in the following figures:[1]

Year	Average net income[a] per worker engaged in agriculture	Wage income[b] per employed industrial worker	Per cent agricultural income is of industrial
1940	$ 531	$1,273	42
1941	733	1,495	49
1942	1,041	1,847	56
1943	1,362	2,156	63
1944	1,456	2,360	62

[a] Realized aggregate net income of farm operators (this includes all cash income from marketings, government payments, value of home consumption, and rental value of dwellings minus expenses of agricultural production) plus wages of hired laborers, divided by average farm employment. U.S. Department of Agriculture, Bureau of Agricultural Economics, *1945 Agricultural Outlook Charts*, November, 1944, p. 6.

[b] Annual earnings of factory, railroad, and mining workers divided by average employment. Source of data is same as for footnote *a*.

[1] The relevant comparison does not lie in the absolute differences between the two sets of per-person dollar income, but in the changes that have occurred in the ratio between them, shown in the last column.

OVERPOPULATION IN AGRICULTURE AGGRAVATED
BY INDUSTRIAL UNEMPLOYMENT

The most readily recognized effect on agriculture of industrial unemployment is the loss of income and consequent curtailed purchasing power of unemployed workers. The full impact of industrial unemployment on agriculture is in fact more penetrating. Unemployment in industry is a barrier to migration. It holds people back in agriculture even as the high rate of population increase on farms and the growing use of labor-saving techniques create a surplus in farm labor. With these adverse conditions, it is inevitable that the income of agricultural workers falls in relation to the income of employed industrial workers.

In 1920, agricultural workers earned 53 per cent of the average wage earnings of industrial workers; by 1939, only 42 per cent. In studying the disparity between rural and industrial earnings, Colin Clark[1] found that, of the countries investigated, the disparity had become greatest in Canada and the United States. The migration of people from farms was not large enough to check the downward drift of earnings in agriculture.

During the period 1920–1939 there was a net migration from farms of 10 million persons. This appears large at first glance, but it was only a little more than the natural increase of the farm population, which in 1939 was only a little more than one million smaller than it was in 1920.

	Millions of Persons[a]
Farm population January 1, 1920....................	31.6
Natural increase 1920 to 1939......................	8.7
	40.3
Net migration from farms, 1920–1939.................	−10.0
Farm population January 1, 1939....................	30.3
Net decrease in farm population during interwar period.	1.3

[a] *Farm Population Estimates, 1910–1942*, U.S. Department of Agriculture, Bureau of Agricultural Economics, November, 1942, p. 2.

[1] *The Conditions of Economic Progress*, Macmillan & Company, Ltd., London, 1940, p. 228.

Distribution of the Labor Force and Earnings

It was the severe industrial unemployment of the thirties that intensified the excess labor problem in agriculture. From 1920 to 1930 the proportion of the working population engaged in agriculture declined at about the same rate that had prevailed for upward of a century. From 1930 to 1940 this trend changed abruptly. There is no evidence that the rate of industrialization in the United States should have tapered off. Had it continued, along with the historical migration out of agriculture, at the time the war started approximately one-fifth of the total farm population, or about 6 million persons, would have been living in towns and cities instead of on farms.[1] The last column of Table V shows how small a change occurred in the distribution of the working population (from 21.6 per cent in agriculture in 1930 to 19.9 per cent in 1940) during the decade of the thirties.

What are we to infer from the parallel movements of "net migration from farms" and "prices received by farmers"? Does it mean that higher farm prices induce workers to leave farming? It may be suggested that what matters is not the farm-price drift in itself, but how farm prices change relative to other producer prices. This, however, does not dismiss the contradiction, because when farm prices have declined they have dropped more than did other prices, and they also have led other prices when they have advanced.

General knowledge of this period indicates that the course of both prices and migration was determined by more general forces, that is, by the great depression and the wartime expansion. If this surmise is true, then it follows that the

[1] Louis H. Bean, "The Farmer's Stake in Greater Industrial Production," *Yearbook of Agriculture, 1940*, U.S. Department of Agriculture, Washington, D.C., p. 351. "The total working population comprised about 54,500,000 people 10 years of age and over, of whom 11,500,000 were attached to agriculture. On the basis of the long-time trend in the proportion of the population in agriculture, these figures represent an excess of about 2,500,000 of working population and 3,500,000 others living on the land. This excess amounts to about 6,000,000 persons, or one-fifth of the total farm population, who under normal conditions would be living in towns and cities instead of on farms."

recovery and expansion from 1923 to 1929 and again from 1935 to 1944 did not go far enough to make the resulting relative rise in farm prices a factor that would check the transfer of labor resources out of agriculture. The inference

TABLE V

MOVEMENT OF PERSONS FROM FARMS, CHANGES IN FARM PRICES AND INCOMES RELATIVE TO THE INCOMES OF INDUSTRIAL WORKERS, AND THE PROPORTION OF WORKING POPULATION ENGAGED IN AGRICULTURE, IN THE UNITED STATES, 1920–1924 TO 1940–1943

Year	Movement of persons to farms from nonfarm areas, in millions[a]	Movement of persons from farms to non-farm areas, in millions[a]	Net migration from farms, in millions[a]	Agricultural income per worker in per cent of industrial wage income[b]	Prices received by farmers[c] (1910–1914 = 100)	Terms of exchange of agriculture[d]	Per cent of working population of the United States in agriculture[e]
1920–1924	5.4	8.7	3.3	43	151	109	26.1 (1920)
1925–1929	7.8	10.7	3.0	48	149	115	21.6 (1930)
1930–1934	6.7	7.7	1.0	33	90	81	
1935–1939	4.0	6.8	2.8	45	107	100	19.9 (1940)
Total...	23.9	33.9	10.1				
1940–1944			5.0	56[f]	144[f]	114[f]	15.0 (1944)

[a] *Farm Population Estimates, 1910–1942*, U.S. Department of Agriculture, Bureau of Agricultural Economics, November, 1942.

[b] *Agricultural Outlook Charts*, U.S. Department of Agriculture, Bureau of Agricultural Economics, November, 1944, p. 6.

[c] *Index Numbers of Prices Received by Farmers, 1910–1943*, U.S. Department of Agriculture, Bureau of Agricultural Economics, February, 1944, p. 36.

[d] Obtained by taking prices received by farmers as a per cent of prices paid by farmers, a simple average of the yearly indexes all based on 1935–1939 = 100. Prices paid by farmers do not include feed, seed, and food.

[e] From Table IV, p. 87, of this chapter.

[f] Based on four-year average, namely, 1940–1943.

is that the mechanism of relative prices (farm prices relative to other prices) was superseded. A transfer of labor occurred, not in response to changes in relative prices but in spite of them. When farm prices fell relative to other producer prices, as happened in 1929 to 1933, the price mechanism was again superseded by other forces and was not effective in determining the transfer of labor resources. Not prices, therefore, but the existence of job opportunities—the opportunity to migrate—takes farm people off farms or requires them to stay put. This suggests an important deviation from accepted thinking concerning price as a balance wheel in the economy. *The mechanism of relative prices is not effective in inducing a redistribution of the labor force; that is, in transferring the excess supply out of agriculture, unless a fuller use of resources exists than prevailed at any time from 1920 to 1944.*

FARM POPULATION ESTIMATED FROM NONAGRICULTURAL
EMPLOYMENT LEVELS, 1920-44 COMPARED WITH ACTUAL FARM
POPULATION ESTIMATES, 1910-44*

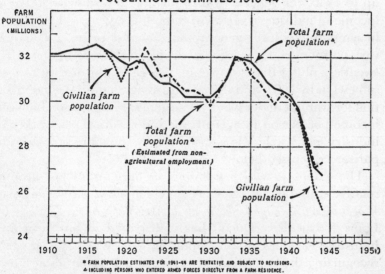

* FARM POPULATION ESTIMATES FOR 1941-44 ARE TENTATIVE AND SUBJECT TO REVISIONS.
△ INCLUDING PERSONS WHO ENTERED ARMED FORCES DIRECTLY FROM A FARM RESIDENCE.

U. S. DEPARTMENT OF AGRICULTURE   BUREAU OF AGRICULTURAL ECONOMICS

COMPARATIVE EARNINGS OF WORKERS
IN AGRICULTURE

There is no doubt that if earnings in agriculture rose far enough relative to wage income in industry, there would come a point at which some workers in industry would elect to transfer to farm work. As such a point was approached, the mechanism of relative prices should become effective in determining which way labor resources would transfer. During the interwar years, however, there was so wide a gap between agricultural and industrial earnings per worker that even when this gap was narrowing, farm people hastened to leave agriculture when jobs were available in industry. Because of this gap, the migration of persons from farms was not in response to changes in relative prices but to the availability or nonavailability of jobs.

Drop in Earnings from 1920 to 1940

Throughout the period, from the close of World War I up to 1940, the general drift of income in farming relative to income in industry was down, though there were fluctuations in sympathy with the general movement of prices. The relative position of farm people dropped sharply in the early twenties, plunged far down in the early thirties, recovered somewhat by 1937, and then declined again until the mobilization for war got under way. The general comparison between income per person in agriculture and earnings per worker in industry (see Table VI) is sustained by the more precise comparisons discussed below.

The extent to which earnings in agriculture lost ground relative to industrial earnings is evident in a careful study of *Wages of Agricultural Labor in the United States* recently made by Louis J. Ducoff.[1] Ducoff has endeavored to put farm and industrial earnings on as comparable a basis as possible, while recognizing the limitations of the statistical materials at hand.

Farm Wage Rates and Hourly Factory Earnings

From 1910 to 1920, the course of farm wage rates and hourly factory earnings was upward and roughly similar, as the indexes in Table VII show. Then they separated widely; earnings of both groups fell, but hourly earnings of farm laborers dropped much more than hourly factory wages.

[1] Louis J. Ducoff, *Wages of Agricultural Labor in the United States*, U.S. Department of Agriculture, Washington, D.C., September, 1944.

The two never came together again—in fact, the disparity widened until the war production made itself felt.

TABLE VI

INCOME PER PERSON IN AGRICULTURE COMPARED WITH EARNINGS PER WORKER
IN INDUSTRY, UNITED STATES AND CANADA, SELECTED YEARS, 1913 TO 1944

	United States			Canada
	(1)	(2)	(3)	(4)
Year	Per cent average net income per person engaged in agriculture is of wage income per employed industrial worker[a]	Per cent average income of hired farm worker is of factory worker[b]	Per cent farm labor earnings per farm in 9 northeastern states are of wage income per employed industrial worker[c]	Per cent average of yearly earnings of hired male farm laborers is of those of manufacturing employees[d]
1913	64	67 (1910–1914)	101	59 (1915)
1919	82	64	122	69 (1920)
1923	42	47 (1920–1924)	78	56
1925	50	41 (1925–1929)	82	59
1930	39	29 (1930–1934)	65	49
1933	32	25 (1935–1939)	31	35
1937	47		41	37
1940	42	24	50 (1939)	38
1944	62	36 (April, 1944)		50 (1942)

[a] Computed from *Agricultural Outlook Charts*, U.S. Department of Agriculture, Bureau of Agricultural Economics, November, 1944, p. 6.

[b] Based on Louis J. Ducoff, *Wages of Agricultural Labor in the United States*, U.S. Department of Agriculture, Washington, D.C., September, 1944.

[c] Donald Paarlberg, "Parity and Progress," *Journal of Farm Economics*, Vol. 25, (1943). Calculated from data appearing in Table 1, p. 423.

[d] Canada Dominion Bureau of Statistics, *Monthly Bulletin of Agricultural Statistics* and the *Canada Year Book, 1942*, p. 348. The figure for 1915 was obtained from J. E. Lattimer, *Canadian Political Science Association Proceedings, 1931*.

Wages of Common Laborers and Farm Hands

A closer and a better comparison of the general drift in earnings is to be had in the wage rates of farm and common laborers because the skills required are fairly comparable. The two rates are somewhat closer in absolute terms than are farm wage rates and hourly factory earnings, but the same basic relations are evident. After World War I, farm wages sagged sharply and thereafter continued downward relative to the wages of common laborers.

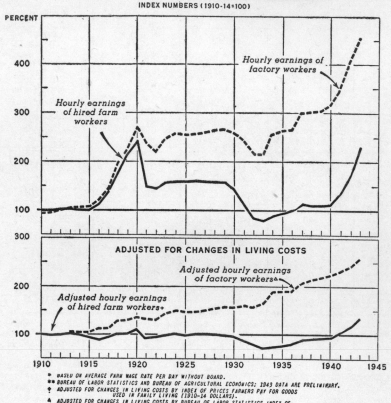

HOURLY EARNINGS OF HIRED FARM WORKERS* AND OF FACTORY WORKERS UNITED STATES. 1910-43**

INDEX NUMBERS (1910-14=100)

* BASED ON AVERAGE FARM WAGE RATE PER DAY WITHOUT BOARD.
** BUREAU OF LABOR STATISTICS AND BUREAU OF AGRICULTURAL ECONOMICS; 1943 DATA ARE PRELIMINARY.
† ADJUSTED FOR CHANGES IN LIVING COSTS BY INDEX OF PRICES FARMERS PAY FOR GOODS USED IN FAMILY LIVING (1910-14 DOLLARS).
▲ ADJUSTED FOR CHANGES IN LIVING COSTS BY BUREAU OF LABOR STATISTICS INDEX OF COST OF LIVING (1913 DOLLARS).

U. S. DEPARTMENT OF AGRICULTURE   BUREAU OF AGRICULTURAL ECONOMICS

Annual Wage Earnings Compared

Indexes of the annual wage of farm and industrial workers show the same structure and trend as those of hourly earnings. However, there is a little less disparity between the two following 1920, when they start moving apart.[1]

[1] Ducoff points out that the reduced length of the industrial work week during

TABLE VII

AVERAGE HOURLY EARNINGS OF FARM LABORERS, WORKERS IN MANUFACTURING INDUSTRIES, COMMON LABOR IN INDUSTRY, AND COMMON LABOR IN ROAD BUILDING, SELECTED PERIODS, UNITED STATES, 1910–1944

Period	Average hourly earnings, cents				Hourly earnings of farm workers as per cent of hourly earnings of		
	Farm laborers[a]	Workers in manu- facturing industries[b]	Common labor in industry[c]	Common labor in road building[d]	Workers in manu- facturing industries	Common labor in industry	Common labor in road building
1944 (April)	36.9	101.2	....	68.0	36	..	54
1943	32.7	96.1	....	71.0	34	..	46
1942	24.9	85.3	63.5	58.0	29	39	43
1941	19.3	72.9	56.6	48.0	26	34	40
1940	15.9	67.0	50.7	46.0	24	31	35
1939	15.6	64.4	50.0	42.0	24	31	37
1935–1939	15.0	60.8	47.0	40.4	25	32	37
1930–1934	14.5	50.5	38.8	37.6	29	37	39
1925–1929	22.8	55.4	34.2[e]	38.8	41	67	59
1920–1924	24.4	52.3	....	....	47		
1920	34.6	57.8	....	....	60		
1919	30.3	47.7	....	....	64		
1918	25.4	40.8	....	....	62		
1917	19.8	31.1	....	....	64		
1916	15.8	26.1	....	....	61		
1915	14.4	22.9	....	....	63		
1910–1914	14.2	21.2	....	....	67		

[a] Based on rates per day without board, using a 10-hour workday as an annual average.

[b] U.S. Department of Agriculture, Bureau of Labor Statistics and Bureau of Agricultural Economics, Washington, D.C.

[c] U.S. Department of Agriculture, Bureau of Labor Statistics, Washington, D.C.

[d] Federal Works Agency, Public Roads Administration; records.

[e] 1926–1929 average.

SOURCE: Louis J. Ducoff, *Wages of Agricultural Labor in the United States*, U.S. Department of Agriculture, Washington, D.C., September, 1944, Table 35, Chap. 6.

Wages Per Man-year of Work

That farm laborers fared much worse than did workers in industry in the three and a half decades since World War I

the depression accounts for the main difference between the hourly and annual comparisons, as would be expected.

is evident also from a comparison of wages paid per man-year of work. In 1910–1914, farm wages were at 46.5 per cent of industrial wages; then there was a steady decline, 1930–1934 finding farm wages at 27.6 per cent of industry wages. Only

ANNUAL WAGE INCOME PER HIRED FARM WORKER* AND PER INDUSTRIAL WORKER△, UNITED STATES, 1910-43
INDEX NUMBERS (1910-14=100)

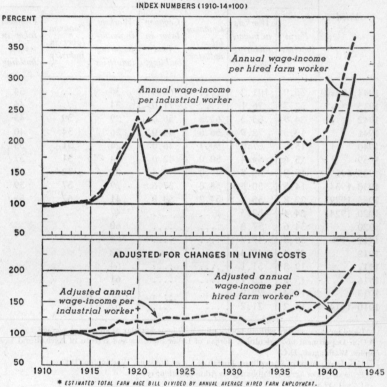

* ESTIMATED TOTAL FARM WAGE BILL DIVIDED BY ANNUAL AVERAGE HIRED FARM EMPLOYMENT.
△ BUREAU OF AGRICULTURAL ECONOMICS; ESTIMATES BASED ON PAYROLL AND EMPLOYMENT DATA FOR FACTORY, MINING, AND RAILROAD EMPLOYEES.
○ ADJUSTED FOR CHANGES IN LIVING COSTS BY INDEX OF PRICES FARMERS PAY FOR GOODS USED IN FAMILY LIVING (1910-14 DOLLARS).
+ ADJUSTED FOR CHANGES IN LIVING COSTS BY BUREAU OF LABOR STATISTICS INDEX OF COST OF LIVING (1913 DOLLARS).

U. S. DEPARTMENT OF AGRICULTURE   BUREAU OF AGRICULTURAL ECONOMICS

a partial recovery has been effected by the war markets for labor as well as farm products. In 1943, agricultural wages per man-year were 37.2 per cent those of industry (Table VIII).

TABLE VIII

COMPARISONS OF WAGES PER MAN-YEAR OF WORK FOR INDUSTRIAL AND AGRICULTURAL WORKERS, FIVE-YEAR AVERAGES, 1910–39, AND SINGLE YEARS 1940–1944, UNITED STATES

| Years | Industrial workers[a] | Hired farm workers[b] | | | Farm Wages as a per cent of industrial wages |
		Total	Cash	Value of perquisites	
1944[c]	$2,360				
1943	2,156	$803	$679	$124	37.2
1942	1,847	616	503	113	33.4
1941	1,495	473	382	91	31.6
1940	1,273	390	309	80	30.6
1935–1939	1,149	362	282	80	31.5
1930–1934	1,038	287	209	78	27.6
1925–1929	1,316	433	323	110	32.9
1920–1924	1,275	450	332	118	35.3
1915–1919	877	394	281	113	44.9
1910–1914	583	271	191	81	46.5

[a] Includes factory, mining, and railroad employees; estimates are based on Bureau of Labor Statistics and Interstate Commerce Commission data on average employment and pay rolls. *Agricultural Outlook Charts*, U.S. Department of Agriculture, Washington, D.C., November, 1944, p. 6.

[b] Total farm wage bill divided by annual average hired farm employment.

[c] Preliminary.

SOURCE: Louis J. Ducoff, *Wages of Agricultural Labor in the United States*, U.S. Department of Agriculture, Washington, D.C., Table 47, Chap. 6. Ducoff points out that this comparison does not overstate in any significant sense the spread between farm and industrial wages per man-year by the value placed on perquisites furnished hired farm hands. Such perquisites are a very small proportion of the total wage bill.

Farm Family, Hired Farm Workers, and Industrial Workers

We have put considerable stress on the wages of hired farm workers, although three-fourths of the labor force in agriculture are self-employed. This was done because the data are available and direct comparisons can be made.[1]   A final and

[1] Ducoff (*op. cit.*, pp. 181–182) adds that the 4 million people who work for wages in agriculture are concentrated on the larger and more productive farms, and that they make possible much more than one-fourth of the total farm production even though they represent only a fourth of the total agricultural labor force.   Hired farm laborers are a mixture of lower-income farmers, members of farmers' families, people who work part time in town and cities, youths who attend school in the winter, migratory workers who follow the crop harvest, and the year-round hired men.

important comparison to be made is that between the wage incomes of industrial workers, of hired farm workers, and the net farm income of family workers including farm operators. The income of family workers, adjusted for changes in living costs, declined significantly during the interwar years relative to wage incomes, and in the depression years of 1921, 1931, and 1932 they dropped to about the same level as the wages of hired farm laborers.

WAGE INCOMES OF INDUSTRIAL WORKERS AND OF HIRED FARM WORKERS AND NET FARM INCOME OF FAMILY WORKERS, ADJUSTED FOR CHANGES IN LIVING COSTS*, UNITED STATES, ANNUAL AVERAGES PER WORKER 1910-43

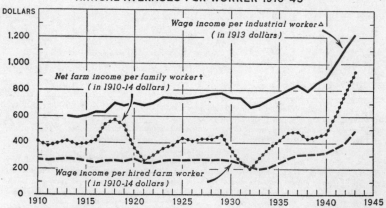

*INCOME PER INDUSTRIAL WORKER ADJUSTED BY THE BUREAU OF LABOR STATISTICS INDEX OF COST OF LIVING; INCOME PER HIRED FARM WORKER AND PER FARM FAMILY WORKER ADJUSTED BY THE BUREAU OF AGRICULTURAL ECONOMICS INDEX OF PRICES PAID BY FARMERS FOR COMMODITIES USED IN FAMILY LIVING.
△ INCLUDES FACTORY, MINING, AND RAILROAD EMPLOYEES   ESTIMATES FOR 1943 ARE PRELIMINARY
† INCLUDES FARM OPERATORS AND UNPAID FAMILY WORKERS

U. S. DEPARTMENT OF AGRICULTURE   BUREAU OF AGRICULTURAL ECONOMICS

Comparative Earnings within Agriculture

Treating American agriculture as a homogeneous entity is permissible only as a first and very rough approximation. There are over five hundred distinct types of farming areas in the United States. A full understanding of earnings from farming requires awareness of the differences among these areas with respect to the four major factors affecting agricultural labor: (*a*) the rate at which new labor-saving technological improvements have been introduced; (*b*) the rate of natural increase in the farm population; (*c*) the pattern of change in demand for different farm products accompanying increased consumer incomes; and (*d*) the nature of the "barriers" to migration. With respect to the movement of labor, these areas vary importantly in proximity to industrial centers, in the level of education, in the wealth of the farm community from which workers migrate, and other factors. As a consequence, there are very significant differences from one farming region to another in the earnings per person engaged in agriculture, differences caused by the varying excesses of labor that have accumulated. This study does not permit discussion of these variations, significant and real as they are. It must suffice to call attention to their existence and to suggest some general consequences for the earnings problem.[1]

The more important advances in labor-saving technology have been made on the level farms and on the larger farms, rather than on the small, hilly farms. In terms of the major crops, most of the improvements in machinery have been adapted to wheat and to corn and not as yet to cotton and tobacco. The natural increase in population has been largest in regions that already have the most excess labor. In the main, the effects of increased consumer income on demand have been more favorable to farming areas having the least excess of labor, because increases in income improve the

---

[1] Ducoff (*op. cit.*, pp. 37–38) stresses the differences in the status of farm laborers, calling attention to three quite distinct historical types of farm labor. One of these has been the apprentice wage hand, not infrequently a neighbor's son. In such circumstances the "hired man" may climb the agricultural ladder until he reaches full ownership. This type of hired man has been characteristic of the North Central and Northeastern states. A second group, prototype of the sharecropper and the hired farm laborer in the South, was the slave laborer. The farm laborer in this group has always had a lower status and less access to alternative job opportunities than the hired farm hand in the North. A third group has put in an appearance where industrial techniques have been introduced into farming. When farmers employ fairly large numbers of laborers in large-scale production, the status differential between the farmer and his workers becomes wide, much wider than on farms where the hired laborer works alongside the farmer.

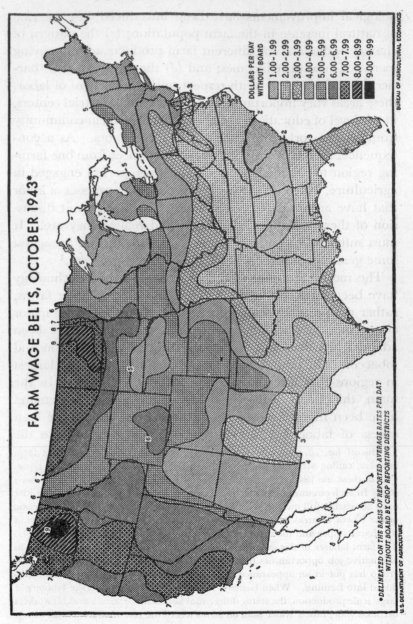

FARM WAGE BELTS, OCTOBER 1943*

DOLLARS PER DAY
WITHOUT BOARD

1.00–1.99
2.00–2.99
3.00–3.99
4.00–4.99
5.00–5.99
6.00–6.99
7.00–7.99
8.00–8.99
9.00–9.99

BUREAU OF AGRICULTURAL ECONOMICS

*DELINEATED ON THE BASIS OF REPORTED AVERAGE RATES PER DAY
WITHOUT BOARD BY CROP REPORTING DISTRICTS

U.S. DEPARTMENT OF AGRICULTURE

demands for animal products (profiting the corn belt and the milksheds), and for the products of the highly specialized fruit and vegetable areas.

The problem of excess labor is at its worst, therefore, in a large portion of the South, in some parts of the intermountain areas, in the cutover regions of the lake states and in the Appalachians; much less excess labor has accumulated in the corn belt, in the dairy areas, and in the fruit and vegetable areas of the Pacific Coast states. The severe droughts of the middle thirties forced hundreds of thousands of people out of the plains states, and this altered substantially the population and labor resources of that major region.

Finally, what fragmentary evidence there is available suggests that since 1940 relatively more people have been drawn out of the least overpopulated farming areas than out of the most overpopulated, if we use as a gauge of the migration the changes in wage rates paid to hired farm workers and the net agricultural income of farm operators.

The differing geographical divisions remained essentially in the same relation to each other with respect to wages during most of the interwar period. The pattern of wages for the years 1910–1914 and for January 1, 1939, is shown in Table IX, page 112. The only major change was the notable worsening of farm wages in the West North-central division, which dropped from an index of 180 to 133. Five years later, however, we see the sharp rise in farm wages (column 3) in the Pacific Coast states, for example, relative to those in the South Atlantic and East South-central states. The fact that there continues to be a very wide disparity in the earnings within agriculture suggests that very considerable differences remain in the distribution of the excess labor in agriculture.

What these differences mean for national policy after the war should be clear. The primary long-run objective of national policy should be to bring about a better distribution of the labor force within the United States, in order more

TABLE IX

INDEX OF FARM WAGE RATES (WITH BOARD) PER MONTH BY GEOGRAPHIC DIVISIONS

Region	(1) 1910–1914	(2) Jan. 1, 1939	(3) Jan. 1, 1944
South Atlantic...................	100	100	100
East South Central..............	101	93	93
West South Central.............	119	109	138
Middle Atlantic.................	152	164	177
East North Central.............	162	154	170
New England...................	165	188	209
West North Central.............	180	133	175
Mountain......................	222	187	229
Pacific........................	229	250	335
United States.................	159	150	181

SOURCE: *Farm Labor*, U.S. Department of Agriculture, Bureau of Agricultural Economics, January, 1944. The farm wage rate per month, with board, of the South Atlantic division was taken as the base with $14.62 for 1910–1914 = 100; $16.54 for Jan. 1, 1939 = 100; and $35.20 for Jan. 1, 1944 = 100. (*Agricultural Statistics* 1940, Table 698, p. 580.)

nearly to approach a general equilibrium measured in terms of the value productivity and earnings of workers. Agricultural programs should not only be consistent with this end but should make a positive contribution to it. So also should industrial and labor programs. Each will fruitfully bear testing against this criterion.

V. EFFECTS OF THE RATE OF INDUSTRIAL EXPANSION ON AGRICULTURE

THE failure of industrial output to expand during the thirties was the basic factor in the worsening of the agricultural situation.[1] The main cause for the underproductive employment and low earnings in agriculture was the unemployment in industry. Fluctuations in industrial output are a great part of the rise and fall of the terms of exchange of agriculture.[2] Tied as it is to the exchange economy, if agriculture is to enjoy economic well-being, the rate of expansion in the secondary and tertiary industries[3] must be

[1] The performance of industry may be measured in terms of the level and also the fluctuation of its production and employment. In this chapter we are concerned with the effects on agriculture of the level of production and the rate at which it expands over time and not with the problem of the short-term fluctuations in industrial production and employment. In this study no attempt is made to ascertain the cause for low levels of industrial production and for its inadequate rate of expansion. This represents a bigger task than the one undertaken here. However, the impact of the level and the fluctuations of industrial production and employment appear direct and significant to the economic well-being of agriculture. Thus it is exceedingly important to agriculture that we diagnose and correct the causes of this poor performance of industry.

[2] To be considered in the next chapter.

[3] The terms "secondary" and "tertiary" industries are used here to denote industries other than primary. Allan G. B. Fisher in "Production, Primary, Secondary, and Tertiary," *The Economic Record* (1939), discusses the origin of these terms in the literature of Australia and New Zealand and points to the usefulness of these concepts. It would serve economic analysis better to classify industries in accordance with the income elasticity of the demand for the products of each. In such a classification primary industries might well be defined as those whose products had an income elasticity of .5 or less; secondary industries as those with an income elasticity falling between 1 and .5; and tertiary industries as those with an income elasticity greater than 1. The lines of demarcation would be a matter of convenience. The main consideration is this;

substantially greater than it is in agriculture. During most of the interwar period this condition was not fulfilled, and agriculture, already at a disadvantage, lost further ground relative to other major sectors of the economy.

In this chapter we shall present briefly empirical evidence on the relationships between the rates of expansion in industry and agriculture in the United States. There have been four distinct periods since 1895. The duration of the first was from 1895 to 1915; the second, from 1915 to 1919; the third, from 1920 to 1939; and the fourth, from 1940 to 1945. In the first of these periods, American agriculture enjoyed the largest measure of sustained prosperity that it has had in its history.

THE GOLDEN ERA OF AMERICAN AGRICULTURE

In the twenty years from 1895 to 1915 industrial output expanded at a rate much higher than that of agriculture. At the end of the period industrial production in the United States was one and one-half times greater than it had been at the beginning, while the output of American agriculture had increased only one-half; hence the industrial rate of increase was three times that of agriculture.

Wages paid to farm workers rose 17 per cent relative to wages paid industrial laborers. (During the last five years, 1911 to 1915, the average net income per person engaged in agriculture was about $370 compared to $595 per worker engaged in industry.[1]) The improvement in agriculture from 1895 to 1915 was, however, considerably larger than the

---

if the concepts "primary," "secondary," and "tertiary" are to be of maximum usefulness in economic analysis, they should be based upon the income elasticity of the products that the industries produce.

[1] *Agricultural Outlook Charts*, U.S. Department of Agriculture, Washington, D.C., November, 1944, p. 6. The focus here is not on the dollar totals but upon the ratio of the earnings of the two groups. In 1910–1914 the ratio between farm income and industrial wages per person engaged stood at 65 per cent. Agriculture did not attain such a high ratio throughout the entire interwar years, in fact not until 1943.

TABLE X

INDEXES OF INDUSTRIAL AND AGRICULTURAL PRODUCTION, AGRICULTURAL TERMS
OF EXCHANGE, CHANGES IN RELATIVE EARNINGS, AND PROPORTION OF THE
WORKING POPULATION IN AGRICULTURE, 1895–1915

(1895 = 100)

Year	(1) Industrial production[a]	(2) Agricultural production[b]	(3) Agricultural terms of exchange[c]	(4) Earnings per farm laborer relative to earnings of workers engaged in manufacturing[d]	(5) Proportion of the working population in agriculture,[e] per cent
1895	100	100	100	100	39.3 = 100
1900	120	119	98	110	36.8 = 94
1905	174	130	105	117	
1910	198	132	124[f]	115	31.2 = 79
1915	256	150	115	121	28.6 = 73

[a] Solomon Fabricant, *The Output of Manufacturing Industries 1899–1937*, National Bureau of Economic Research, New York, 1940, Table 1, p. 44. The index for 1895 was obtained from Warren M. Persons, *Forecasting Business Cycles*, John Wiley & Sons, Inc., New York, 1931, Table 12, pp. 170–171, and adjusted to the same basis as that employed in the study by Fabricant.

[b] Louis H. Bean and Frederick Strauss, *Gross Farm Income and Indices of Production and Prices in the United States, 1869–1937*, Technical Bulletin 703, U.S. Department of Agriculture, Washington, D.C., December, 1940, Table 59, p. 125.

[c] Louis H. Bean and Frederick Strauss, *Gross Farm Income and Indices of Production and Prices in the United States, 1869–1937*, Technical Bulletin 703, Table 77, p. 140 and *Index of Wholesale Prices, 1890–1927*, U.S. Department of Labor, Washington, D.C., 1928. In 1895 the index of farm prices was 60.4 and the index for 70 industrial products was 72.5. The ratio between them is 83, which is the base of 100 for the series in column 3.

[d] Based on Paul H. Douglas, *Real Wages in the United States 1890–1926*, Houghton Mifflin Company, Boston, 1930, Table 147, p. 392. In 1895 the average annual earnings of farm laborers were 52 per cent of those of workers engaged in manufacturing. Thus 52 = 100 in column 4.

[e] P. K. Whelpton, "Occupational Groups in the United States 1820–1920," *Journal of the American Statistical Association* (1926), p. 339. It is estimated that in 1895, 39.3 per cent of the working population of the United States was in agriculture. Thus 39.3 = 100 in column 5.

[f] Pulled up considerably by the sharp rise of farm prices in 1909 and 1910.

changes in current incomes would indicate, because of the appreciation that took place in the capital value of the real estate, livestock, and other farm property. Significantly, the proportion of the total working population in agriculture moved downward from 39.3 to 28.6 per cent, a relative drop of more than one-fourth.

Foreign demand was strong, but agricultural exports did not increase appreciably, chiefly because of the rapidly expanding domestic market.[1] The terms of exchange became more favorable to agriculture from about 1895 to 1909, at which time prices generally leveled off and the ratio of prices paid to prices received by farmers remained remarkably steady up to World War I.[2] This was American agriculture's golden era. It was a period in which the industrialization that took place was sufficiently rapid to absorb (*a*) the growing output of agriculture and (*b*) an increasingly larger share of the working population. The substantial gains in the earnings of farm people, both in absolute terms and relative to the earnings of workers in industry, were a consequence largely of this one factor. In numbers, the farm population appears to have stayed fairly constant after reaching about 32 million, in spite of a natural increase estimated at about 650,000 a year at the close of the period. In the latter years of this twenty-year period the net migration from farms was sufficient to offset fully the natural population growth.[3]

[1] There is no satisfactory index of the quantity of agricultural exports for this period. The dollar value of agricultural products exported rose about as much as did the wholesale prices of farm products. Accordingly, we infer that the quantity exported did not change appreciably. Meat exports dropped. Cotton exports rose from about 6.5 (1895–1900) to 8.8 million bales (1910–1915) and wheat declined from about 180 to 100 million bushels annually. (1914 and 1915 wheat exports were very large, however, chiefly as a result of the war.) (*Agricultural Statistics, 1942*, U.S. Department of Agriculture, Washington, D.C.)

[2] The index of wholesale prices of farm products rose from 61.2 in 1895 to 86.5 in 1908; fuels, from 65.9 to 87.7; building materials, from 68.3 to 91.8; house furnishing goods, from 77.3 to 91.6; clothing materials, from 77.3 to 93.8; and chemicals and drugs, from 80.7 to 99.2. *Index Numbers of Wholesale Prices on Pre-war Base, 1890–1927*, U.S. Department of Labor, Washington, D.C., 1928, Table 1, pp. 3 and 5. (The U.S. Department of Agriculture statistics on prices paid and prices received by farmers do not extend back of 1910.)

[3] The critical reader may well ask at this point, why did our economy perform so well during this period, attaining the essentials of full employment? Did the steadiness (and only gradual rise) of the price level furnish the requisite conditions? Many farm people have long held the view that the prosperity from 1895 to 1915 had its foundation in the steady value of the dollar and that it is in fiscal-monetary policy that the remedy for the unemployment in our cities and the chronically depressed state of agriculture is to be found. With respect to the basic elements of the problem, farm people holding this view have been and continue to be right. Fiscal-monetary policy is the *first line of defense* against a

CHRONIC AGRICULTURAL SURPLUSES

The two decades that separated the great wars were in marked contrast to the two decades that preceded 1915. A sharp recession succeeded the boomlet that followed the 1918 armistice. Then the prewar trends in production reasserted themselves temporarily in industry and in agriculture through the middle and later twenties. After that came economic disintegration. In spite of new and better technology at hand and an increase in population, physical output remained low and stagnant. In place of the 150 per cent rise that marked the two decades prior to 1915, industrial output from 1919–1939 expanded less than 50 per cent. The annual rate of increase was less than one-third as great as that of the years preceding World War I. In agriculture the course of production became uncertain after 1930, with a low point in the middle thirties caused largely by droughts and, to a minor extent, by government programs to restrict production. During the period as a whole, there was only a small increase in agricultural production.

The terms of exchange ran heavily against agriculture. They declined sharply in the early twenties, then recovered, reached a high for the entire interwar period in 1925, and stayed fairly constant until 1929, when with the break in the structure of prices generally they dropped in 1932 to an unprecedented low of 54 per cent of the level of 1920. Although they recovered considerably by 1937, a downward course was again in evidence in 1938 and 1939 and well into 1940. Stagnation in industry and dwindling export outlets meant so adverse a pressure on agricultural prices that all the efforts of government—spending billions of dollars to curtail production, to subsidize exports and consumption, and to provide additional demand by storage—may have tempered but were not sufficient to keep the terms of trade from becoming very

---

fluctuating and stagnant economy. The question is examined in Part IV of this study with other problems of policy.

unfavorable to agriculture. Agricultural surpluses were the order of the day and back of these surpluses was the excess labor force accumulating in agriculture.

We have already pointed out that the proportion of the working population in agriculture broke its historical trend during the great depression. It continued down at its old rate through the twenties, declining from 26.1 to 21.6 per cent. But in the next decade, the thirties, this trend came to an abrupt stop; the excess workers in agriculture, because of industrial unemployment, had no place to go.

These two decades appear to have given us the necessary conditions for a depressed and overpopulated agriculture. The low rate—in fact, the virtual stagnation—of industrial expansion and the deterioration of foreign trade were undoubtedly the primary causes of "the farm problem," that loomed so large and had become so chronic in its unmanageable surpluses.

WORLD WAR I PRECEDED BY FEW UNEMPLOYED RESOURCES AND WAGED WITHOUT PRICE CONTROLS

The experiences of World War I are noteworthy in that the bulge in production was small and the advance in prices large compared to what has happened as a consequence of the economic mobilization during World War II. The expansion in industrial output from 1914 to 1918 was at a rate not appreciably different from that which had been in process since 1895.[1] Likewise, the increase in agricultural production, in spite of the extraordinary efforts to produce more food during the war years, was also essentially a continuance of the rate of increase that had been under way for two decades.[2]

[1] Solomon Fabricant (*The Output of Manufacturing Industries, 1899–1937*, National Bureau of Economic Research, New York, 1940, p. 45) presents a chart on a ratio scale from which it is apparent that, although there was a very sharp increase from 1915 to 1916, in the war years as a whole there was merely an extension of the trend that had been under way for fully two decades.

[2] Frederick Strauss and Louis H. Bean (*Gross Farm Income and Indices of Pro-*

Effects of the Rate of Industrial Expansion

In 1918 industrial production was 17 per cent and agricultural
5 per cent larger than in 1915.   The relative rates of increase

TABLE XI

INDEXES OF INDUSTRIAL AND AGRICULTURAL PRODUCTION, AGRICULTURAL TERMS
OF EXCHANGE, CHANGES IN RELATIVE EARNINGS, AND PROPORTION OF THE
WORKING POPULATION IN AGRICULTURE, 1920–1939

(1920 = 100)

Year	(1) Industrial production[a]	(2) Agricultural production[b]	(3) Agricultural terms of exchange[c]	(4) Income per person engaged in agriculture relative to earnings of industrial workers[d]	(5) Proportion of the working population in agriculture,[e] per cent
1920	100	100	100	100	26.1 = 100
1925	120	105	99	94	
1930	121	106	86	74	21.6 = 83
1935	116	99	86	83	
1939	145	115	82	79	20.6 = 79

[a] *Federal Reserve Bulletin*, (February, 1944), p. 179.

[b] *Farm Income Situation*, U.S. Department of Agriculture, Bureau of Agricultural Economics, December, 1943, p. 15.

[c] *Index Numbers of Prices Received by Farmers, 1910–1943*, U.S. Department of Agriculture, Bureau of Agricultural Economics, February, 1944, p. 22.   In 1920 the index for prices received by farmers was 211, and that of prices paid by farmers was 212.   Thus our base is a ratio of 99.5 = 100.   The index of prices paid by farmers includes all commodities both for use in production and for family maintenance other than food, feed, and seed.

[d] *1944 Agricultural Outlook Charts*, U.S. Department of Agriculture, Bureau of Agricultural Economics, October, 1943, p. 6.   In 1920 the average net income per person engaged in agriculture was $753, and wage income per employed industrial worker was $1,411.   Thus our base is a ratio of 53 = 100.

[e] For 1920, see P. K. Whelpton, "Occupational Groups in the United States 1820–1920," *Journal of the American Statistical Association*, 1926, p. 339.

For 1930 and 1939, see *United States Census*, 1940, Vol. III, Part I, p. 25.   In 1920 the per cent of the working population engaged in agriculture was 26.1 = 100.

had been approximately three to one in favor of industry
before the war and remained so during the war.   The prin-

duction and Prices in the United States, 1869–1937, Technical Bulletin 703, U.S.
Department of Agriculture, December, 1940) include a ratio chart, Fig. 42,
p. 125, which shows that the increase in output that was attained during World
War I was no larger than might have been expected from a continuation of the
pre-1915 trend.

cipal structural change came in prices. All prices rose rapidly, but farm prices outdistanced other prices and the terms of exchange in 1918 were approximately 23 per cent more favorable to agriculture than they had been in 1915. Why did not agricultural output increase more with the inducement of high farm prices and decidedly more favorable terms of exchange? There was little slack in resources in agriculture when World War I started; nor were there at hand important improvements in farm technology. It was clearly an inelastic supply situation.

In administering the economy during World War I, the government (in contrast to World War II) did not impose many price controls. The small response in production coupled with the great increase in demand gave inflation its head, and it expressed itself more fully in farm prices than in other major categories of prices.

Agricultural earnings made singular advances and in 1918 came closer to the wage incomes of industrial workers than at any previous time in the United States. That year the average net income per person engaged in agriculture was $882, compared to the wage income per employed industrial worker of $1,064. This represented an increase in agricultural earnings relative to industrial earnings of 36 per cent over 1915.

It was not so much the expansion in industrial output (relative to the agricultural expansion) that tipped the scales in favor of agriculture as it was the enlarged demand for food, especially for shipments to the Allies. It has been estimated that the crop acreage required to produce the net exports of major farm products during the years immediately preceding World War I was about 50 million acres. By 1915, exports absorbed the output of about 70 million acres. The greatly heightened export demand improved agriculture's terms of exchange and pulled farm earnings up with it.

A striking fact is that there was no marked departure of

labor out of agriculture as a factor bettering earnings per worker. The farm population continued its downward trend at roughly the same rate that had prevailed during the

TABLE XII

INDEXES OF INDUSTRIAL AND AGRICULTURAL PRODUCTION, AGRICULTURAL TERMS OF EXCHANGE, CHANGES IN RELATIVE EARNINGS, AND PROPORTION OF THE WORKING POPULATION IN AGRICULTURE, 1915–1920

(1915 = 100)

Year	(1) Industrial production[a]	(2) Agricultural production[b]	(3) Agricultural terms of exchange[c]	(4) Income per person engaged in agriculture relative to earnings of industrial workers[d]	(5) Proportion of the working population in agriculture,[e] per cent
1915	100	100	100	100	28.6 = 100
1916	119	96	101	110	
1917	118	99	124	138	
1918	117	105	123	136	
1919	102	106	113	134	
1920	111	107	112	87	26.1 = 91

[a] Solomon Fabricant, *The Output of Manufacturing Industries, 1899–1937,* Table 1, p. 44.

[b] Frederick Strauss and Louis H. Bean, *Gross Farm Income and Indices of Farm Production and Prices in the United States, 1896–1937, Technical Bulletin* 703, U.S. Department of Agriculture, December, 1940, p. 125.

[c] *Index Numbers of Prices Received by Farmers, 1910–1943,* U.S. Department of Agriculture, Bureau of Agricultural Economics, p. 22; and *Agricultural Statistics, 1943,* U.S. Department of Agriculture, Washington, D.C., p. 394.   In 1915 the index of prices received by farmers was 99 against an index for prices paid by farmers of 105, giving a ratio of 94.2 = 100.   The index of prices paid by farmers includes all commodities bought for use in production and family maintenance.

[d] *1944 Agricultural Outlook Charts,* U.S. Department of Agriculture, Bureau of Agricultural Economics, October, 1943, p. 6.   In 1915 the average net income per person engaged in agriculture was $381 compared with wage income per employed industrial worker of $622, giving a ratio of 61 = 100.

[e] P. K. Whelpton, "Occupational Groups in the United States 1820–1920," *Journal of the American Statistical Association,* 1926, p. 339.   In 1915, taking the mid-point between the 1910 and 1920 censuses, the proportion of the total working population engaged in agriculture is 28.6 = 100.

previous two decades, no more rapidly.   About 32.5 million people were in agriculture in 1915; in 1920 there were 31.6 million.   The transfer of labor is the most significant difference between the effects of World War I and World War II on agriculture.

WORLD WAR II PRECEDED BY MANY UNEMPLOYED RESOURCES AND WAGED WITH PRICE CONTROLS

Industrial production during World War II climbed at the extraordinary rate of 30 per cent a year, and agricultural output at the equally astounding rate of 5 per cent. Contrast this with the peak production attained in 1918, when an average yearly rate of growth of 5.7 per cent in industry and 1.7 in agriculture had been realized. The expansion of 1940–1943, however, came after the stagnation of the thirties. It was possible because of the tremendous backlog of unemployed resources both in industry and in agriculture.

TABLE XIII

INDEXES OF INDUSTRIAL AND AGRICULTURAL PRODUCTION, AGRICULTURAL TERMS OF EXCHANGE, CHANGES IN RELATIVE EARNINGS, AND PROPORTION OF THE WORKING POPULATION IN AGRICULTURE, 1940–1943

(1940 = 100)

Year	(1) Industrial production[a]	(2) Agricultural production[b]	(3) Agricultural terms of exchange[c]	(4) Income per person engaged in agriculture relative to earnings of industrial workers[d]	(5) Proportion of the working population in agriculture,[e] per cent
1940	100	100	100	100	19.9 = 100
1941	130	102	115	117	
1942	159	114	131	133	
1943	191	116	149	150	15 = 75

[a] *Federal Reserve Bulletin*, February, 1944, p. 179.

[b] *Farm Income Situation*, U.S. Department of Agriculture, Bureau of Agricultural Economics, December, 1943, p. 15.

[c] *Index Numbers of Prices Received by Farmers, 1910–1943*, U.S. Department of Agriculture, Bureau of Agricultural Economics, p. 22. The index for prices received by farmers was 100 in 1940, and that for prices paid by farmers for all commodities for use in production and family maintenance (other than food, feed, and seed) was 92, giving a ratio of 92 = 100.

[d] *Agricultural Outlook Charts*, U.S. Department of Agriculture, Bureau of Agricultural Economics, November, 1944, p. 6. The average net income per person engaged in agriculture in 1940 was $531 and wage income per employed industrial worker was $1,273, giving a ratio of 42 = 100.

[e] *United States Census, 1940*, Vol. III, Part I, p. 25; and current estimates of the U.S. Department of Agriculture and U.S. Department of Labor.

The improvement in the terms of exchange of agriculture was twice as rapid during World War II, when price controls were applied generally, as it was during World War I, when price controls were used sparingly. Why? Mainly responsible for this peculiar twist in prices were:

1. The very considerable increase in the demand for food— for lend-lease, for civilian consumers with greatly expanded incomes to spend, and for the armed forces.

2. Price legislation, formulated in such a way that it actually contributed to widening the terms of exchange in favor of agriculture. Price controls were more effective in checking the rise of prices of many commodities that farmers buy than in checking the prices received by farmers. Farm prices were tied by Congress to the parity formula, which permits them to spiral upward because the index of prices paid by farmers includes food, feed, and seed. These represent 33.6 per cent of the weights of all commodities in the index, though they are in fact commodities that farmers also sell.

3. The terms of exchange for agriculture were at a very low point at the beginning of this period, reflecting the weight of the depression.

With increasing agricultural production (some of which was a temporary phenomenon, however, resulting from bumper crops and the conversion of large reserves of feed and wheat into animal products), with rapidly improving terms of exchange, and with the departure of many workers out of agriculture, farm earnings were lifted to a hitherto unknown high. In 1940 the average net income per person in agriculture was 42 per cent of the wage income per employed industrial worker. In the extraordinary war-time market, dollar agricultural earnings rose from $531 in 1940 to $1,362 in 1943, those of industrial workers from $1,273 to $2,156. By 1943, earnings in agriculture were therefore 63 per cent as large as those of industrial workers. It should be noted, however, that relatively the farmer had only regained the position he held just prior to World War I.

Significant changes for the long pull ahead have also come in the transfer of labor resources. Since 1940 millions of workers have migrated from farms to cities, and many others maintaining their residence in agriculture have given up farm work to take other employment. In four years the proportion of the nation's labor force engaged in agriculture dropped from about 20 to 15 per cent.

RATES OF EXPANSION COMPARED

Comparing the two periods of peace, the twenty years that we have called the "golden era of American agriculture" and the two decades of chronic agricultural surpluses differed markedly in the rate of industrial expansion. During the two decades 1895–1915 industrial expansion was three times what it was from 1920 to 1939. The agricultural rate of output followed suit.[1]

The two war periods show an equally great contrast. Industry has expanded five times as rapidly during World War II as it did during World War I.[2] With all due credit to those who have carried the burden of administering the American economy as it has been mobilized for war since 1940, this great increase in production was possible in large part because of the tremendous amount of unemployed resources that had accumulated in the economy both in industry and within agriculture. Agriculture has also

---

[1] During the period before World War I prices were rising and the drift in the terms of exchange favored agriculture to the extent of a .75 per cent increase a year on an average. This is in contrast to a drop of nearly 1 per cent a year for the postwar period, when surpluses and the farm problem were constantly in the foreground.

[2] These calculations are based on the production index of industry prepared by the research staff of the Federal Reserve Board. It may be argued that this index overstates the increase in production. This is a debatable point. However, even if some overestimation should be inherent in the index, there would remain all told a very pronounced increase in favor of industry from 1940 to 1943.

expanded at a much greater rate than during World War I—more than three times as rapidly—notwithstanding the transfer to industry of a very considerable proportion of the labor resources formerly in agriculture.

TABLE XIV

CHANGE IN RATES OF INDUSTRIAL PRODUCTION, AGRICULTURAL PRODUCTION, TERMS OF EXCHANGE, AGRICULTURAL RELATIVE TO INDUSTRIAL EARNINGS, AND DISTRIBUTION OF THE WORKING POPULATION; AVERAGE FOR YEARS 1895–1915, 1920–1939, 1915–1918, AND 1940–1943[a]

(In per cent)

Period	(1) Industrial production	(2) Agricultural production	(3) Agricultural terms of exchange	(4) Agricultural earnings relative to industrial earnings	(5) Distribution of the working population
I. During peace:					
1895–1915	7.80	2.50	0.75	1.05	−1.35
1920–1939	2.37	0.79	−0.95	−1.11	−1.11
II. During war:					
1915–1918	5.66	1.66	7.66	12.00	−0.83
1940–1943	30.33	5.33	16.33	16.66	−8.33

[a] Based on the four preceding tables in this chapter.

What do these data on the behavior of our economy point to? What bearing have they upon national policy for agriculture after the war?

We have tried to test, in a preliminary way, one of the major hypotheses underlying this study. This hypothesis is that one of the fundamental conditions necessary for economic progress in agriculture is the expansion of secondary and tertiary industries, at a rate considerably greater than the rate in agriculture. On the assumption (a) that the income elasticity of farm products is decidedly less than it is for the products and services of what we have called "secondary and tertiary industries";[1] (b) that the rate of reproduction of the

---

[1] Because available production statistics are not classified by secondary and tertiary industries, it is necessary in this rough approximation to employ indus-

farm population is considerably larger than that of the non-farm population; and (*c*) that the introduction of labor-saving technology in farming is at a rate as rapid as that in secondary and tertiary industries taken as a whole—it becomes necessary for industries other than agriculture to expand more rapidly than agriculture, if the use of agricultural resources is to be held in approximate equilibrium with the rest of the economy, an essential condition if agriculture is to prosper.

The performance of the American economy since 1895 appears to bear out this hypothesis. In good times and bad, in war and peace, the rate of expansion in industrial output has, in fact, been several times as large as that of agriculture. What is revealed by the foregoing documentation of agricultural-industrial relationships over a fifty-year period is how large the average rate of expansion in industry must be to ensure prosperity in agriculture.

It seems likely that after the war, when relief needs have been filled and the granaries restocked, agriculture can be fairly prosperous—*if during the first two decades after the war the annual rate of increase in nonagricultural output reaches 4 to 6 per cent.*[1] This would probably make room for an expansion in agriculture of upward of 2 per cent per year. Should this rate prevail, the greatest part of the old farm problem, which in the years between the two wars looked as though it were here to stay, would gradually disappear. A yearly rate of expansion in the nonagricultural industries of about this magnitude should be sufficient to absorb most of agriculture's

---

trial production as covering both categories, realizing that most services are not included. As an economy develops, most of the nonfarm production not included as industrial production has an even higher rate of potential expansion than does industrial output, because the income elasticity of this output (chiefly services) is even higher than that of industrial products.

[1] An annual rate averaging somewhere between 4 and 6 per cent is not too large to expect starting from full employment, for the gains to be had from advances in technology, accumulation of capital, improvement in skills and better organization are about of this magnitude.

excess labor force. It would not be likely to occasion any considerable change in the terms of trade of agriculture. They could be expected to advance somewhat; this improvement and a substantial increase in the output per farm worker would bring about an equilibrium in the economy as earnings in agriculture rose relatively and became comparable to the incomes of workers in industry.

A reverse set of circumstances can obviously be seen in the preceding analysis. The lower the rate of expansion in nonagricultural industries, the more severe will be the maladjustments in agriculture—surpluses, low prices, overpopulation, and very low incomes. If the industrial rate of growth should fall to half the above figures or less, we may expect economic dislocations and distress to prevail in agriculture and we may again find it necessary to have farm programs involving billions of dollars of public funds, primarily for relief.

Another major interaction between the output of industry and the economic well-being of agriculture lies in the fluctuation in the terms of exchange. The causes of the wide swings from year to year will be examined next.

VI. BUSINESS FLUCTUATIONS AND
AGRICULTURE

Ⅰⅆⱱⱥ growing dependence on the exchange system makes
agriculture increasingly vulnerable to business fluctuations.
In an industrial economy, this dependency may well be the
Achilles' heel of agriculture. Such vulnerability has already
given rise to a host of price and income problems in agriculture. It is these problems, rooted in the instability of
industrial production and employment, and mainly short-run
in duration (in that at times the situation improves quickly
and then worsens quickly), that have claimed most of the
attention of farm groups, legislators, and the public. For
the most part, they have crowded from the scene the fundamental task of correcting the widespread underemployment in
agriculture.

To establish a few bench marks with regard to long-run
forces at work affecting the value of farm products and
resources and the well-being of farm people, we examined in
the three preceding chapters the slowly occurring structural
changes of a developing economy as they affect agriculture.
What of the short-run problems confronting agriculture?
In this we shall restrict our inquiry to the effects of business
fluctuations on agriculture.[1]

NATURE OF THE EFFECTS

Business fluctuations may affect agriculture's production,
the distribution of the labor force, price, and income.

In production agriculture has thus far been quite immune to
the disease of curtailing output when business recedes.

---

[1] It would be appropriate to examine the effects of agriculture upon the business economy. Although some weight is given to this relationship in evaluating
compensatory payments later in this chapter, no basic inquiry is attempted.

Farmers do not of their own accord lessen their production efforts when business becomes depressed.[1] Nor are they prone to increase production when business booms. As an illustration:[2] From 1929 to 1932 agricultural production changed only from an index of 99 to 96, although industrial output fell from 110 to 58;[3] from 1937 to 1938, agricultural production merely slid from 106 to 103 (yields were down) compared to a drop from 113 to 89 for industry. When business boomed as it did from 1924 to 1929, with industrial output rising from 82 to 110, agricultural production moved only from 98 to 99 (no appreciable change in yields); from 1933 to 1937, agriculture advanced from 96 to 106 (yields were very high in 1937), and industry from 69 to 113 (Table XVI).

The distribution of the labor force, as has been shown in detail in Chap. IV, is worsened when business declines and improved when business expands, especially when the expansion is sustained over a number of years. Paradoxical as it may seem, it is a fact that since World War I the movement of workers into and out of agriculture has not been in accord with changes in farm prices. As farm prices fell, more people stayed in agriculture; as farm prices rose, the migration from farms increased. During the early thirties, when farm prices broke into and fell relative to other prices, the movement of people from farms not only dwindled but actually reversed itself. From 1939 to 1944 farm prices in the United States doubled, and also rose more than other product prices, but this was accompanied by an unprecedented migration out of agriculture. From this we infer that the mechanism of relative prices in this particular sphere, looked at cyclewise, is not effective in inducing the desired redistribution of the labor resources, that is, lessening the excess supply of labor

---

[1] A depression in business may curtail the inputs of fertilizer, and in some areas less hired labor may be employed while self-employed workers do more of the farm work.

[2] These figures strictly speaking do not measure the "production effort of farmers."

[3] Both the agricultural and industrial indexes are based on 1935–1939 = 100.

dependent upon farming for its income. Another economic force has superseded changes in relative prices. The availability or nonavailability of jobs has been the dominant force.[1]

The prices received by farmers move in close sympathy with the fluctuations in business, rising when industrial production and employment expand and falling when they contract. The amplitude of farm-price fluctuations, however, is greater than that of prices generally. Since agricultural output is not altered significantly, it follows that the changes in farm income associated with business fluctuations are transmitted to agriculture through farm prices. Next in importance to the overlarge supply of labor, the underemployment problem that burdens agriculture in a developing economy is the extraordinary *instability of farm income*—a burden placed on agriculture primarily by business fluctuations.[2]

AGRICULTURE'S UNSTABLE TERMS OF EXCHANGE

How much can farm people buy with the cash income they receive from the sales of crops and livestock? Here we are concerned not with long-time averages but with the cyclical changes in the purchasing power of the products that the farmer sells, specifically the changes that are associated with business fluctuations. The terms of exchange of agriculture are very unstable. To illustrate this instability let us take a corn belt farmer, a farmer with an annual interest obligation of $600, producing for sale each year twenty-five choice butcher hogs. He would have received enough income from his hogs in 1937 to pay this interest; but in 1940 the check from the sale of his hogs would have covered only half of his interest obligation; and in 1933 the twenty-five hogs when marketed would have fetched less than a third enough to pay the $600 of interest.

[1] See Chap. IV for a fuller treatment.

[2] A few figures make evident the staggering instability of farm income. The index of cash income from farm marketings, with 1935–1939 = 100, dropped from 142 in 1929 to 59 in 1932; from 111 in 1937 to 96 in 1938. It rose from 102 in 1921 to 138 in 1925; from 59 in 1932 to 111 in 1937.

Major Propositions

Certain assumptions with regard to the governing conditions that characterize business fluctuations and the terms of exchange of agriculture[1] are warranted by the fifty-year period we have reviewed. These assumptions may be put in terms of four major propositions:

1. The prices that farmers receive for farm products are very sensitive to changes in economic expectations of the urban-industrial community generally; this means that the prices of farm products reflect quickly a bullish or bearish turn.

2. The prices that farmers pay for the products of secondary and tertiary industries, including services, are comparatively insensitive to changes in business outlook: and this means that prices of nonfarm products and services do not reflect quickly an optimistic or pessimistic turn.[2]

3. Agricultural production in the aggregate responds slowly, or not at all, to the changes in economic expectations associated with business fluctuations.

4. The output of industry is highly responsive to changes in economic expectations, with production rising sharply when the outlook turns bright and falling abruptly when it becomes gloomy.

The causality here runs from the changes in economic expectations to increases and decreases in industrial output (not in industrial prices) and to rises and falls in farm prices (not in farm production). If these propositions are true in fact, we would expect a close positive connection between the ratio of industrial to agricultural output and the ratio of prices received to prices paid by farmers (see Table XV).

[1] The terms of exchange of agriculture may be analyzed not only in a long-run context to ascertain how they are altered by the forces operating in a developing economy, but also in a short-run setting to determine how business fluctuations affect them. In this chapter we shall focus wholly on the latter, the short-run changes.

[2] Most industrial prices will not change upward or downward many times within a year, while most farm-product prices change daily, many even hourly.

The courses taken by these two sets of ratios are not a case of similar responses to a more general economic force playing on each of them. The general economic force in this context is the changes that occur in economic expectations in the community generally. The crucial fact is that agriculture and industry do not adjust their production or the prices at which their products sell in the same way during business fluctuations. If they did, it would follow perforce that the terms of exchange between farm and nonfarm products and services would remain essentially constant. But this is not what occurs. Instead, when demand contracts during a depression, industry produces relatively little and manages fairly successfully to maintain prices, while agriculture continues at high production and farm prices drop sharply. Only one conclusion can follow with regard to agriculture's terms of exchange: What farmers receive in exchange per unit of product is made highly unstable by business fluctuations.

To restate the major consequences: When business contracts, agricultural production does not drop, while the prices received by farmers for their products decline more than the prices they pay for goods and services used in farm production and for family maintenance. Conversely, when business expands, industry's output rises more than agriculture's, and the prices of the goods and services that farmers buy rise less than the prices of crops and livestock that farmers sell. This basic relationship between the volume of industrial and agricultural output and what farmers receive in exchange for what they sell is in one sense elementary, but it is fundamental to an understanding of the main cause for the cyclical instability of agriculture's terms of exchange.[1]

---

[1] It should be noted for the critical student that this instability in the terms of exchange occurs in spite of the low income elasticity of farm products, which acts as a dampening influence when national income falls and rises. Suppose the income elasticity of farm products were unity (1) instead of .25, then the expansion or contraction of income (per capita) associated with business fluctuations would occasion a proportional increase or decrease in the demand for farm

Parity and Disparity

Because of the growing disposition to remedy agriculture's ills by cutting down production when industry cuts its output, the effects of curtailed production deserve further treatment. The following hypothetical situations make evident the manner in which one section of the economy can pass along to other sections a part of the burden of contraction in production. If agriculture were to curtail its operation to one-half of its normal output and industry were to produce at a high level, plainly what would happen would be a switch in the exchange ratio between farm and industrial products decidedly in favor of farm products. By the same logic, if industrial output is curtailed to a low figure while agriculture continues in full production, the exchange ratio between farm and industrial products must turn decidedly unfavorable to those selling farm products.

In the record of the past quarter century, as shown in Tables XV and XVI, we note that

1. Agricultural production from one year to the next, even with widespread drought, has been remarkably steady.

2. Industrial production has varied greatly, rising rapidly for a series of years and falling in like fashion.

3. When industrial output is large relative to agricultural production, farm prices are high relative to the prices of the products that farmers buy; conversely, when industry produces little, agricultural prices are low relative to industrial prices.

4. There is a close connection between the year-to-year changes in agriculture's terms of exchange and the changes in the relative output of agriculture and industry.

From these short-run interactions between the ratio of agricultural to industrial production and prices received to prices paid by farmers, several inferences may be drawn:

products and with given price elasticities and given changes in relative production would cause even greater swings in farm prices.

1. If farmers want a more favorable "parity price" in any given year, they may attain this objective by curtailing farm output.

TABLE XV

RATIO OF INDUSTRIAL TO AGRICULTURAL PRODUCTION AND OF PRICES RECEIVED
TO PRICES PAID BY FARMERS IN THE UNITED STATES[a]

Year	Ratio of industrial to agricultural production	Ratio of prices received to prices paid by farmers
	(1940 = 100)	(1940 = 100)
1940	100	100
1941	125	115
1942	140	131
1943	162	151
1944	155	144
	(1930 = 100)	(1930 = 100)
1930	100	100
1931	80	79
1932	65	66
1933	77	71
1934	87	81
1935	103	100
1936	118	105
1937	115	108
1938	92	86
1939	111	86
	(1920 = 100)	(1920 = 100)
1920	100	100
1921	85	75
1922	98	85
1923	115	92
1924	102	92
1925	113	99
1926	117	93
1927	118	93
1928	118	98
1929	135	97

[a] Based on Table XVI.

2. If industry and labor want to keep their prices and wages high relative to the prices of food and fiber, they may accom-

TABLE XVI
INDUSTRIAL AND AGRICULTURAL PRODUCTION AND PRICES RECEIVED AND PAID
BY FARMERS, 1920–1944
(1935–1939 = 100)

Year	Industrial production[a]	Agricultural production[b]	Prices received by farmers[c]	Prices paid by farmers[d]	Industrial production in per cent of agricultural production	Prices received in per cent of prices paid by farmers
1920	75	92	197	163	82	121
1921	58	83	116	128	70	91
1922	73	91	123	120	80	103
1923	88	94	134	120	94	112
1924	82	98	134	120	84	112
1925	90	97	146	122	93	120
1926	96	100	136	121	96	112
1927	95	98	133	119	97	112
1928	99	102	141	120	97	118
1929	110	99	139	119	111	117
1930	91	98	120	115	93	104
1931	75	102	84	103	74	82
1932	58	96	64	92	60	69
1933	69	96	67	91	72	74
1934	75	93	84	100	81	84
1935	87	91	102	98	96	104
1936	103	94	107	98	110	109
1937	113	106	114	102	107	112
1938	89	103	91	102	86	89
1939	109	106	89	100	103	89
1940	125	110	93	100	114	93
1941	162	113	116	108	143	107
1942	199	124	149	122	160	122
1943	239	129	180	129	185	140
1944	235	133	182	136	177	134

[a] *Federal Reserve Bulletin* (February, 1945), p. 167.

[b] *Farm Income Situation*, U.S. Department of Agriculture, Bureau of Agricultural Economics, December, 1944, p. 1.

[c] *Agricultural Outlook Charts*, U.S. Department of Agriculture, Bureau of Agricultural Economics, November, 1944, p. 1.

[d] U.S. Department of Agriculture, Bureau of Agricultural Economics, from data made available by Dr. O. C. Stine, Head, Division of Historical and Statistical Research. Prices paid for all commodities used in production and for living and maintenance excluding feed, food, and seed.

plish this in the short run by producing little while agriculture produces plentifully.

Both courses of action outlined above are, however, in conflict with the general interest and in addition give only temporary advantages to the group pursuing such a negative policy. *It is necessary for each group to produce more and not less, for to do otherwise is to curtail the wealth of the nation.*[1]

Farm people stand to gain very considerably from a high rate of industrial output, and nonfarm people gain appreciably from a large, steady volume of agricultural output. Agriculture, in the main, has fulfilled its part of these conditions in behalf of the general interest, but industry, with its wide fluctuations in output, has not done so.

As a depression unfolds, business curtails its output and unemployment spreads. Agriculture, not responding to the business scene, continues its production efforts. Is this stubborn nonconformity of agriculture an asset or a liability? Would it be better for the national economy if agriculture acted in concert with other industries? There is, in fact, a school of thought that holds it desirable to make agricultural production a variable, adjusting it downward when demand drops and upward when the demand is strengthened by the cyclical behavior of the rest of the economy. On many counts this is a shortsighted view. Agriculture's steady output effort, year after year, regardless of the performance of industry and in spite of the wide fluctuations in purchasing power of consumers, is very much an asset rather than a liability to the economy as a whole. Much of the farm problem that loomed so large in the years between the two wars was not the result of maladjustments within agriculture but of poor and erratic performance elsewhere in the economy. The remedy, for the most part, did not lie in agriculture, in

---

[1] Only in a short-run, business-fluctuation context; as an economy develops, it becomes necessary to shift resources away from some lines of production, thus curtailing them relatively and often absolutely.

curtailing the output of food, feed, and fiber, but in attaining an expanding and steady production by other producers.

In a choice between policies to lessen the instability of farm income caused by business fluctuations, it is better to preserve, and if possible even enhance, the steadiness of agricultural production[1] than to undertake measures to pull agricultural production down when business recedes and push it up when business rises. Furthermore, it is better (with qualifications in the case of some semidurable farm products that can be stored) so to price farm products that they will move readily into internal and external trade, and to provide compensatory payments to farmers to sustain farm income when business recedes and unemployment spreads, rather than to attempt a program of price supports.[2] In Chap. X we present a proposal that is countercyclical and that does not disturb agricultural production and trade when business becomes depressed.

[1] Not in the sense that the same amount of exactly the same products should be produced one year after another, for it is essential that agricultural production adjust to secular changes in the supply and demand for farm products. Thus this goal of steadiness in production applies to the short run, specifically to business fluctuations.

[2] The merits and limitations of the present program of support prices are considered in Chap. XII.

VII. OPPORTUNITIES FOR AGRICULTURAL
IMPORTS AND EXPORTS

THE main issues concerning our future foreign trade in agriculture come clear if put as questions. As for imports, has the United States been, or is it destined to become, a major importer of food and fiber? When incomes here are high, the amount and the variety of food demanded are large. Something of the effect of increased employment and high wages on the demand for food has been revealed by our wartime experiences. To satisfy a strong domestic demand will it be necessary or cheaper to import a considerable volume of agricultural products?

On the export side, the United States has highly specialized agricultural resources that are suited, and have been developed, to produce for export. Because of the nature of these resources, must this country continue as a major exporter of farm products? In spite of poor demand abroad and the efforts of the AAA during the thirties to curtail production of the leading export crops (notably cotton, wheat, tobacco, and rice), we have emerged with a volume of production still far in excess of domestic requirements. Confronting us, therefore, is the question: Is our farm economy such that we would gain by making possible the export of a considerable volume of certain farm products?

Other less visible issues must be considered before a "yes" or "no" can be given to that question. Our major export crops belong in a class known as "exploitative" crops. They do not help conserve our soil resources; instead they contribute to soil losses, especially soil erosion, and soil losses entail a cost. Does the world price at which these products sell include that cost? If these costs have escaped the price-making mechanism, then we have been subsidizing such exports to the extent of the soil losses. What is the nature of the evidence on this point?

During most of the interwar period, the markets of the world were burdened by chronic surpluses of staple agricultural products—wheat, cotton, coffee, and sugar were examples. The United States is the world's largest supplier of cotton and is high on the list among suppliers of wheat. What level will world markets for these products attain after the war? Even with high industrial production and with world trade free from serious restrictions, are agricultural surpluses likely to recur?

Most important among the unsettled questions is the relation of our domestic agricultural policy to foreign trade. Evidence will be presented that the United States has much to gain from foreign trade in food, feed, and fiber. But it has embarked on an agricultural policy that before the war had raised the internal price of certain of our export products above their world price. After the war these policies will merely widen the gap. Inevitably this will mean conflict between our foreign trade and agricultural policies.[1] The extent to which any one segment of the agricultural economy departs from the structure of world prices, and the vested interest that becomes established as a consequence, will measure the seriousness of the conflict. The background of this developing inconsistency between trade policy and agricultural policy is reviewed here.

Prewar Developments. Farm programs from 1933 to 1941 did not give rise to any major problem between trade and agricultural policy—except for the loans of the Commodity Credit Corporation. AAA parity payments up to 1937 and FSA grants and aids were largely relief measures for the distressed conditions in agriculture caused by the industrial depression. The commodity loans of CCC, however, had

[1] This problem has been discussed by Theodore W. Schultz in "Which Way Will Farmers Turn?" *Foreign Affairs*, July, 1945.

important price effects and for that reason they did complicate foreign trade.

The Agricultural Adjustment Act, which dominated the national farm scene, was designed to curtail production. The AAA programs were for the most part production and not price measures. The acreage allotments of AAA had no appreciable price effect because they did not, except to a limited extent in the case of cotton, actually succeed in reducing the amount of farm products produced; as a consequence the effects upon foreign trade were negligible.[1]

The loan rates of the CCC became a major price-determining factor during the 1933–1941 period. When these commodity loans were higher than the prevailing market prices, they had adverse effects upon trade. Both domestic and foreign sales contracted, and stocks accumulated except as they were moved by resort to subsidies. But in the main the problem was concentrated in wheat and cotton, in which extraordinary stocks accumulated. There was little dispersal of the cotton hoard even during the war period.

Wartime Developments. In 1941 the center of gravity in agricultural policy shifted away from acreage allotments, designed to check production, to support prices planned to encourage expansion in some crops and livestock. By 1944 support prices had been extended to most farm products. The government came to rely largely on its price programs to shape and guide farm production. This shift from production to price measures on the part of the Department of Agriculture has far-reaching implications for both internal and external trade. The character of present legislation, especially the procedures under which the Department of Agriculture announces and maintains support prices, involves commitments of a type that preclude a satisfactory pricing of farm products for trade after the war.

[1] In the next chapter, agricultural controls are discussed and the acreage, production, and price effects of the AAA's program of acreage allotments are analyzed.

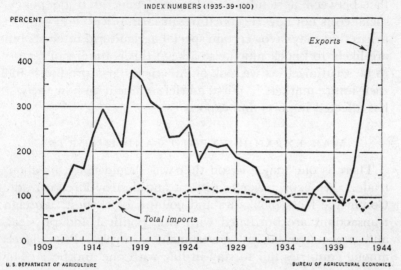

VOLUME OF EXPORTS AND IMPORTS OF FOOD
PRODUCTS, UNITED STATES, 1909-43

INDEX NUMBERS (1935-39·100)

Farm Prices and Trade. It is in the pricing of farm products that trade and agricultural policies are likely to diverge, the one seeking to enlarge markets and the other acting to restrict them. Support prices have a legitimate purpose, namely, that of maintaining farm incomes when depression in business reduces sharply the purchasing power of consumers. The monkey wrench in the machinery is the type of pricing legislation that has been devised to accomplish this objective. The present program of support prices will create obstacles to both internal and external trade in farm products. That such a program of support prices will make depressions more costly is a certainty; that it may defeat its own purpose is a very real hazard.

It should be anticipated that support prices for farm products will dominate agricultural policy and programs after the war. They cannot therefore be dismissed. They represent a new focusing in agricultural policy which has come as a consequence of the war and has powerful political support within the Administration and in the Congress.

· 141 ·

Specialized resources developed for export channels, conflict between agricultural policy and general trade policy,
social costs not now reckoned in our farm prices, and support
prices that may favor certain special agricultural interests but
are likely to knock much else askew: this is the list of factors
to be scrutinized as we look at American farm products and
their future markets.[1] First, a brief comment on how the war
has affected imports and exports.

WAR EXPANDS EXPORTS AND IMPORTS

There is one major lesson that war should teach us about
trade. We expect war to disrupt and destroy foreign trade.
Commerce faces blockades and counter blockades. Foreign
transactions are burdened with risk, political and physical,
and are narrowed by government controls. Price levels
among countries fail to stay in line with one another. The

[1] These questions and problems must not be divorced from their larger setting.
Agricultural imports and exports cannot be studied in isolation. Agricultural
products must be seen as an integral part of the whole world economy if the
requirements of agricultural foreign trade are to be understood. The economic
machinery that coordinates the actions of producers and consumers of this and
other countries in national and international markets has functioned very
clumsily. Few would describe it as an automatic mechanism. There is
general agreement that it did an exceedingly poor job during the period from
1920 to 1939. It behooves us to overhaul and improve this mechanism so that
it will do a better job after this war. It is remarkable how freely we have
improvised in economic machinery during the war. We have created
both new agencies and procedures, lend-lease being a conspicuous example.
For relief and rehabilitation more agencies and arrangements have been
developed.
   In the over-all economic mechanism many parts affect agriculture. It is not,
however, within the province of this study to explore, for example, the policies
appropriate for international monetary authorities—foreign investments,
exchange rates, import and export quotas, commodities agreements, tariffs,
and other measures that fall in this field. Nor can we examine here the many
internal programs (except in agriculture) of public agencies and of private
firms that influence what we buy from other countries and what we sell. In this
inquiry these are dealt with simply under two general types of consequences,
namely, (*a*) for the structure of relative prices, and (*b*) for the general level of
production.

"most-favored-nation" principle is shunted aside as we proceed with an eye to economic warfare.

War may destroy but it also creates trade. In some respects it is like the crest of a flood, cutting new channels. Both during World War I and during World War II, the foreign trade of the United States expanded and flourished. We may venture the judgment that both our imports and exports of the war periods reflected the comparative cost structure better than they did during the interwar period. To the extent that this is true, it would mean that the foreign trade carried on during the war made "economic sense" in the use of world resources accessible to us. The United States not only made way for imports but went after them, even urging her neighbors to produce more, and (here is the significant fact) encouraging them to produce and sell to us the things in which they excelled. In the last analysis, this is the fundamental test as to whether or not foreign trade adds to the wealth of a nation. From Canada and Mexico, as an example, we import chiefly agricultural products. Instead of blocking the efforts of these two countries to sell in our markets, as we did persistently during peacetime, we have bought so much during the war that they have found it advisable to protect themselves from the resulting high prices and from what has appeared to them an insatiable American demand.

This experience is not cited to suggest that war does not wreck most of our peacetime international machinery for carrying on foreign trade, but to call attention to the actual changes that have occurred in exports and imports. An expanding economy, such as a war begets, has the capacity to open the channels of trade even though most of the "normal" marketing machinery is put out of use. Contrast this with a stagnant economy, such as prevailed during much of the interwar period, which nurtured political attitudes favoring protectionism and the erection of trade barriers isolating the national economy. The ability to export and the willingness to import are certainly enhanced when the economy is expanding;[1] unemployment breeds a spirit of defeatism—both at home and in the sphere of foreign trade.

AGRICULTURAL IMPORTS LIKELY TO RISE

What is the probable future position of the United States as an importer of agricultural products, food as well as industrial raw materials? Agricultural imports of the United States rose during the interwar period, in spite of the great depression and the disintegration of world commerce. They increased in quantity from an index[2] of 61 in 1920 (which incidentally was the same as that of 1915) to 106 in 1929. They dropped again to a low of 79 in 1932, then recovered and reached a peak of 116 in 1936. Agricultural imports were fully 50 per cent greater in quantity during the years just prior to 1939 than in the years immediately preceding 1914. In spite of shrinking exports, a low level of industrial activity, and the many trade barriers that were erected, agricultural imports rose.

What these figures do not show is how much larger the increase would have been given (*a*) a high production, (*b*) a structure of relative prices within the United States more comparable to foreign prices,[3] so that we could have imported more than we did, and (*c*) a better balance in the distribution of the labor force between industry (including both the secondary and tertiary fields) and agriculture, so that earnings would have been about the same in both sectors of the economy. None of these three conditions was met during the interwar period, nor are they likely to be satisfied fully in the period after the war. To the extent that they are attained, the volume of agricultural imports is likely to increase. The pull of each is in the same direction, namely, to increase the

[1] An excellent case in point is that the feed-producing areas in this country did not raise political opposition to the wartime imports of feed grain from Canada, which amounted to 246 million bushels in 1943 compared to 5 million bushels in 1939.

[2] Calendar years 1924–1929 = 100.

[3] The main obstacles here are, of course, tariffs, export subsidies, and various forms of dumping and quotas.

foodstuffs and the agricultural raw materials imported by the United States.

The United States may be destined to become a much larger importer of food, surpassing any other country except the United Kingdom. This is not, however, the most relevant point for our inquiry. Of more significance are the conditions that bring about the expansion in imports. The nation as a whole stands to gain to the extent that imports increase because of (*a*) a higher level of production accompanying a high level of employment and income of the working population generally, (*b*) a better fitting together of our structure of prices with the prices of other countries, and (*c*) a better allocation of resources within the United States. As each of these conditions is attained, we add to the aggregate productivity of the economy. The fact that this increased productivity would increase agricultural imports is incidental, for increases of particular imports are merely one of the consequences of the expansion of real incomes within the United States.[1]

What We Import

About one-half of the total imports of the United States have been agricultural products. This was true before World

[1] The strategic position of the rate of industrial production in affecting aggregate productivity cannot be overstated. To make this evident we need only name the negative effects of subnormal industrial output. First, it increases the number of people that engage in agriculture, making farm labor cheap (whether measured in terms of wages paid to workers or in terms of income obtained by farmers). When labor is thus made abundant and cheap in agriculture, the stage is set for the production of cheaper farm products, sufficiently cheap to keep out some imports that otherwise would enter. Then, too, in an atmosphere of depression, little if any headway may be made in removing the barriers that force the relative prices within the United States out of line with those of other countries. Second, when industrial production is curtailed, it is all but impossible to bring about a better balance in the distribution of the labor force between industry and agriculture. At best what is accomplished is to "balance the incidences of the depression." The emphasis is on relief and not on the discovery of adjustments in production that would add to the national output. Negative policies carry the day, partly for relief, partly as a retreat, but largely because the scarcity of resources is no longer the primary limiting element determining how much we produce.

War I, persisted during the twenties, and was still true in 1939 at the start of World War II. Many of these products are not, and cannot be, grown in the United States. This is true of most of the agricultural products of the tropics—raw silk, coffee, rubber, cocoa beans, bananas, tea, spices—which do not compete with but "complement" our farm economy. Additional products can be included as "complementary" if the factor of seasonality is taken into account. For example, fresh vegetables grown in the Caribbean countries and in Mexico for table use in the United States during the winter months are also "complementary" in this sense.[1]

[1] The U.S. Department of Agriculture classifies agricultural imports in two groups, namely *complementary* imports (including coffee, raw silk, cocoa beans, rubber, wool for carpets, bananas, tea, and spices) and *supplementary* imports (products similar to agricultural products grown commercially in the United States). In value the two groups are about even, as the following figures for 1937, which are typical, show:

	In Millions
Total domestic imports	$2,331
Total agricultural imports	1,155
Complementary	567
Supplementary	588

The U.S. Department of Agriculture statistical series, dividing agricultural imports into complementary and supplementary products, does not go farther back than 1924. The quantity of these imports for selected years was as follows:

(1924–1929 = 100)

Year	Complementary	Supplementary
1925	96	100
1929	110	101
1932	94	60
1935	106	98
1937	102	80
1939	113	87

Agricultural Statistics 1942, U.S. Department of Agriculture, Washington, D.C., Table 687, p. 537, and Table 691, p. 541.

The weight of United States imports in world trade is seen in the following figures for six commodities: during 1934–1938, 67 per cent of the total world trade in silk entered the United

TABLE XVII

QUANTITY OF MAJOR AGRICULTURAL PRODUCTS ENTERING WORLD TRADE, 1934–1938—ANNUAL AVERAGES AND COMPARISONS FOR THE UNITED STATES[1]

Product	World Exports, in thousands	United States, in thousands	Per cent United States is of world trade
Raw silk, lb..............	88,550	59,497 (imports)	67
Coffee, lb...............	3,668,000	1,748,000 (imports)	48
Rubber, tons.............	1,205	486 (imports)	40
Sugar, tons..............	12,534	4,814 (imports)	38
Vegetable oil,[a] lb.........	10,056,000	1,593,000 (net imports)[b]	16
Tea, lb..................	973,000	84,000 (imports)	9
Wool, lb.................	2,438,000	200,000 (imports)	8
Beef and veal, lb..........	1,845,000	50,013 (net imports)	3
Lard, lb.................	351,000	197,000 (exports)	56
Cotton, bales............	13,808	5,532 (net exports)	40
Tobacco,[c] lb............	1,213,000	344,000 (net exports)	28
Pork, lb.................	1,289,000	151,000 (exports)	12
Wheat, bu...............	640,431	22,535 (net exports)	4
Rice, lb.................	17,155,000	374,000 (net exports)	2
Mutton and lambs,[d] lb....	728,000		0
Corn, bu...............	400,781	(33,000 in, and the same amount out, yearly average)	

[a] Soybeans, cotton seed, flaxseed, peanuts, palm kernel, sesame, copra, rapeseed, and colza. Weight is in oil equivalent.

[b] Coconut, linseed, palm, olive, peanuts, and cotton oil and oil equivalent of sesame seed, palm kernel, rapeseed, and soybeans.   [c] 1935–1938.   [d] Four major exporting countries total.

[1] Compiled from various tables in Henry C. Taylor and Anne Dewees, *World Trade in Agricultural Products*, New York, The Macmillan Company, 1943, and *Agricultural Statistics, 1942*, U.S. Department of Agriculture, Washington, D.C.

States; 48 per cent of the coffee; 40 per cent of the rubber; 38 per cent of sugar; 16 per cent of vegetable oil; and 9 per cent of tea.

AGRICULTURAL EXPORTS HAVE DWINDLED

In agricultural exports, the United States lost much ground in the period between the two wars. They shrank, by any measuring stick. In dollar volume, they exceeded the $2 billion mark for one or two years during the middle twenties, but dropped to $800 million and less after the depression.[1] The decline in physical volume was also severe. (Cotton exports, most important of them all, dropped from an average of 8.52 million bales during 1924–1929 to 5.42 million bales during 1936–1939.)

Agricultural exports also shrank relative to total United States exports. In 1910, 51 per cent of all United States exports were agricultural products; this figure fell to 41 per cent in 1925 and to 20 per cent in 1939.[2] Agricultural exports also dropped during this period in relation to farm income. They contributed fully 15 per cent of the gross farm income in 1910 and less than 10 per cent in the thirties.[3]

[1] The following table is taken from a study by Hal B. Lary, *The United States in the World Economy* (Economic Series 23, U.S. Department of Commerce, Washington, D.C., 1943), p. 60.

Commodities exported	Average 1922–1924, in millions	Average 1937–1939, in millions
Cotton (unmanufactured)	$810	$280
Wheat (including flour)	275	76
Cured pork	106	11
Lard	119	18
All other farm products	628	375
Total	1,938	760

[2] *Agricultural Statistics, 1942,* U.S. Department of Agriculture, Washington, D.C., Table 687, p. 537.

[3] The contribution of exports to the gross income of each of the major commodities exported also dwindled, in most cases markedly. Nevertheless, the export demand had an appreciable effect upon farm income. Clawson and Black, after examining the income of agriculture in relationship to the export market for the period 1910–1940, are of the view that export outlets importantly affect gross farm income. "In the prewar years [1910–1915], annual income was more than one billion dollars higher than the indices of price level and real income would have indicated; since 1934, from one-half to one billion dollars lower." They ascribe this difference to the changes that have occurred in the export situation. See Marion Clawson and John D. Black, "Agricultural Income and the Export Market, 1910–1940," *Journal of Farm Economics,* Vol. 24 (1942), pp. 770–771.

The study by Frederick Strauss on the *Composition of Gross Farm Income Since the Civil War,* National Bureau of Economic Research, *Research Bulletin* 78, 1940,

Opportunities for Agricultural Imports and Exports

Outlook for Exports

Once the postwar relief period is closed, what are the prospects for farm exports? Are they likely to drop back to the low levels that prevailed prior to the war? As with imports, three basic factors will determine the fortunes of our agricultural exports.

These factors will be pivotal: (a) the general level of production in this country, which means primarily production in the industrial sector since agriculture remains in full gear whether times are good or bad; (b) the extent to which the relative price structure within the United States corresponds with prices presented to us by other countries;[1] and (c) the extent to which the prices of agricultural products that enter export channels are permitted to reflect prevailing costs, with the reductions in cost attained by advances in farm technology. We propose to discuss each of these in turn.[2]

Increasing Our Employment and Production

Changes upward in the level of industrial production contribute to agriculture's welfare both directly within the American economy and indirectly through effects upon foreign countries.

Full employment and high production expand the domestic

p. 18, gives the following figures on the contribution of exports to the gross income of each of the major commodities.

Years	Cotton	Wheat	Tobacco	Pork products	Beef products
1934–1937	44	8	37	3	0.5
1909–1913	68	18	41	13	5
1889–1893	68	35	43	18	16

[1] Here, again, we focus upon the price effects of such trade barriers as tariffs, export subsidies, and quotas.

[2] Though factor (c) is basically contained in (b), it is convenient to state it as a separate factor in order to focus attention upon decreases in cost not yet fully reflected in prices of such products as cotton and wheat.

demand for virtually all farm products, including those that enter export channels. The price of cotton, our top export crop, is exceedingly sensitive to changes in business conditions and the amount used domestically moves in close and direct response to changes in industrial activity.[1] (Domestic demand for wheat and rice, also export crops, is not so closely associated with high employment.) The improved demand for farm products not on an export basis—meats, milk, chickens, and eggs—that accompanies high industrial activity is even more significant, since this induces farmers to shift some resources away from their export crops to feedstuff production for the increase of livestock. This shift to products for home consumption is likely to be of considerable magnitude should the United States attain and maintain a high rate of nonagricultural activity for as long a period as five to ten years. The most important outcome, however, is that high production puts into motion forces that help redistribute the working population, drawing people out of agriculture and adding them to the labor forces of secondary and tertiary industries, thus bettering the earnings of those who remain in agriculture. A shrinking of the output of export crops is thus achieved by the altered pattern of demand and the movement of farm people, especially out of those parts of agriculture most overcrowded and underproductive in per capita terms, notably the cotton South.

A high production within the United States increases incomes of people in other countries, since the United States buys more from them. The enlarged volume of dollar exchange made available to buyers abroad opens the door to

[1] The marked rises in domestic consumption of cotton commonly associated with the cyclical rises of business activity overstate considerably the increase in the demand for cotton which may result from an increase in real income per person in an expanding economy. The long-pull secular increase in incomes is not likely to bring any marked increase in the demand for cotton goods, at least in the American market. It appears that the income elasticity of cotton, like that of farm products generally, is low, probably falling within the range of .25 to .50 and perhaps at the lower end of this range. In the market abroad the income elasticity of cotton is much higher.

the purchase of American goods and services, and to investments in American property.

Splicing Outside and Inside Prices

That the economic welfare of the country demands high employment and production has by now become a maxim in postwar thinking. There is much less appreciation of the gains that may be obtained (by the nation as a whole as well as by farmers engaged in producing for export) from bringing together our prices and prices outside of the United States.[1] To the degree that this end is attained, the competitive position of the farmer producing export crops will be improved.

First, it will lower the price of many of the things that farmers buy. This is often overlooked by leaders in industry and by spokesmen for organized labor. The emphasis of farm leaders upon the cost to agriculture of the prevailing high industrial tariffs, and their insistence that the benefit payments of the AAA were simply an offset for the extra cost to them of industrial protectionism should not go unnoticed. Provided the trade barriers are removed, the industrial economy of Great Britain and of a number of the western European countries has had, and will again have, the capacity to make a number of products available to producers and consumers in the United States at prices considerably below those that have hitherto prevailed. This would reduce living costs for farmers and for the rest of our consumers and it would also cut farmers' production expenses, measurably improving the competitive position of precisely those farmers who are engaged in producing for export.

Second, splicing relative prices inside and outside the United States will also induce us to buy more industrial products from the workshops of the Old World. The added dollar income of foreigners improves foreign demand for American

[1] Especially through the removal of tariffs, quotas, and various price-raising programs.

goods, services, and investments, and thus the demand for farm products of the United States.

Farm Technology Has Cut Cost

In many farming areas in the United States production expenses have been lowered substantially during the interwar years by the advances in farm technology. Since producers in other countries have not made similar progress, the competitive position of such American farmers has improved. Internal price policy, however, has obscured some of these developments and the added competitive strength has not given American farmers the advantage that it should have in bidding for markets abroad.

Rice. What farm technology can accomplish has been illustrated by the extraordinary change in our position as a producer of rice. From 1860 to 1900 about half the rice consumed in the United States was imported, even though domestic ricegrowers were sheltered by a tariff that kept the price of rice from 30 to 50 per cent above the prevailing world price. Patently, rice growing in the United States at that time was at a distinct comparative disadvantage. About the time of World War I, as a consequence of a revolution in rice-growing technology (with the opening of the prairies of southeastern Louisiana and parts of Texas and Arkansas), the industry changed from an essentially manual basis to one of modern machinery. American farmers producing rice now grow it cheaply enough not only to supply all domestic needs, but to take a place among rice exporters. Just prior to the war (1936–1940), rice exports averaged almost 10 million bushels annually.[1]

[1] It should be noted further that rice farmers in Louisiana, Texas, and Arkansas have been among the more prosperous of their region, able and willing to pay somewhat higher wages than the neighboring cotton and sugar growers although rice is sold in direct competition with countries of which it is a chief export, namely, India, Siam, and Indo-China. The crucial fact, of course, is quite evident. A rice farmer in Texas, for instance, using the most modern large-scale machinery, may harvest about 10,000 bushels of rice a year. His Oriental competitor depends on a water buffalo, a crude plow, a hoe, a sickle,

Soybeans are a comparatively new crop, introduced into general farming after the other war. For a time they appeared to be at some disadvantage in competition with other crops and certainly in competition with soybeans grown abroad. Since then, however, with the adaptation of the plants to our soil and climate (through breeding and selection of seed, improvements in cultivation, and especially with the use of mechanical machinery for planting and harvesting), the comparative position of this crop has so much improved that it may well be to the advantage of the United States in the postwar period to export some soybeans and soybean products.

In *wheat growing*, also, appreciable technological advances were made during the interwar period. These came not so much from improvements in varieties as from the mechanization of the cultivation and harvesting of the crop. With wheat loans fixed in accordance with 1910–1914 price relationships, wheat prices have not, however, reflected fully these changes in cost.

Cotton has not benefited in the recent past (except in some parts of Texas and Oklahoma) from any marked improvement in technology comparable with those in rice, soybeans, and wheat. This does not mean that cotton has necessarily lost ground, or that it should be withdrawn from export. Cotton appears to be entering a far-reaching mechanical revolution, as vast in its social and economic implications as the change from the scythe and cradle to the reaper in grain crops. This will take cotton growing from the hilly to the more level land, and it is likely to improve the competitive position of American cotton considerably.

MANY EXPORT CROPS LINKED WITH SOIL EROSION

The soil losses in the United States caused by erosion have been enormous; soil erosion has become one of America's

---

and a flail. For each day's work the American farmer may produce from 20 to 50 times as much rice as the Oriental farmer.

major problems. The large acreages devoted to row crops (notably corn, cotton, tobacco, and grain sorghum) have caused much soil erosion. The row crops not only draw heavily upon soil nutriments, thus exhausting the fertility of the soil, but they also change the structure of the soil, making it vulnerable to erosion.

Crops and cropping practices that bring about a diminution of soil productivity are of two classes: (*a*) those that do not disturb the structure of the soil sufficiently to bring about erosion, which means that the soil may subsequently be restored simply by adding certain soil nutriments and, accordingly, the depletion and rebuilding are reversible processes— one representing disinvestment and the other investment in the productive property of the soil; and (*b*) those that alter the structure of the soil to the point where wind and water erosion take place, in addition to the depletion of the soil fertility.

Soil erosion is not an easily reversible process, as is the depletion of soil fertility, because to restore soil that has been eroded usually entails a very high cost—a cost much larger than either the additional income that was actually obtained from the production of the crops that contributed to the erosion, or the additional output that may be obtained after the land has been restored. In other words, there is an important gap separating the added income that is obtained by the disinvestment through erosion and the much larger cost involved in restoring the soil once erosion has taken place.

Much of the cost of soil erosion escapes the private ledger of individual farmers, to be borne subsequently by society. This means that the price of the farm product does not include all its costs. Since this is true, should the United States discourage the export of these crops? Presumably we sell them at a net loss.[1]

---

[1] There is a close parallel in the case of Great Britain or any industrial country. Should such a country take steps to restrict the export of industrial goods because manufacturers' prices do not include the social cost of the smoke that their plants belch forth?

In the practical world with its many risks and uncertainties, niceties on the cost side of production of the kind entailed in soil erosion are usually lost among the larger, and what appear to be the more important, variables. But the soil losses from erosion represent too serious a cost not to be brought into the accounts. Fortunately, there is a fundamental solution at hand. It lies in overhauling the institutions that govern production in agriculture,[1] in order to reduce the divergency between the social and private cost of producing the crops that cause erosion. Although considerable headway has been made in this direction during the last decade, much more needs to be accomplished.

Transfer of Soil

There is a social cost of another type that should be recognized, though, unlike the price of soil erosion, it is not one that we are called upon to face in the immediate future. The shipment of staple farm crops, whether they enter external or internal trade, is, among other things, a transfer of soil nutriments. This transfer occurs even when crops are grown under conditions that do not give rise to soil erosion, inasmuch as farm products are composed of certain amounts of nitrogen, potash, phosphorus, and other elements drawn out of the soil. Historically, there has been substantial transfer of productive soil elements from one locality to another. The agricultural land of both Denmark and Holland has been developed to a considerable extent by importing feed for livestock, then using the manure to improve the soil. This transfer has also gone on apace within the United States. We have, for instance, been building up the soils in most of the milksheds at the expense of other farming areas that produce the feed the dairymen purchase for their cows.

It may be remarked that we have in fact maintained the

---

[1] The growing awareness of farmers of the effects of erosion on soil productivity is an important advance. The main defect in our farm tenure is its failure to provide compensation for unexhausted improvements.

price of our important export crops substantially above what would have been their world "equilibrium price." We have not been selling these products to buyers abroad except at prices somewhat higher than what would have been their "normal price."[1] This has been done, however, as a price-stabilizing or price-raising measure related to the support of farm income, and not with an eye to the cost to society of the erosive crops.

Overpopulation and Erosion

It is important to bear in mind that as long as millions of people are "crowded" into agriculture, as is the case in the South because of the stagnation of industry, it is necessary to find the best alternative employment for such labor resources. Under the present distribution of labor, the value productivity of many workers engaged in farming has been maximized by producing cotton, wheat, and other crops for export. For example, if we were to deny export outlets to cotton or restrict its sale because of soil erosion costs, we would reduce even further the value of cotton and, accordingly, the value of the labor of two to three million people now dependent upon and situated in the cotton economy.

The real shrink in exports should come not from restrictions of this kind but from the transfer of labor resources out of agriculture into industry. Such a transfer would occasion a *recombination of resources in agriculture in favor of the human agent*, and it would, therefore, improve the value productivity, and thus the real earnings, of those persons who remain in farming.[2]

---

[1] Except when specific export sales were receiving outright subsidies.

[2] The changes in farming that the war effort has introduced into Southern agriculture afford clues to the answer to this problem; they suggest how potent a force the growing scarcity of labor has been in altering farming practices and techniques. As the price of labor has risen relative to other factors, labor inputs have been economized by producing less cotton and by turning to more extensive crops (especially those suited to livestock), by farm enlargements, by abandonment of some highly erodible land, and like measures. Most of these facilitate soil conservation. Probably no single development would contribute more to conserving soil in the cotton South than a labor market so strong that it

When our farm exports are reduced through this transfer of labor, we may be assured of a result in a larger total output on the part of the nation. Until this happens, however, it is necessary for those who are in agriculture to produce those crops in which their advantage is greatest. With about half the farm people of the United States situated in the cotton states, we will produce a lot of cotton, even though it is exploitative both of the soil and of the people growing the crop. The exploitation of the soil arises from the divergence between the social and private cost entailed by erosion, but it is intensified by the very serious lack of balance in the distribution of workers between industry and agriculture.

CHRONIC AGRICULTURAL SURPLUSES IN PROSPECT

Wheat, cotton, coffee, and sugar were chronically in surplus during most of the thirties. None of these maladjustments has been corrected. The scarcities of food occasioned by the war merely act as a smoke screen, hiding from our view the dislocations that exist behind it. Soon after the relief period is over, the agricultural surplus problem will put in an appearance again. It will reappear as unsolved and, in a number of instances, as unmanageable from the point of view of a particular country, because the problem presented is so largely international in its scope. Moreover, the list of such surplus commodities may be lengthened by the war. Oilseeds, fats and oils, and even rice are likely to take their place among the products badly out of adjustment.[1]

We cannot examine here the many circumstances in other countries that have contributed to these maladjustments. They are an outgrowth of the general disintegration of world commerce, the many restrictive policies of both producer

---

would draw half or more of the population now on farms in that region into nonagricultural employment.

[1] See Bennett S. White, Jr., and Edith G. Denhardt, "Chronic Surpluses of Agricultural Commodities in the Post-war Period," *Journal of Farm Economics*, November, 1943.

and consumer countries, and, again, the unequal growth of the supply of and demand for agricultural products which results from the long-run forces that were considered in Chap. III. As we look for ways to correct these maladjustments, it should be noted, however, that this group of commodities has certain characteristics in common.

1. The products in this group are staple commodities subject to a world market and a world price. More precisely, each product is sufficiently uniform to permit sales and purchases by grades and standards, and each product is produced and also consumed by a number of trading countries. It therefore follows that when maladjustments in supply and demand develop, not one but all of the trading countries are affected. Likewise, appropriate measures to correct the maladjustments do not rest in the hands of any one nation. The remedy, like the problem, is international in its dimensions. To use our own wheat problem as an illustration: no matter how successful the United States may be internally in developing a positive fiscal-monetary policy to attain full use of the nation's labor force and plant (important as this would be to American agriculture and to the prosperity of the world), this would not in itself be sufficient to solve the wheat problem of the United States, much less that of Canada, Australia, Argentina, and the Danubian countries.

2. These commodities, in chronic surplus during the interwar years, became "political crops" in some producing and also in a few consuming countries. Where a single crop represents most of a nation's exports (coffee in Brazil, for example), the vulnerability of the foreign-exchange position of the country has occasioned governmental controls. In other countries large numbers of producers were hard pressed by the disintegration of world markets, and the government was called upon to provide some measure of relief. As these and other factors arose, public attitudes, political commitments, laws, and governmental agencies took form. An array of public measures was the common result—various systems

of multiple prices, subsidies, concealed dumping, and market quotas (as parts of commodity agreements and separately).

3. Examination of the resources used to produce these surplus commodities shows that in many cases the resources (chiefly land and equipment) are of little or no value in producing any other product. The immobility of labor in many countries, with no real alternative employment open, contributes further to the specificity of the resources. Accordingly, in spite of lower relative prices, producers find it not only difficult, but often quite impossible, to transfer their resources to the growing of some other crop. For example, unless the labor force in the cotton areas is reduced very considerably, there would be great difficulty in shifting from cotton to feed in the South. Likewise, a transfer from wheat to grass is not very feasible in many areas in the plains states and in parts of the prairie provinces of Canada.

Another hurdle to the reallocation of resources, especially within the firm (farm), is the uncertainty of the relationship of one product price to another—for example, cotton to livestock products, cotton to peanuts, and wheat to corn and barley. These relative prices are notoriously erratic. It may take years before farmers can formulate a judgment about changes in the relative prices of products that they happen to produce. Wheat and corn relationships are an excellent illustration. Wheat can be used for feed or, alternatively, a considerable part of the acreage devoted to wheat may be used to grow feed grains. In the years immediately preceding World War I, the farm price of wheat (United States average) was fully 25 per cent higher than that of corn, the leading feed grain in the United States. Now let us suppose that the conditions underlying the demand and supply of wheat have pulled the relative prices of wheat and corn closer together, so that wheat has a value about 10 per cent above corn. At this lowered price, it becomes profitable to use some wheat as feed and to shift some wheatland to the growing of feed. This is essentially what the developments in wheat and corn occurring during the twenties and thirties called for. But with the rapid shifts in the ratio of wheat to corn prices, this long-run drawing together of wheat and corn prices gave the farmer little guidance in allotting his acreage. The price of wheat galloped from 22 per cent above that of corn in 1931 to 4 per cent in 1934 and to 27 per cent in 1935. In 1936 corn prices actually averaged higher than wheat prices, only to be followed by a year in which wheat prices were virtually twice as high as corn. It should be apparent that under the existing system of farm-product pricing, little can be expected from this erratic mechanism of relative prices in guiding or inducing necessary shifts in production.

4. Some of the countries producing commodities likely to be in surplus soon after the war will be unable to transfer labor resources out of agriculture since they do not have the resources that permit industrialization. The basic elements of this particular problem were considered at the close of Chap. III. Consider, as an extreme case, a small trading country producing only wheat, with all nonlabor resources in that country specific to wheat. Let us suppose further that other wheat-growing and exporting countries introduce labor-saving technology which reduces the labor required to produce a bushel of wheat by more than one-half and thus reduces the cost of growing wheat enough to lower the world price one-third. The income per head in our hypothetical country would fall sharply unless a considerable part of the labor force were to leave agriculture, which, under the conditions given, would entail migration to some other country with more diverse resources.

Trade does not in itself avert this difficulty. Better trading conditions, essential as they are to the economic health of nations, cannot keep incomes per head from declining in some countries producing such crops as wheat, cotton, sugar, oils, and fats. This will be true where the nonlabor resources are essentially specific to a particular crop, the potentials for industrialization are insufficient to absorb the excess supply of labor in agriculture, and the opportunity for people to migrate to another country is severely restricted. Cuba, Puerto Rico, and other Caribbean areas, the Danubian countries for the most part, and old Poland are countries faced with these adverse circumstances.

INTERNAL AND EXTERNAL PRICES AFTER THE WAR

Before the war the commodity loans of the CCC acted to separate the internal and external prices of certain farm products. For the most part, no measures were taken to close this gap. The United States in effect withheld American cotton until the world price increased to a level comparable to the domestic price, with the consequence that other cotton-producing countries were encouraged to expand their output and thus supplant American cotton exports in considerable part.[1] For wheat, and occasionally for other products, government subsidies were used to close the gap between internal and external prices. But, in general, the problem was not considered particularly important or serious.[2]

Support prices for a long list of farm products, to be effective for at least two years after the war, have been authorized by Congress. The support prices specified by legislation are likely to overvaluate substantially many farm products, and the result will be a widening of the gap between internal and external prices. Trade, it can be expected, will be further disrupted; agricultural policy and trade policy will become even more inconsistent, a situation already developing prior to the war.

[1] There were also other forces at work. In Brazil the low price of coffee was a factor in making cotton growing more attractive than it otherwise would have been. The inability of some countries to acquire dollar exchange because of our import policy also shifted some demand away from American cotton; nor does this exhaust the many difficulties that have confronted our cotton in world markets.

[2] This view, however, was quite erroneous, since even before the war cotton was being priced too high in both the internal and external markets by the CCC loan rates.

The mountain and Mohammed indicate the choice of alternatives for solving this problem. Either trade policy must be tethered to the agricultural programs, or agricultural policy must be modified so that it shows some cognizance of trade requirements. Unless we prefer to move mountains, it would seem wise to recognize trade requirements by reformulating price policy in agriculture and recasting the role of support prices.[1] Support prices as they now stand are exceedingly defective. They unquestionably will disrupt agricultural exports. They will also succeed in disorganizing the internal trade of farm products, bringing about serious dislocations in resources in agriculture. And if we can weather these maladjustments, we are still faced with the fact that support prices of the type that Congress has directed the Department of Agriculture to announce and maintain will not accomplish their main purpose, namely, that of sustaining farm income when the demand for farm products as a whole drops sharply in the wake of a business recession.

[1] Policies appropriate to this purpose are considered in a later chapter.

PART III

Governmental Programs and Controls

VIII. AGRICULTURAL CONTROLS

AMERICAN agriculture provides an instructive paradox—
many small farmers and big government, much private
management and much public administration, competition
at the farm level and control at the federal. Why do we have
in agriculture more private, and essentially free, enterprise
and also more government programs than in any other major
sector of the economy? Are these not fundamentally inconsistent and contradictory? It is a cherished belief that
government controls, especially the type found in agriculture,
are incompatible with private enterprise.

PARADOX OF PRIVATE ENTERPRISE AND
PUBLIC CONTROL

At the farm level agriculture fulfills, for the most part, the
basic conditions of "pure" competition: large numbers of
producers (6 million before the war) and relatively easy
entry of newcomers. No single producer can affect appreciably the price of the factors he buys or of the products he sells.
Farming is a classic example of production under competitive
conditions. It would appear that production is controlled
by competition and accordingly government programs should
be unnecessary; certainly it should reduce them to a minimum.

Instead, we find a grand array of farm legislation, and
administrative agencies with a large and expert personnel
and budgets that run into several hundred million dollars
annually. This far-reaching and impressive machinery of
government authority would seem to offer all the conditions

required for a state-controlled and managed farm economy with little or no room for private enterprise.

Why these two seemingly inconsistent impressions? Which is real and which merely apparent?

The paradox is not in what we are looking at, but in what we are looking through. It arises out of our ideas; it is an element in our intellectual equipment and not a reality in agriculture. *What we have experienced in agriculture suggests that vigorous, enterprising farms and equally vigorous, well-designed governmental programs may be highly complementary.* One may be a condition necessary to the other. It may be that neither can perform at a maximum without the other—maximum in terms of economic criteria; namely, the best allocation and use of productive resources, and in terms of the social criterion of advancing general welfare.

Conflict or Complement

Instead of searching for an inevitable conflict, our task is to ascertain the conditions needed for a complementary relationship and to see if they exist in agriculture. The test of any hypothesis used can at this point be made from experience, from the trials and errors both of farmers and of the Department of Agriculture and the land-grant system in trying to bring about a more rational use of agricultural resources.

The small family-type farm, which dominates agriculture in the United States, is incapable of doing its own technical and economic research. This has made necessary the establishment of agricultural experiment stations under public auspices. Typical of the lack of economic knowledge or requisite finance is the fact that small private farms do not store enough feed in years of large crops to maintain their livestock in years of small crops. Thus wide swings characterize the volume of livestock production. (That there is a hog cycle is evidence of what happens to the output of pork when thousands of farmers all respond simultaneously to a change in the relative prices of feed and hogs.) The inability of the farm family to finance itself over a period sufficiently long to cover the swings from bad to good weather in the plains states is still another example of the limitations of unassisted, private enterprise in agriculture. Another case is the divergence between private and social cost caused by farm tenancy. Here, again, no remedy is provided by more and freer private enterprise. Nor can one overlook the widespread, uneconomic disinvestment (deterioration involving both erosion and depletion of soil) going on apace on all too many farms in the United States. These experiences raise doubts that the family-type farm can perform satisfactorily, unassisted by government, in the institutional framework of market prices that has prevailed historically in the United States.

At the same time, experience forces the conclusion that government cannot successfully determine the production programs of individual farmers. The intricacy of the resources employed on most farms, with each farm a unique set of resources, indicates that the management decisions required from day to day and from season to season can be made only by someone in constant and close contact with the farm. No matter how far-flung and highly organized an administrative agency the government may establish, the evidence is that it would fail in providing adequate managerial decisions for production operations on individual farms. The limited experience of the Agricultural Adjustment Administration in attempting to determine acreage allotments and quotas for individual farms demonstrated the shortcomings of a government agency in this sphere.

The Federal government has undoubtedly entered into some agricultural undertakings where its efforts have subtracted from, rather than added to, farm production; or, more often, the gain has not been commensurate with the cost, and it therefore has been diseconomy. Enough experience has accumulated to indicate that there are a number of areas inappropriate for government programs of the type that have prevailed. However, there unquestionably are spheres —for example, in soil management, farm tenure, credit, storage, and in the pricing of farm products—where more could be accomplished by appropriate governmental effort.

Measuring the merits and limitations of government programs in agriculture requires some notion of the kind of complement to private enterprise that is functionally required. In what circumstances and under what conditions are we likely to get better results by a combination of government and private efforts instead of one or the other?[1]

The existing governmental programs in agriculture and the policies that they represent may be classified as follows: those established under the emergency conditions that prevailed in the early thirties, and those established more recently to deal with wartime problems.[2]

✓ PROGRAMS TO COPE WITH DEPRESSION

Most of the farm legislation and administrative machinery of the depression years was maintained through the war. How useful will these old agencies be in handling agricultural adjustments and other farm problems now? Are they like certain prewar industrial machines—oiled, covered, and placed aside, to go back into operation as soon as the plant returns to civilian production? Many of the old dislocations in agriculture will require attention again now the war is over. Will these agencies be appropriate for the task?

Each of these agencies has been doing a number of different

[1] The reader will have noted that here we have focused upon "economizing," that is, allocating all resources to their best advantage, and not upon the social efficiency of a people or upon the problem of freedom. Two reasons underlie this orientation. (a) Economic analysis has a major contribution to make in understanding what is entailed in "economy" but probably can offer little to an inquiry into social efficiency and freedom; and (b) the development (chiefly in government) of new institutions affecting agriculture that favor the economic efficiency of the family farm in the United States has, if anything, enhanced both the social efficiency and freedom of farm people.

[2] A third class should be noted, namely, agricultural programs in effect before 1930: primarily credit programs, some regulatory aids, and efforts at education (chiefly through agricultural extension work).

things; hence it is necessary to focus not upon the agency (that is, the Agricultural Adjustment Administration, Commodity Credit Corporation, Farm Security Administration, Farm Credit Administration) but upon the particular *administrative techniques* employed. We shall therefore be examining the more important means used to regulate the agricultural economy—namely, rules and procedures set up to guide, adjust, control, and direct the production, investment, and consumption of farm prople. Of these, acreage allotments and commodity loans are the most important.[1]

Use of Acreage Allotments

Of the many things that the AAA has been doing, the main objective has been to regulate the acreage of certain basic crops. To do this, the AAA has developed a system of acreage allotments, entailing the establishing of acreage limits for each farm growing the crop.[2] Certain benefits were offered to induce farmers to participate and make the required adjustments in their cropping programs, and at an appropriate time the AAA checked compliance and made its payments to farmers.

Acreage allotments have been used for three purposes:[3] (*a*) to curtail production, and thus raise farm prices and income;[4] (*b*) to reduce misuse of the soil; and (*c*) as a basis for making government payments to farmers for participation in the program. In this discussion we are concerned chiefly

[1] The analysis that follows does not consider other administrative techniques—such as credit, grants of materials, technical aids, and managerial assistance—to bring about adjustments in production. They have not received enough systematic study to determine their merit as controls.

[2] Acreage allotments were discontinued during the war.

[3] It should be made plain that we are restricting our attention for the time being to the effects of acreage allotments, only one of the several administrative techniques employed by AAA, albeit the most important one.

[4] The effect of curtailed production on income depends, of course, upon the elasticity of the demand. With the demand near or less than unity, income would be, if anything, reduced. Only with an inelastic demand would farm income be increased.

with the first of these objectives. It may be helpful, however, to anticipate our findings, tentative as they are, to help see some of the essential interplay that has been at work. In our judgment, the AAA acreage allotments reduced the acreage planted and harvested of the main crops subject to this technique, but they probably did not affect total production appreciably (except for cotton) and hence had no substantial price or income effect. The program did contribute considerably to soil conservation by reducing the acreage of both cotton and corn, two of our more "erosive" crops, and by inducing better farming practices on the crop side generally. But the procedure of tying most of the AAA payments to acreage allotments has made the personal-income effects of these payments regressive, larger farms receiving proportionately greater payments than small farms.

Establishing Allotments. To understand the function and economic implications of acreage allotments, it is necessary to look at the way in which such a system is established and administered. The AAA found it necessary to do two things for each crop: (*a*) to determine a total acreage goal and (*b*) to allot a part of this total to each farm on which the crop was produced. The total acreage, set as the national goal, could be either smaller or larger than that which farmers would otherwise plant and harvest. In principle, acreage adjustments may be either up or down. In practice, however, the AAA machinery was used chiefly to curtail acreage and not to expand it; this was true even after 1940 when it was becoming increasingly apparent that because of the war more food and feed would be needed. The acreage goals were set each year not according to any predetermined formula but with an eye to carry-overs, prospective demand, and parity price. The national total was then broken down into state totals which in turn were allotted to individual farms on the basis of their crop history, thus tying the acreage allotment of each farm to what the farm had been producing.

The benefits offered to farmers for participating were of

two kinds: (*a*) direct benefits consisting chiefly of AAA payments, crop loans, reduced prices for fertilizer and other materials (in some areas), and for a time the privilege to participate in the crop-insurance program (mainly in wheat); and (*b*) indirect benefits through higher prices (resulting from the collective action of farmers curtailing output), a storage program to reduce the price and production instability caused by varying crop yields, and soil conservation effected by reducing the most exploitative crops, such as corn, cotton, tobacco, and wheat.

In addition to offering these benefits to induce farmers to participate, the AAA was authorized to institute for some crops a system of marketing quotas with penalties for noncompliance. (Commodity loans and marketing quotas are administrative techniques distinct from acreage allotments which also may be, and have been, employed to regulate production.) For cotton and tobacco, and to some extent wheat, each farmer, each year that marketing quotas were in effect, was given a quota permitting him to market a specified amount. If he exceeded his quota, he was subject to a penalty. So much for the procedure of acreage allotments. What part did they play in AAA policy before the war?

During the twelve years since its establishment, changes in emphasis have taken place in AAA in the use of acreage allotments. In its early days the AAA was operating in a depression with widespread unemployment and only small foreign demand for farm products. Against this background the AAA initiated its program of curtailing basic crops, stressing three major aims: (*a*) to reduce surpluses, (*b*) to increase farm income, and (*c*) to lessen the wastage of soil. In the first stage, up to 1936, the AAA operated on revenue obtained from processing taxes, and it made individual contracts with farmers in which it specified the obligations of the participating farmer and of the government. During this period emphasis was laid upon reducing production, so that it would match more nearly the reduced demand occasioned by the drop in exports and by the depressed domestic market. In 1936, because of widespread drought, the appearance of the dust bowl, and the adverse decision of the Supreme Court in the Hoosac-Mills case, the AAA shifted its attention from reducing production through acreage allotments to conserving soil. Following the extraordinarily large crops of 1937, however, AAA went back to a kind of middle way, stressing both soil conservation and the curtailment of crops. The "ever-normal granary" idea was also given prominence at this time. It appealed both to consumers who had become drought-conscious and concerned about food supplies and to producers who saw in it an outlet for part of their output when crops were as large as in 1937. The storage of crop surpluses was given a larger role in the revised AAA of 1938.

At the time the war started, the AAA was trying to do several things: it was trying to regulate crop production through acreage allotments; it was seeking to facilitate soil conservation by reducing the acreage of the more exploitative crops; it was using the CCC as an agency for leveling big and small crop years through storages; it was asking for and receiving from Congress large appropriations for payments to farmers, to induce them to participate in adjusting output to the acreage allotted and for other purposes. Throughout this period, however, no meaningful criteria were developed for measuring the performance of the AAA. All the basic legislation was tied to the concepts of price and income parity. Parity prices, however, remained in practice a rather distant goal, someday to be attained, though its achievement might be questioned since prevailing farm prices were far below those called for by the parity formula.

The AAA Act of 1933 had given the Secretary of Agriculture considerable administrative discretion in determining acreage allotments. It was not until the Act of 1938 that Congress began to circumscribe the Secretary's powers, by making the parity-price goal much more binding upon the actions of the administrative agencies in agriculture.

To what use can acreage allotment be put in adjusting agricultural production after the war? Does our experience indicate that this administrative procedure is effective in bringing about a better use of agricultural resources than would otherwise prevail? Is it a procedure that complements private enterprise in farming, improving the performance of farms as producing units?

What Did AAA Allotments Do to Crop Acreages? As the table below reveals, the four basic crops subject to AAA control show a cut of over 45 million acres, a 21 per cent decrease for the four crops taken together. How much of the reduction was effected by AAA? A recent study[1] indicates that the drought years pulled corn down about 10 million acres in Nebraska, Kansas, Missouri, and South Dakota, thus accounting for nearly half the reduction in corn. Wheat and cotton, however, were not affected by the drought in the same way as corn, although no similar study has been made for them. Thus, while it is not possible to demonstrate precisely what part of the 45-million-acre cut was brought about by the AAA program, it does seem that most of it may be ascribed to the crop-control features of AAA.

Crop	Acreages without AAA 1931–1933 average, million acres	Acreages with AAA 1940–1942[a] average, million acres	Reduction in per cent
Corn..........	111.0	89.0	20
Wheat.........	67.2	58.7	13
Cotton.........	38.6	23.8	38
Tobacco.......	1.7	1.4	18
Total........	218.5	172.9	21

[a] Acreage planted except for tobacco, which is acreage harvested. Source, U.S. Department of Agriculture, Washington, D.C. Comparing the change in acreage from the five years 1928–1932 to the five years 1938–1942, these four crops dropped from 216 to 180 million acres, a decrease of about 17 per cent.

[1] Theodore W. Schultz and O. H. Brownlee, "Effects of Crop Acreage Control Features of AAA on Feed Production in 11 Midwest States," *Agricultural Experiment Station, Research Bulletin* 298, Ames, Iowa, April, 1942, p. 683.

What Did Acreage Allotments Do to Crop Production? Acres of land are plainly only one of several inputs that a farmer employs in growing crops. If one of the inputs is rationed (in this case the amount of land allotted for a crop), he has several alternatives open to him should he want to maintain, or even increase, production. (*a*) He may remove from production his poorest acres (that is, keep his best acres in corn or cotton or whatever crop is restricted). (*b*) He may intensify the use of the land planted in the restricted crop by applying more capital and labor resources (namely, by using improved seed, more fertilizer, improved tillage, and more labor). (*c*) On the acres restricted by the AAA allotment he may produce substitute crops (for example, such crops as alfalfa, sorghum, and soybeans may under certain circumstances produce even more feed than corn). (*d*) He may substitute future outputs for present output by investing in soil resources (for example, by adopting crop rotations and cropping practices that will build up his soil). The production effects of these various types of substitution on a particular farm depend upon the nature of the soil resources, the crop and livestock enterprise, the technology, the relation between the cost of the factors employed and product prices, and the enterprise of the farmer.

What changes did occur in production of the four crops under consideration?

Crop	Production without AAA[1] 1931–1933, in millions	Production with AAA 1940–1942, in millions	Change in per cent
Corn, bu......	2,635	2,757	5
Wheat, bu.....	750	910	21
Cotton, bales..	14.4	12	−17
Tobacco, lb....	1,318	1,377	4

[1] If the period 1928–1932 is compared with 1938–1942, the average yearly production for corn rose from 2,554 to 2,680 million bushels; wheat from 864 to 878 million bushels; cotton fell from 14.7 to 12.0 million bales; and tobacco rose from 1,427 to 1,480 million pounds.

In spite of the reduction in acres, production actually increased except for cotton. The 17 per cent drop in cotton, however, overstates the reduction because of the very high yields in 1931 (which resulted in a 17-million-bale crop) and the poor crop in 1941 (when less than 10.7 million bales were produced).

The experience in corn illustrates how shifts within the farm will offset production effects of the cut in corn acreage. The Iowa study, analyzing the over-all production of feed in eleven key corn-belt states, indicates:

(1) that aggregate feed production in these eleven states . . . would not have been significantly different without crop acreage control, (2) that the proportion of the total feed supply comprised by corn has been somewhat smaller as a result of corn acreage allotments, (3) that about the same aggregate amounts of feed concentrates other than corn have been produced as would have been grown without AAA, and (4) that feed roughages were not only greater in absolute amounts but made up a greater proportion of the total feed supply than would have been the case without crop acreage control.[1]

Farmers producing wheat and cotton do not have at hand so wide a range of substitute methods to offset a cut in cotton and wheat acreage. The corn farmer has been in a unique position, because he has had a number of effective alternatives in recombining his resources and thereby has not only maintained but in many instances increased his total output of feed. Examining the production consequences of the crop allotment feature of AAA, the upshot seems clear: *There has been enough substitution of the type described to have made the crop acreage allotments, ruling out the vagaries of weather, ineffective in regulating production.* Drastic cuts in acreage do reduce output the first year or two, but even with programs as severe as those administered in cotton, it appears that within a few crop seasons the total output recovers remarkably even in the face of a 40 per cent cut in acreage.

Our tentative conclusion, therefore, is that acreage allotment as practiced by the AAA is not a satisfactory means for

[1] *Ibid.*, p. 678.

regulating production, especially if unemployed resources exist. Under a condition of fully employed resources, acreage allotments might be more effective.

The effects on the volume of production are not, however, the whole of the story. Did the AAA allotments bring about a more or less economic use of resources by farmers? One result appears to be good; a second is unquestionably bad. The AAA programs did hasten the adoption of better agricultural techniques. Cotton, corn, and wheat farmers were for the most part using farm practices that did not give them the most productive use of their resources. The AAA occasioned a kind of increased returns by forcing a recombination of factors and the introduction of newer and better farming practices. But a contrary effect—that is, a misuse of resources —came as the result of farmers' acquiring a vested interest in their acreage allotments, owing to the fact that sizable benefit payments were distributed in accordance with the acres allotted to the farm and the per-acre output of the land. Consequently, shifts among crops that normally take place during a span of years have been arrested. Cotton has not moved sufficiently out of the eastern sections of the cotton belt into the Mississippi delta area, particularly into parts of the delta more recently brought into cultivation. Wheat acreage has been maintained in some areas with a high climatic hazard—acreage that would have been abandoned and allowed to return to grass had it not been for the "freezing" effect of the AAA wheat allotments and the benefit payments made to those who kept their allotments active.

It may be well to repeat that our purpose in this section has not been to evaluate the accomplishments of the AAA program in its entirety. Instead, we have focused attention on one main purpose of the program—crop control, and on only one means of achieving it—acreage allotments. It should be remembered, however, that the AAA was meant to serve other purposes, though they were secondary to crop control, and that it had other means at its disposal besides acreage allotments. The acreage allotments, moreover, have been used for other purposes: to reduce misuse of the soil and as a basis for distributing government payments to farmers.

Use of Commodity Loans

The Commodity Credit Corporation, begun in 1933, had made commodity loans and purchases aggregating just under $3 billion at the time the United States entered the war. They had been distributed as follows:

Commodity	Accumulative Loans and Purchases by CCC, 1933 through 1941, in Millions
Cotton	$1,159
Wheat	709
Corn	552
Others	576
Total	2,996

SOURCE: *Agricultural Statistics*, U.S. Department of Agriculture, Washington, D.C., 1942, p. 732.

In making the loans to farmers, the CCC has used essentially the same procedure as its ill-fated predecessor, the Federal Farm Board. It so happened, however, that the Farm Board started its loan operations as prices were being pulled down by the great depression, while the CCC, launched in 1933, had the strong current of rising prices in its favor. Crop shortages following the severe droughts of the middle thirties also aided the CCC, and the crop-control features of AAA were intended to safeguard CCC operations by holding production in check when reserve stocks became too large. In spite of all these advantages, the CCC had accumulated excessively large stocks as loan collateral and was in a critical position at the time the war started. At the end of 1940 it owned and had loans outstanding on 10.7 million bales of cotton; its holdings of corn went to a peak of 477 million bushels in 1941; and at the end of 1942, 519 million bushels of wheat were owned by or pledged to CCC.

War-induced Demands Saved CCC. The war rescued the CCC, by converting into valuable assets (except for cotton) the huge inventories that the CCC was instrumental in accumulating. Since the war has bailed the CCC out of its difficulties, we start the postwar period with a clean slate in farm products other than cotton. We have the opportunity to begin anew and to profit from past mistakes.

Are we to infer from the experiences of CCC that with the rules and regulations now governing its operations, rising prices, unprecedented droughts, and a world war once each decade are required for it to succeed? This is too harsh a judgment.

The technique of commodity loans may make a substantial contribution if it is used to attain a better use of agricultural resources and not to correct particular dislocations in farm income. The CCC loans have had significant effects upon farm production, prices, and incomes. The loan technique is not a blunt instrument like acreage allotments; it is a sharp tool that cuts quickly and deeply. It can do much harm or much good, depending upon how it is administered. Appropriately used, commodity loans can guide the production of farm crops and regulate the storage of farm products. However, the loans may be used, and have been used, in ways that lead to waste and a misuse of resources.

CCC commodity loans have had two basic characteristics: (*a*) they have been nonrecourse loans and thus in effect minimum prices, and (*b*) the rate of the loan has been established from year to year in accordance with the parity price formula.

CCC Loans as Minimum Prices

Being "without recourse," the rate of the loan has been in effect a minimum price. This feature was extended to cover both principal and accumulated interest. Thus when a farmer elected not to redeem the cotton, wheat, corn, or tobacco that he had pledged as collateral, he satisfied all claims against him both as to principal and interest by giving the CCC full title to the commodity. Since the loan rate has acted as a minimum price, as it approached and equaled the market price all the difficulties involved in pricing a commodity have arisen. Questions of quality differences, locational differentials, and the time element in pricing a commodity have vexed the administration of CCC. It is not easy to administer a set of minimum prices in the form of loans or by any other procedure. The difficulties have not merely been headaches for the administrators. They have made themselves very evident in the markets for the crops.

Cotton Loans Have Overpriced Low Grades and Short Staples. In the case of cotton, the low-grade, short-staple varieties have been overpriced in the loan rate relative to the better grade and longer staple lengths; as a result, as one would expect, the carry-over soon consisted largely of the lower grade and shorter staple lengths, either owned by CCC or pledged to it as collateral. Most of the huge reserve of cotton now on hand is of these less desirable types.

TABLE XVIII

Total Production, Total Quantity under Loans and Purchases (1933–1941), and Largest Quantity Owned by CCC and Pledged to Secure Loans—Cotton, Wheat, Corn, Tobacco, Rye, and Barley

(1)	(2)	(3)	(4)	(5)	(6)	(7)
Commodity	Total production 1933–1941[a]	Total quantity under loans and purchases 1933–1941[b]	Largest quantity owned by CCC and pledged to secure loans[c]	Per cent (3) is of (2)	Per cent (4) is of (3)	Per cent (4) is of average crop
Cotton, million bales	112	21.6	10.7[d]	19	50	86
Wheat, million bushels	6,648	879	519[f]	13	60	70
Corn, million bushels	20,620	1,029	477[e]	5	46	20
Tobacco, million pounds	12,442	647	370[e]	5	57	26
Rye, million bushels	353	8	4[f]	2	50	10
Barley, million bushels	2,121	24	16[f]	1	67	7

[a] *Agricultural Statistics, 1942,* U.S. Department of Agriculture, Washington, D.C.
[b] *Agricultural Statistics, 1942,* U.S. Department of Agriculture, Washington, D.C.
[c] *Agricultural Statistics, 1940, 1941,* and *1942,* U.S. Department of Agriculture, Washington, D.C.
[d] January 1, 1940.
[e] January 1, 1941.
[f] January 1, 1942.

Flat Rate for Corn. The early administration of the corn loans illustrates the problem of geographical differentials; a flat loan rate was employed, which meant in effect that this minimum price per bushel was the same regardless of location. As a result, the storage of corn by farmers in order to obtain a loan, and the subsequent accumulation of corn owned by CCC, took place largely in the middle and western parts of the corn belt.[1]

The most serious difficulty, however, has arisen in what may be considered the time element, namely, that the loan rates at particular times were not in line with other prices. It is apparent that this is what happened to cotton in 1937, to corn in 1939, and to wheat in 1940. The overpricing by the loan continued in each of these commodities until the sudden lift of prices caused by war demands. In wheat, subsidizing wheat for feed served as a corrective, inducing farmers to use the unprecedented quantities of 315 million bushels for feed in 1942 and 390 million bushels in 1943. But even war demand has not been effective in correcting the overpricing of the CCC loans on cotton, and more than 10 million bales are essentially locked up by the high loan rates and by the legislation governing the disposal of this cotton.

Backward- or Forward-looking Loans. There is considerable evidence that loan rates for durable crops, employed to assure farmers of minimum prices for the crops they produce, may be an effective administrative technique for guiding farm production. When this procedure was used in 1942 and 1943 with soybeans, peanuts, and flaxseed, it was instrumental in inducing farmers to double their acreage of these three oil-bearing crops. The significant fact, however, is that they were *forward-looking loan rates*. They were announced in advance, at a time when farmers could make plans and

[1] See Professor Geoffrey Shepherd's study, *Controlling Corn and Hog Supplies and Prices*, Technical Bulletin 826, U.S. Department of Agriculture, Washington, D.C., June, 1942. See also a brief article by Theodore W. Schultz and O. H. Brownlee, "Our U.S. Iowa Corn Granary and How It Has Affected Hogs in the Corn Belt," *Iowa Farm Economist*, 7(1) Ames, Iowa, 1941.

proceed to prepare for and plant the crop. They were not loans announced and made available to farmers after the crop had been produced, as was the case in cotton, wheat, corn, tobacco, and other loans and purchases made by CCC over an eight-year period and to a total of nearly $3 billion. Such loans can have only an indirect and remote effect on production plans.

Loan rates employed as minimum prices may be used to establish a comprehensive future market for durable farm products. Thus employed, they would make explicit the relative price structure to which farmers may adjust and fit their production operations. But apart from an emergency use of loans in the case of a few crops (the oil crops during the war), the CCC loans have not been used for this purpose or in this manner.[1]

Loans Tied to Parity

The second feature of the CCC commodity loans, that of determining the rate of the loans in accordance with the parity price formula, has passed through several stages. In the AAA Act of 1933, the Secretary of Agriculture was given wide latitude in setting a loan rate. The 1938 Act, however, circumscribed the authority of the Secretary by specifying that the commodity loans were to be made at rates ranging between 52 and 75 per cent of parity. In 1941 legislation made all loans mandatory at 85 per cent of parity. In 1942 the rate was raised to 90 per cent of parity except for crops that would adversely affect the feeding of livestock, and the stipulation was added that these loan rates were to extend to the expiration of the two-year period beginning with the end of the January following the close of the war.[2] (The

[1] In this context commodity loans can be made an integral part of a system of forward prices for farm products. We shall indicate the general rationale for such a system later in this study.

[2] For an elaboration of the parity concept, see Theodore W. Schultz, *Redirecting Farm Policy*, The Macmillan Company, New York, 1943.

loan rate on cotton has since been advanced to 92.5 per cent of parity.)

The most serious defect of the legislation under which the CCC is administered is the use of loan rates tied to the parity price formula. The existing formula is wholly obsolete, and it can only bring serious dislocations when put into effect. This became very evident following 1939, after Congress limited the authority of the Secretary of Agriculture and fixed the loan rates in terms of the parity price formula. After the war, this particular price-loan base will be even more obsolete. Any attempt to enforce the farm-price relationships that prevailed prior to World War I (namely, during 1909–1914) is bound to distort seriously the price structure appropriate to agriculture.

Before the loan technique developed by the CCC can be used for positive purposes in guiding production, the first and most important step to be taken is to revise the basic legislation under which the CCC functions. The loan rates must be detached from the parity price formula of 1909–1914, and the purpose of CCC should be made that of inducing adjustments in production and of regulating storage stocks to counter fluctuations in yields and, within limits, in demand.[1]

Acreage allotments and commodity loans are only two, though the two most important, of the numerous administrative techniques employed as controls in agriculture prior to the war. Other means were used to promote soil conservation, to finance and rehabilitate farmers, and to encourage output adjustments. They are not covered in this study as no adequate basis for an appraisal is at hand.

[1] See the following by Geoffrey Shepherd: *Commodity Loans and Price Floors for Farm Products*, Iowa State College Press, Ames, Iowa, 1943; "Stabilization Operations of CCC," *Journal of Farm Economics*, Vol. 24 (1942); and "Basis for Controlling Agricultural Prices," *Journal of Farm Economics*, Vol. 24 (1942). See also appraisal of loans and storages, Theodore W. Schultz, "Economic Effects of Agricultural Programs," *American Economic Review*, Vol. 30 (1941).

Agricultural Controls

WARTIME CONTROLS

Except for price supports, the food and farm-product controls that were part of the war mobilization of the economy are likely to become obsolete and fall into disuse as the demand for food recedes.

Price Ceilings

The fixing of maximum prices on food and farm products has been the most important wartime control affecting agriculture. Food prices are likely to stay at or near ceiling levels until agricultural production in Europe recovers and food requirements for military and relief uses decline. The 1945 crop in Europe was planted under great difficulties. There can be no recovery in food production until the 1946 crop is harvested. That would be the earliest date; it may take longer. When these needs have been met, however, the demand for food is likely to contract sharply, and farm prices will start their downward course. At this juncture the support prices already authorized by Congress will come into play.

Before the support-price stage is reached, the mistake may be made of removing the price ceilings prematurely. Uncertainty as to postwar demand for food may unsettle farm prices, especially prices of those products that are sold in highly speculative commodity markets. This uncertainty may cause some farm prices to recede for a time appreciably below the maximum set by government controls. If at this critical time the price ceilings on farm and food products are removed, the stage will be set for a pronounced rise in farm and food prices like that following World War I. An early postwar farm-price inflation, starting from the already high prices caused by the war, would feed the flames of the land boom and distort price relationships, and would do as much, if not more, harm to agriculture as the inflation of

November, 1918, to May, 1920, when the farm price index went from 210 to 235.[1]

Rationing of Farm Machinery and Equipment

The shortage of certain critical materials has limited the manufacture of farm machinery and equipment. The output was reduced at the very hour when demand increased,[2] and it thus became necessary to ration the distribution of new farm machinery and equipment. In 1943, ninety-one types of farm machinery were put under rationing rules by the U.S. Department of Agriculture.

Production of new farm machinery and equipment needs to be expanded rapidly. Farmers now have money and want to buy these capital goods, both because they have been increasingly adapted to the family-type farm and because they have proved their worth in saving labor and reducing costs. Another consideration making the expansion of farm machinery production important is the fact that the sale of $2 to $3 billion's worth of farm machinery and equipment in the first two years after the war may go a long way toward checking the land boom that is under way.[3] Farm earnings used for buying farm equipment will subsequently mean lower costs of production; if used for buying land, they will, in too many instances, be dissipated in bidding up the price

[1] *Index Numbers of Prices Received by Farmers*, U.S. Department of Agriculture, Bureau of Agricultural Economics, Washington, D.C., 1944, p. 22.

[2] As indicated earlier, the wartime demand for labor has reduced the supply of labor available to agriculture. This has made it necessary for farmers to recombine the factors of production in order to maintain and increase farm output. Demand for additional farm machinery and equipment has been supported by the enlarged income of farmers and by the fact that intensive wartime use has made for more rapid wearing out and depreciation of farm implements.

[3] This inference is made on the belief that additional purchases of farm machinery and equipment would absorb a considerable part of the extra funds that farmers might otherwise spend on land. More efficient machinery and equipment will, however, induce some farmers to enlarge their farms and thus add to the demand for land.

of land and thereby worsening the competitive position of farmers.

As the supply of new farm machinery and equipment is increased, control of its distribution will obviously no longer be required. The rationing of farm machinery is one of several wartime controls that are self-liquidating. Too great emphasis cannot be placed on the need to hasten the expansion of output of new farm machinery and equipment.

The Rationing of Fertilizer

The amount of fertilizer used increased during the war years, with the 1944 supplies substantially larger than those of the preceding year. The controls for fertilizer were minimal. The demand for fertilizer will remain large while farm prices are high and the incentive for intensifying production is thus maintained.

The controls of other materials employed in agricultural production or in farm-family living have followed the same course as the controls of fertilizer and farm machinery. The lumber supply available in 1943 was about 50 per cent of the 1940 level, creating a severe shortage of lumber for farm use, and it has been rationed through the county war boards. There have been severe shortages of other materials—copper wire, milk cans, insecticides, and fungicides—which have necessitated various types of distribution controls. But as supplies increase, these controls will automatically become unnecessary and will disappear.

Facilitating the Movement of Labor

To alleviate acute local scarcities of farm labor, the government has initiated programs to recruit, train, and place farm workers. The United States Crop Corps has lent a hand in some local mobilization. Federal appropriations have been

· 183 ·

given to the state extension services, which aid intrastate movement of farm workers, paying, for example, all or part of the cost of transporting workers within the state from areas of temporary surplus to areas of critical need. Measures have also been taken to increase the interstate movement of workers and to obtain foreign workers from Mexico, the Bahamas, and Jamaica. The Federal government has operated some farm-labor supply centers as well, using buildings and equipment formerly utilized for the Farm Security Administration, the Civilian Conservation Corps, and NYA camps.

These various programs have been integrated through the Office of Labor of the War Food Administration. This office has had authority, also, over wage stabilization for agricultural workers, although this has had no particular import since employers of agricultural labor have been free to raise wages up to $2,400 per annum at their own option,[1] except for particular crops, areas, and classes of employers. Maximum wage rates have been set for several crops in areas of California and Florida.

To stabilize employment in agriculture during the war, the Manpower Commission ruled that the U.S. Employment Service before referring a farm worker to essential war work out of agriculture should consult with the county agent and issue a statement of availability to the worker. Insofar as these regulations were observed, they substantially lessened the mobility of farm workers.

Whether or not some of these controls may be maintained to facilitate the demobilization and the redistribution of the labor force is not clear. Obviously we do not yet have adequate machinery for handling this very serious problem. It is as important to bring about a more orderly distribution of the labor force as the nation mobilizes for peace as it was in mobilizing for war.

[1] For a detailed treatment of farm wages during the war see Louis J. Ducoff, *Wages of Agricultural Labor in the United States*, U.S. Department of Agriculture, Washington, D.C., Chap. 8, "Wartime Regulation of Farm Wage Rates."

Support prices are already earmarked as an important government control in agriculture after the war, however. The problem that they present and the contribution they might make is considered in some detail in Chap. XII.

PART IV

Problems in Agricultural Policy

IX. UNDEREMPLOYMENT AND THE ATTENDANT LOW EARNINGS IN AGRICULTURE

THERE is no paved highway connecting "economic analysis" and "public policy." For the most part it is an unmapped, badly maintained, and hazardous stretch to travel. A word of caution is needed before starting down this road: it is one thing to analyze accurately the basic forces reshaping the supply and demand for farm products and their effects upon the employment and income of farm people, but it is quite another to translate these findings into *principles, rules and procedures*, and programs appropriate to public policy. Public policy is seldom, if ever, single-purposed; virtually every policy consideration entails a number of values. In the belief, however, that the findings growing out of economic inquiry may be better understood and thus made more useful in the field of public affairs, economists must, at least, keep on trying to interpret the results of their studies into the language and in terms of the values underlying policy considerations. This is the essence of what we have attempted in Part IV, in what is essentially a series of notes on *problems in policy*.

GROWING DEPENDENCY OF AGRICULTURE UPON THE REST OF THE ECONOMY

Farm families have become less self-contained; their production and their consumption have been oriented increasingly toward markets and away from production for their own household use. Farm people have gained from the fuller integration of their production and consumption into the exchange system, insofar as they have shared the benefits that come from the extension of the national and international market, from the division of labor that this makes possible, from advances in technology occurring in other fields, and from the increasing range of goods and services made available to them. The level of living of most farm families has improved over the years. In becoming dependent upon markets, farm people have also incurred certain liabilities. These liabilities were not for the most part anticipated; having appeared, they have come to claim much attention in agricultural policy.

As farm families have become more dependent upon selling and buying, they also have become more vulnerable to the actions of other groups in the economy. The well-being of most farm families is now directly linked with decisions of other "firms" affecting production, consumption, and savings. More specifically, the production and price policies of management and of organized labor, imperfections in competition, the periodic destruction of aggregate demand, the lack of sufficient expansion outside agriculture to provide employment for all available labor, equipment, and plants, and to put to account advances in technology, the strangling of world trade by growing regionalism, and the inadequacy of government policies, especially in the monetary-fiscal sphere—these private and public actions have come to have a direct significance for farm prices and income.

The experiences of the interwar years indicate that American agriculture at times paid dearly for its dependence on the exchange system. In spite of their steady output of a large volume of food and fiber, produced year after year with ever-rising efficiency, farm people have found themselves pitched about by the forward and backward surges of other sectors of the economy. Small wonder that farm people have organized into interest groups seeking ways to lessen the burdens that the exchange economy has placed on them.[1] In their efforts to cope with the emergency of the thirties, farmers accepted production control. In this they were following the footpaths, so they felt and were told, of industry; the thing to do when the demand shrinks is to curtail output and thus at least to maintain prices. But it was soon evident that production control was inadequate as a solution either for the underemployment and the attendant low earnings in agriculture or for the instability of farm income.

Public policy concerning agriculture will have to be determined in three distinct areas:

1. Social security including farm relief.
2. Business fluctuations.
3. The normal functioning of a developing economy.

The forces in an expanding economy that have caused the chronic, depressed conditions in agriculture, particularly its underemployment, have been detailed in preceding chapters. We have also examined briefly the agricultural price and income problems associated with business fluctuations. We have not, however, dealt with farm relief and social security except in a most incidental manner. Adequate security and relief measures have not yet been developed for agriculture— whether the emergencies arise from such natural causes as droughts and floods, from sharp curtailment in demand and from depressed prices, or from needs associated with old age, sickness, accidents, and unemployment (in the case of hired farm laborers). In this respect, legislation has not reached the stage that has been attained in providing relief and

---

[1] Farmers on the more commercialized farms are organized into commodity groups and into general farm organizations, and their price and income problems have been given strong representation and expression. Commercialized farms are not necessarily large; the greater per cent of them are family-type farms. There are, however, a larger group of farm families still comparatively self-sustaining, essentially unorganized, and accordingly less articulate. Their problems, for the most part, receive little or no public attention. (See Table XIX for a classification of American farms.)

security for industrial workers. The problems of agriculture in this sphere are so specialized and of such major importance that they deserve special treatment. They have been omitted from this study, since the object here is to examine the role of agriculture in a developing economy and to give some consideration to the problem of trade fluctuations; policy and programs appropriate for farm relief and social security for farm people are too important to be treated in an incidental manner.[1]

In turning now to policy considerations we shall therefore weigh only two of the three major questions. First, how may we achieve a better balance between agriculture and industry in the allocation of resources? Labor will be the focal issue. Second, how may we remedy the instability of farm income? To treat these it will be necessary to consider also production adjustments and farm prices as problems in policy.

THE UNDEREMPLOYMENT PROBLEM IN AGRICULTURE

Mobilization for war went a long way in diminishing the overlarge supply and thus the underemployed labor in agriculture. The distribution of the nation's labor force between agriculture and other occupations has been considerably improved in the past five years. In fact, at no time since World War I has there been less agricultural underemployment. Nevertheless, the migration out of agriculture, particularly out of the poorer farming areas, has not and will not have proceeded anywhere near far enough for the earnings of at least one-third, more likely one-half, of the people engaged in farming to reach a level comparable to the earnings of the less well paid labor in other occupations. Many

[1] The Agriculture Committee of the National Planning Association has approved a series of recommendations for the extension of old-age and survivor benefits to farm people. A study made by Professor M. R. Benedict accompanies these recommendations.

more people will have to leave agriculture before the earnings inside and outside agriculture become essentially equal. As we look ahead, major emphasis therefore must be put on creating job opportunities in other occupations—industrial and service jobs that may be available to men and women in farm localities, especially to workers now crowding the less commercial low-production farming areas.

What will demobilization bring? Will most of the gains that have come to agriculture from the redistribution of the labor force be lost? Will war workers drawn from agricultural areas be compelled by the lack of jobs to return to the locality from which they came? What is done in conversion and demobilization will affect the distribution of the nation's labor force for many years to come.[1] We are too likely to lose sight of the fundamental, long-run requirements of agriculture if, as is probable, demobilization occurs while many farmers still feel the pinch of wartime labor shortages, and while farm prices still are high and people look upon agriculture as being prosperous.[2]

[1] A section of south central Alabama, which the present writer had occasion to study briefly during the early part of 1945, offers a graphic instance of this problem. The area about a hundred miles from Mobile had been a highly congested farming area prior to the war. Upward of two-fifths of the prewar hired farm laborers and about one-fifth of the sharecroppers and even tenants had left agriculture. One-tenth of the farmers who had received tenant-purchase loans had given up their farms (in which most of them had acquired some equity) and left to take nonagricultural jobs. In addition, many farmers (operators on small farming units, for the most part) were making the trip to the Mobile shipyards each working day (about 200 miles a round trip), where they had earned in 1944 as much as $3,000 per person.

For such an area, demobilization will carry long-run consequences. If most of those who have left find it unnecessary to return, a great forward step will have been taken in improving the economic status of the people still on the land.

[2] Developments in early 1945 in the area described in the footnote above are evidence of this danger. Several thousand workers in the shipyards of Mobile were dismissed and the hours of many others reduced. Since there is no other industrial area near by to which they could go, and since the prices of cotton and peanuts were still very high, many ex-farm workers were in the process of returning to the farming area they had left, a few of them buying a farm or seeking to "reclaim" the one they had abandoned.

Outlook for the Long Pull

We cannot escape the slowly moving, persistent secular forces that reshape the demand and supply of farm products, forces that were at work long before World War I and are likely to make themselves felt with added strength during the next two or three decades. We cannot ignore, therefore, the fact that the growth of the demand for farm products, certainly for food, is slowing down. For one thing, the population that buys the bulk of the output of American agriculture is increasing at a slower rate than formerly, with the prospect that it will stop increasing altogether. Moreover, as we better our level of living, people spend proportionately less of their income for products of the farm. But while the demand for farm goods is growing at a diminished rate, the supply is growing at an accelerated rate. Better farm practices and techniques will employ more capital and more skill, and these will produce more feed, food, and fiber. But they unmistakably will call for fewer workers in agriculture. Nature takes little or no cognizance of these facts: the net reproduction rate of the farm population continues higher than that in any major occupational group, and far above what is required to supply agriculture with labor.

WHAT NOT TO DO

Measures to be avoided in solving the excess supply of labor in agriculture can therefore be identified quite easily. Not so easily, those to be followed.

Back to the Land

What do the opportunities for new farm operators look like? How many farm operators are likely to retire in the first few years after the war? Will farms be available for veterans?

Various studies indicate that because of the depression fewer farm operators retired during the decade of the thirties

· 191 ·

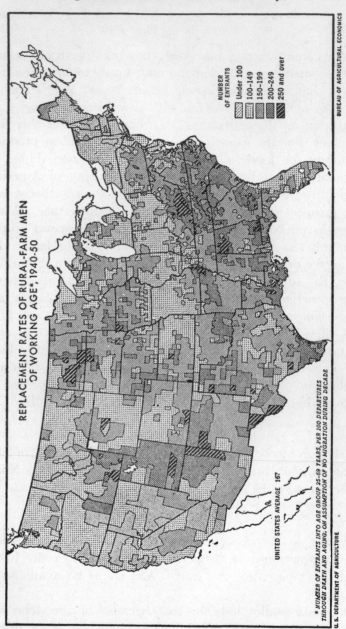

REPLACEMENT RATES OF RURAL-FARM MEN
OF WORKING AGE*, 1940-50

NUMBER
OF ENTRANTS

Under 100
100-149
150-199
200-249
250 and over

UNITED STATES AVERAGE 167

* NUMBER OF ENTRANTS INTO AGE GROUP 25-69 YEARS, PER 100 DEPARTURES
THROUGH DEATH AND AGING, ON ASSUMPTION OF NO MIGRATION DURING DECADE

U.S. DEPARTMENT OF AGRICULTURE

BUREAU OF AGRICULTURAL ECONOMICS

than would have retired in normal circumstances. About 110,000 more operators over fifty-five years of age had delayed retirement as of 1940, compared to the decade of the twenties. The war years have necessitated a further post-ponement in retirements because of the lack of younger men to replace aging operators; upward of another 110,000 oper-ators have carried on beyond their normal retirement age.[1] Accordingly, about 220,000 farm operators might be expected to retire in favor of younger men at the end of the war. But there are two important qualifications. First, nearly half the operators referred to above are on farms that in 1939 pro-duced $600 or less. Farms so low in productivity hardly offer full employment for returning soldiers or for war workers returning to agriculture.[2] The second qualification is that against these estimates of expected retirements of farm oper-ators must be set the wartime decline in the total number of farms. The Census of 1940 listed just over 6 million farms; the number certainly has decreased as a consequence of the mobilization for war. Although no official figure will be available until the 1945 Census of Agriculture has been

[1] Based on the testimony of C. C. Taylor of the Bureau of Agricultural Eco-nomics, before the Senate Special Committee on Postwar Economic Planning, May 11, 1944, p. 3, and upon a study by Margaret J. Hagood and Louis J. Ducoff, *Farm Population and Utilization of Resources in the Postwar Period*, U.S. Department of Agriculture, Bureau of Agricultural Economics, January, 1944.

[2] The U.S. Department of Agriculture Interbureau Report, *Farming Oppor-tunities, Outlook, Problems, and Policies*, December, 1944, indicates the following: In addition to the 220,000 farm operators who have postponed retirement, the yearly expected rate of retirement of farm operators may be about 50,000 per year during the rest of the decade of the forties. The report estimates that the upsurge in sales of farms, occasioned by the war—through (a) farmers retiring, (b) farmers changing to other occupations, (c) sales of farms subdivided in two or more farms, and (d) sales of family-operated estates where operator discon-tinues farming—made a net total of 50,000 to 60,000 in 1943, or about the num-ber of expected annual retirements after the war. The report then points out that if the demand for farm products warrants, the expansion, improvement, and division of some farms and the irrigation, drainage, and clearing of suitable land would make feasible the adding of another 225,000 farm-operator opportunities. The probabilities are, however, that the postwar demand will not support this type of development.

tabulated, a number of convincing bits of evidence suggest that the number of farms may have declined by as much as one-tenth. To economize on labor, farmers have found it necessary to recombine the factors of production, with the result that many farms have been enlarged into somewhat bigger operating units by the consolidation of small farms or parts of other farms. The increased use of farm machinery

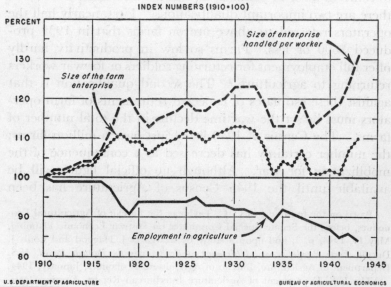

RELATION OF EMPLOYMENT IN AGRICULTURE TO THE SIZE OF AGRICULTURAL ENTERPRISE

INDEX NUMBERS (1910=100)

U.S. DEPARTMENT OF AGRICULTURE   BUREAU OF AGRICULTURAL ECONOMICS

is facilitating this consolidation. Then, too, there has been some abandonment of farms that had been essentially self-contained, as the people on such farms migrated. The number of farms in the United States may therefore be as low as 5½ million (or less).[1]

It has been estimated that the number of farms that may become available during the next five years will not exceed

[1] The Bureau of Agricultural Economics in *Net Farm Income and Parity Report: 1943*, July, 1944, Table 8, p. 16, includes estimates of the number of farms for 1943 as 5,570,000.

· 194 ·

750,000.[1] This number will not take care of the demand, for upward of a million men in the armed forces will seek opportunities in farming. Most of these men will want to become full-time farmers. Another half-million returning soldiers will want part-time farms. It is quite likely that anywhere from a hundred thousand to upward of a million war workers (depending upon the amount of unemployment that occurs during the transition), who left agriculture during the war to do industrial work, will be wanting farms or some kind of work in agriculture.

Let us not repeat the mistake made by many countries following World War I, of initiating land-settlement programs to help returning soldiers. In the United States such programs were undertaken by a number of the states, and similar programs are again under consideration. The illusion that open space offers economic opportunity should have been dispelled by the failure of these schemes during the interwar years.[2] Agriculture, of all the major industries, is most likely to have a chronic excess of labor.

Plans to drain, clear, and irrigate millions of acres for the purpose of settling returning soldiers on the land lose sight of the prospect that agricultural surpluses are highly probable as soon as military and relief food needs have been met. Some programs to bring land into use have merit in terms of local or even regional production situations and market developments, and in terms of the cost of bringing such additional land into agricultural production.[3] But in terms of the over-all demand-and-supply situation, additional investments

---

[1] See *Farms for Veterans*, National Planning Association, Washington, D.C. (Prepared by Lowry Nelson, 1945.)

[2] For a careful analysis of land-settlement experiences see *Farming Opportunities Outlook, Problems, and Policies*, a preliminary report prepared by an Interbureau Committee of Post-war Agricultural Programs of the U.S. Department of Agriculture, Washington, D.C., December, 1944.

[3] An estimate of the irrigation projects being proposed for the ten plains states suggests 2,550 settlement opportunities from 1944 to 1950 and about 17,500 after 1950.

of this kind are in general probably not warranted. The early postwar period is likely to be misleading simply because food will continue to be unusually scarce and farm prices relatively high for a short time after the war effort in other fields is over. Should this sequence of events occur, it might exaggerate expectations of income from farming at a time when the labor force engaged in farming happens to be at a minimum. Popular support could then readily be obtained for measures to develop additional land for agricultural use and to encourage people to farm, despite the fact that low farm prices, cheap food, and farm surpluses are just around the corner.

Many war workers are likely to return to farms of their own accord, and so will many members of the armed forces who came from farms. The real task will be to keep this voluntary movement of people back to the land at a minimum, rather than to embark on land-settlement programs to induce returning soldiers to enter farming.

Farms for Veterans. Returning members of the armed forces who will want to farm can be grouped as follows:[1]

1. Veterans reared and experienced at farming who will return of their own accord either as farmers or as farm workers to farms of efficient size, and who will have the necessary capital from their own savings or by drawing upon family resources. This group of men will find their way into agriculture by their own effort and in their own right.

2. Veterans with farm background who want to become established on efficient-sized farms but who will not have access to a farm nor will they have sufficient resources to buy and equip one. The veterans in this group will know what they want, will have the competence and experience that is needed, but they will find it difficult, if not impossible, to enter farming without credit and other types of assistance.

[1] This section follows closely the recommendations of the Agriculture Committee of the National Planning Association in its policy statement in *Farms for Veterans*, 1945.

3. Veterans who entered the armed forces from farming areas that are depressed because of low earnings caused by the inefficient size and organization of the farms, who may wish to return to these farms despite the adverse situation. It is very important that every effort be made to keep the veterans in this group from commiting themselves to submarginal farming opportunities. They should be encouraged to seek a farm that is efficient in a type of agriculture that has promise, or they should enter some nonagricultural occupation.

4. Veterans with little or no farm experience, who nevertheless believe they would like to become farmers. They should be informed that agriculture has been overmanned and that in a developing economy it has been shrinking and will continue to shrink, relative to secondary and tertiary industries; that economic opportunities are, accordingly, more limited in agriculture than in many other fields; and that farming has come to require highly developed skills. Veterans in this group should be encouraged to take advantage of the educational provisions in the G.I. Bill to obtain some technical schooling in agriculture by attending an agricultural college. They should also seek first-hand experience at farming. With such training and experience they will be better equipped to appraise and reassess their desire to farm and also the opportunities that are likely to be available to them in American agriculture.

Low-production Farms

Also on the list of what not to do are programs to increase the number of so-called "subsistence farms." It is one thing to make room for more subsistence farms to provide relief for people when there is mass unemployment in industry, as was the case during most of the thirties; it is quite another matter to embark on a long-run program to facilitate more low-production, essentially self-contained farms in the United

States.[1] It might be contended that farm families have become altogether too vulnerable to the effects of business fluctuations and that we should look for arrangements that will make farmers less dependent upon markets, that is, more self-contained. This whole approach, which has strong support in some groups on cultural and sociological grounds, too often overlooks the very high price that self-containment exacts from farm families. Most of the social problems in agriculture associated with bad health, poor nutrition, inadequate housing, and substandard education are concentrated heavily in the farming areas that are most self-contained. These are our rural slums. It is the farms with the least cash income that present, in terms of social criteria, the most difficult and, in many respects, also the most significant problems in American agriculture. (In the South this problem is greatly complicated by the status of the Negro.)

A measure of farm poverty is that one-half of all individual farms in 1939 received $625 or less as the value of all farm products traded, sold, or used in the producing households.[2] Over one-fifth of our farms are already classified as "low-production family farms" (Table XIX). Here we have a measure of the extent of the self-containment that prevailed in agriculture just prior to the war. There are altogether too many farms in the United States at or near a subsistence level, farms essentially divorced from markets, with incomes too small to provide a level of consumption adequate to assure social efficiency. It is not unlikely that fully two-fifths of the farm families of the United States are too self-contained to afford and enjoy the good life consistent with the resources and values of our society. The argument against too great self-containment of farm people patently is not an argument against increasing the efficiency of workers engaged in farm-

[1] These observations are not applicable to industrial workers who supplement their incomes by part-time farming activities.

[2] Based on the 1940 Census. The basic data for this calculation are given in Table XXI, Chap. X.

TABLE XIX

CLASSIFICATION OF FARMS BY INCOME AND TYPE IN 1940, EXCLUSIVE OF SHARECROPPERS[1]

	1940	Per cent
I. FAMILY-TYPE FARMS		
1. Moderate- to high-production family farms		
Farms having a value of products at 1939 prices equivalent to at least $600 and less than $10,000. Farms dependent primarily upon family and operator for labor............................	3,125,000	56.3
2. Low-production family farms		
Farms, usually located in poor land areas, having value of products in terms of 1939 prices of less than $600, whose operators are under sixty-five years of age and who work off the farm less than 100 days.....................................	1,150,000	20.7
3. Part-time family farms		
Farms having a value of products at 1939 prices of less than $600, off-the-farm work by the operator amounting to 100 days or more..............	625,000	11.2
4. Residential family farms		
Farms, rural and suburban, used chiefly for residence, having a value of products at 1939 prices of less than $600, whose operators are 65 years and over, and work off the farm less than 100 days...	575,000	10.4
II. NONFAMILY FARMS		
5. Large nonfamily farms, including plantations		
Farms dependent mainly upon hired labor, tenants, and croppers. Farms having a value of products amounting to $10,000 or more at 1939 prices, and employing wage labor equivalent to 750 days; plantations in the South employing five or more croppers, share, standing, or cash tenants, or employing one cropper or tenant and sufficient wage hands to make a total equivalent of five or more croppers or tenants....................	80,000	1.4

[1] Adapted from U.S. Department of Agriculture Interbureau Committee Report, *Farming Opportunities, Outlook, Problems, and Policies*, December, 1944, p. 40. Figures are based on article by M. R. Benedict, F. F. Elliott, H. R. Tolley, and Conrad Taeuber, "The Need for a New Classification of Farms," *Journal of Farm Economics*, November, 1944, pp. 694–708.

This classification of farms is still far from satisfactory for purposes of analyzing the resources and income problems existing in American agriculture. To develop a more significant classification, it is necessary to define the family-type farm rigorously in terms of its labor requirements as a farm dependent upon the work of the farm family, including the operator. This would give a dichotomy with one group classified as family farms and the other as nonfamily farms. It would be necessary to subgroup the first of these, both according to productivity and according to purposes for which the farm is employed.

CUMULATIVE DISTRIBUTION OF TOTAL VALUE OF AGRICULTURAL PRODUCTS, UNITED STATES, 1939

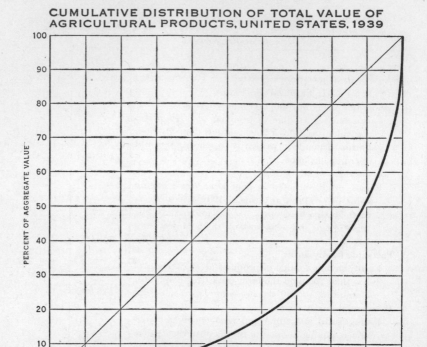

DATA FROM 1940 CENSUS OF AGRICULTURE

U. S. DEPARTMENT OF AGRICULTURE   BUREAU OF AGRICULTURAL ECONOMICS

ing. Ways and means must be found to increase the low earnings that are the principal cause for the poverty characterizing so much of agriculture. Accordingly, programs that improve the output and consumption of farm families through grants and aids, through extension of certain social benefits to farm people who are burdened by too much self-containment, are important. The main contribution of the FSA may prove to have been its work in this sphere. An orderly program to facilitate farm enlargements is in order when enough people have left agriculture. But the restrictions of the Tarver amendment, forcing the FSA to establish undersized farms in its farm-ownership program, are a move in the wrong direction.

Barriers to Migration

Another item on the list of things not to do is putting obstacles in the way of farm people who would prefer to take jobs in nonfarm employment. The movement of people from farms is at best difficult. The entry of workers into many fields is hedged by restrictions, some imposed by organized labor. Federal programs regulating the supply of farm labor during the war have added to the barriers to interstate migration dictated by the Pace amendment. The agricultural extension services of the several states were authorized by Congress to mobilize intrastate farm labor. These services did, in the main, a creditable job within the states, but the very decentralization of this wartime control has meant less development of interstate channels for the movement of agricultural workers.

Present social-security legislation also hinders the movement of people from one state to another. Barriers stemming from the race problem, intrenched in customs and traditions, play a decisive part in sections of the South in checking migration from farms. If race tensions become more acute because of the unemployment that will attend demobilization, great harm may be done in checking the movement, particularly of Negroes, out of agriculture in the South, thus damming up too much of the nation's labor force in the very farming areas now most seriously overpopulated. Lack of knowledge, poor health, and insufficient funds to change residence are in themselves major obstacles to migration. These are greatest in the farming areas where migration is needed most.

POSITIVE MEASURES TO REDUCE THE UNDER-EMPLOYMENT AND THE LOW EARNINGS IN AGRICULTURE

Of the action likely to make a positive contribution in reducing underemployment in agriculture, we place first and foremost the growth of business in the economy as a whole and its capacity to stay on keel. These should have first attention.

Growth of Secondary and Tertiary Industries

The expansion of nonagricultural industries (including service industries and government) will probably have to be at a rate about three times as rapid as that of agriculture to keep the underemployment in agriculture at such a level that farming is not chronically depressed. How much agricultural production is likely to expand during the first decade after the war cannot be stated with exactness. It will obviously depend on the level of farm prices, on the availability of farm machinery, equipment, fertilizer, and the like, on advances in farm technology, and on future land developments. The war has fully demonstrated that the potential increase is very large. Under peacetime conditions, with farm prices at 90 per cent of parity, an expansion of at least 10 per cent, and probably as high as 15 per cent, seems likely in the first decade after the war. A rate of expansion for agriculture of 15 per cent for the first decade[1] would mean that expansion in other industries of upward of 45 per cent during the period would go a long way toward absorbing agriculture's excess labor, and would be the most important single factor in bringing the earnings of workers in industry and in agriculture into a more comparable relationship than at any time during the last three decades.

[1] The U.S. Department of Agriculture index for volume of all agricultural products for sale and consumed in the farm home stood at 129 in 1943, with 1935–1939 equal to 100. This overstates production of a continuing character, because of the very large yields in recent years and the large reserve of corn and wheat that has been fed to livestock, pulling up the volume of livestock. It seems likely that more normal yields and no extra feed reserves will reduce the index several points. If, after this leveling off, agricultural production starts from an index of about 125 and an expansion of 15 per cent is attained during the first decade after the war, the index would have risen to about 144 ten years after the war. Again, it should be noted that this growth is based on the assumption of farm prices as high as 90 per cent of parity.

Farm people, therefore, have a major stake in policies affecting nonagricultural employment and production. They stand to gain much from fiscal-monetary measures and other programs that seek to lessen the fluctuations of business and to keep production at a general level sufficiently large to absorb all the available resources and advances in technology. When this objective is attained, the distribution of the labor force between agriculture and other occupations will improve greatly. This redistribution may not solve fully, certainly not in a decade, the low-income problem of farms that are essentially self-contained, but it would set the stage as no other development could for facilitating the correction of even this deeply rooted problem in agriculture. The cure would be slow, but the gain would be important; its importance cannot be exaggerated.

More Leisure on Farms

After the war farm people with improved incomes may be able to trade part of their excess labor supply for additional leisure. Between the wars, conditions in agriculture were such that it was difficult for most farm people to reduce the hours they worked in order to have more leisure.[1] Earnings were for the most part very low, and the declining value of farm property reduced the savings and equity of farm people. Most farmers were short of capital and were subject to much capital rationing.[2] Farmers worked hard and long. In such circumstances leisure was not as valuable as the additional expected earnings from the work.[3] For the most part, farm

[1] Some reduction in hours worked in the better farming areas did occur.

[2] By capital rationing we mean that although the rate of return from extra capital inputs on a farm is greater than the interest rate on capital, the farmer, largely because of the burden of economic uncertainty confronting him, either does not want to borrow the additional capital or could not obtain it if he tried.

[3] Two observations are called for: (*a*) On farms in one-crop farming areas and in areas where subsistence farming predominates, a lack of enough work during much of the year is one of the main causes for the low annual productivity of farm people. This problem is obviously quite separate from that of increasing leisure time for farmers, since it is underemployment due in part to technical

families were too close to the margin of insolvency to afford more leisure.

The contrast between agriculture and industry in attaining and adjusting to a shorter working schedule is worth notice. Organized labor has been in a strong position to acquire more leisure, often with little loss in weekly earnings. The farmer as an individual has been less favorably situated to reduce the amount of time he works and not experience some loss in income. The two sets of institutions, that created by organized labor and that controlling farm people, are both somewhat extreme in their results. In industry many laborers might prefer to work some additional time in order to have the added earnings instead of the free time that the shorter work week may make obligatory; in agriculture many farm families would undoubtedly prefer more leisure, but the loss in income appears to them too large under the competitive conditions prevailing in agriculture.

Postwar developments may bring more leisure for some farmers after the war. The reduced labor force in agriculture has occasioned a recombination of resources that has improved, relatively, the value productivity of many of the farm people who remain. Farm earnings as a whole have risen, but earnings per person have risen even more markedly. Savings have been high and in most sections debts have been reduced. If these gains are not dissipated in a postwar land boom, and if farm prices do not decline as a whole more than a fourth to a third from their ceiling levels, agricultural incomes will be high enough to induce many farm people to increase their leisure time. Moreover, the new farm machinery and equipment, adapted as it is to the requirements of a family-type farm, will be chiefly labor-saving in character. It will make

---

features of the crop and other institutional conditions. (*b*) If farmers producing livestock and livestock products (the section of agriculture with longest average workdays) were to reduce the number of hours worked by 10 or even 20 per cent, the total revenue of such farmers would probably not be reduced because of the nature of the demand for these farm products.

possible one of two things: (*a*) more leisure time for the farmer, or (*b*) enlargement in the size of the farm. There is wisdom in making explicit to farmers that a choice will be open to them. Each farmer should see that some of the time saved may be converted into leisure. Educational programs ought to focus on this choice so that farm families sense the full import of the decision they make.

Governmental Machinery for Equalizing Labor Supply

There is need to develop a national administrative service that will at least inform workers—not alone in agriculture but also in other occupations—of job opportunities. In many respects the labor market is one of our most imperfect markets. Farm workers are especially isolated; they lack knowledge of the type of jobs, working conditions, and earnings that may be available elsewhere.

The *National Agricultural Outlook* has been developed since 1923 into a most useful instrument for bringing economic information to farmers and to others interested in agriculture. Under a similar procedure, information about industrial job opportunities could usefully be provided by analyzing the supply-and-demand forces playing upon labor in various industries and in various localities. A *National Outlook* to serve all labor is long overdue. Such an information service should be supplemented by a national employment service assisting workers more directly and immediately from day to day, bringing them into contact with jobs. Grants and aids to cover some of the expenses of migrating are also needed, to facilitate the movement of workers out of the more overpopulated and distressed farming areas.

Public Investments in Farm People, Particularly in the Young

Among the important positive measures that will make for a better distribution of the nation's labor force over the years are certain investments in people, investments that enhance a person's productivity and add to his mobility. Education, medical services, nutrition, and housing all fall into this class. A strong case can be made for greatly enlarged public grants and aids to rural-farm communities and families for such investments. For the most part it is the better equipped young people in rural areas who leave for the cities. Rural-farm people bear a wholly disproportionate share of the cost of rearing and educating the children of this nation—cost reckoned in terms of food, clothing, shelter, medical attention, and education.

There are no convincing reasons why these necessary replacement costs of the population should be borne so largely by rural-farm people, as is now the case because rural-farm net reproduction rates are higher than urban-industrial. All these costs are borne by the family, except education, which falls, in most of the United States, largely upon the local school district. This means that the necessary cost inherent in maintaining the social efficiency of the individual—a cost that constantly rises in our society—is, as things now stand, borne primarily by the family and locality.

As a consequence, out of their low incomes, farm people now pay a very much larger than proportional share of the replacement cost entailed in bearing, rearing, and educating the next generation. Since people migrate from rural-farm communities in which they are reared to urban-industrial communities, it should be evident that both communities are affected by the character and level of investments made in people. Certainly the urban-industrial communities that receive, and in large measure depend upon, the influx of rural-farm-reared people are interested in adding individuals of good health, who have received a high level of education, and who have, among other things, a social horizon and understanding that make them adaptable to the new environment and thus valuable citizens. Certainly the nation has a vital interest in this matter. Investments of this type enhance very appreciably the economic productivity of the individual and, especially significant in a developing economy demanding considerable labor migration, they increase his mobility as a factor of production.[1]

The report of the committee on *Postwar Agricultural Policy* of the Association of Land-Grant Colleges and Universities stresses the significance of rural living conditions and social facilities. Emphasizing the fact that the youth from the farms help maintain the urban population, the report points out that the income of many farm families is simply too small to provide an adequate level of living. (It does not, however, relate the public investments, which it deems essential in this sphere, to migration—that is, to bringing about a better distribution of the labor force of the nation.) It urges that rural schools be given more support. To better the quality of teaching personnel, rural teachers' salaries must be raised very considerably and their living quarters improved. Schools in most rural areas will need better sanitary facilities, recreational equipment, and modern buildings, if well-trained teachers are to be attracted to this work in the future. "The major solution for the financial problems of rural schools," the report concludes, "is greater state and federal aid."[2]

The report does not stress sufficiently, however, that where vocational training is offered, it should prepare farm children as much for nonagricultural employment as for farming. The report makes evident the need for more doctors, dentists, and nurses to serve rural communities, as well as public facilities for medical diagnosis and care, with medical centers and with special ambulance service for rural areas. Inasmuch as only one-fourth of farm families at present have diets that meet nutritional standards,[3] the provision of school lunches and improvement of education in health and nutri-

[1] For somewhat more extended treatment of this point see Theodore W. Schultz, *Redirecting Farm Policy*, The Macmillan Company, New York, 1943, Section on "Family and Nation," pp. 68–71.

[2] *Postwar Agricultural Policy*, Report of the Committee on Postwar Agricultural Policy of the Association of Land-Grant Colleges and Universities, October, 1944, p. 51.

[3] *Ibid.*, p. 53.

tion is urged. Better houses are desirable, electrification is urgent, telephone services should be expanded, roads are essential, and better recreational facilities are long overdue. All these expenditures are important not only for improving the level of living on farms but also for increasing the mobility of people and thus enabling farm people to improve their lot.

X. POLICY TO LESSEN
THE INSTABILITY OF FARM INCOME

DESPITE its many ingredients, most of the farm problem boils down to issues affecting the level of farm income. Most farm people find themselves in the nation's lowest income brackets. In 1929 the income per person on farms, from farming, was $223, and the income of those not on farms was $870; in 1932 these figures were $74 and $442, respectively; in 1937 they were $197 and $671; and in the war year 1942 they climbed to $389 and $1,023.[1] Whole sections of agriculture have had chronically "depressed" incomes. Fully half the farm people of the United States are in the South, where incomes from farming are unbelievably small.[2] It is not meant to imply, however, that all farm people or that all parts of American agriculture have incomes far below

[1] It is not our contention that these dollar figures are strictly comparable, but their lack of comparability is insignificant when we consider the difference between the two sets of figures. In ascertaining the net income per person from farming, the Department of Agriculture takes the cash income from the marketings of farm products and adds the following: government payments, value of products consumed on the farms where they are produced (including those consumed by farm laborers and their families as well as by the operator's own household), and rent of farm dwelling (computed so as to include an allowance for maintenance and interest of farm dwellings, a proportionate share of taxes on farm real estate, and insurance on farm buildings). The expenses of agricultural production are then subtracted from this gross farm income and a correction is made for inventory differences. The resulting figure gives net income of farm operators from farming, to which are then added farm wages of farm laborers living on farms.

See *Agricultural Statistics, 1943*, U.S. Department of Agriculture, Washington, D.C., Table 496, p. 406.

[2] One should not infer from this generalization that all farm families in the South are necessarily poor. Many farming units are very large, some are exceedingly efficient, and some have benefited greatly from the "cheap" labor that has burdened this region.

the income level of people in other occupations. Most of the farm people in the corn belt, in the milksheds, and elsewhere have enjoyed high productivity and fairly high earnings, and these incomes are reflected in good homes, schools, and roads, and in a high standard of living. But the income level of fully one-half of our farm people is too low to permit them to have housing, medical service, education, and even diets that do not fall far below standards considered a minimum by most American people.[1]

The level of income per person in agriculture can be improved substantially by a better allocation and a fuller use of the nation's labor force. This has already been discussed.

Much has been said and written in this country about the desirability of the family farm as a social-economic goal. This much is fairly clear; a family-type farm—meaning a farm dependent primarily upon the operator and his family for its labor—on which the family can use its own labor force effectively by having at its disposal modern farm technology along with sufficient land and other capital resources to establish an efficient farming unit would go far in increasing the productivity and the level of income of the people engaged in farming. There are, however, many hurdles to this goal, widespread capital rationing in agriculture and the excess supply of labor being among them.

Variations in the distribution of income within agriculture, as in other parts of our economy, are wide and there is a growing public concern about both the extreme ends. Some farm programs of the prewar period, especially the income payments of the AAA and some of the commodity loans of the CCC, did not have the effect of pulling the two ends toward the wide middle but actually contributed to a further widen-

[1] Another facet of this problem, in fact, the reverse of the question, is seen if agriculture is evaluated as a potential market. Consumption in the farm sector of our economy has been much smaller than the number of people would seem to warrant: a fifth of our total population possessing about a tenth of the income. Since farmers spend a proportionately larger share of their income on durables, the market for current consumer goods and services is held in check all the more.

ing of the income range.[1] The AAA parity payments, for example, were somewhat regressive, in that farmers with large incomes received, relative to the size of their incomes, larger payments from the government than did farmers with small incomes.[2]

The distribution of income within agriculture in part reflects differences in efficiency along with differences in property incomes, inasmuch as some farmers have little or no capital while others have considerable capital earning income for them. In considerable part it tells of poor allocation of resources. Whole regions in agriculture do not have access to modern technology, again because of a capital shortage and because of the cheapness of labor.[3] When we turn to consumption and take stock of how people live, what kind of education they give their children, and the effect these factors will have upon the future population of the country, the wide range in the distribution of income becomes most significant. Most of the farm families in the lower half of the income hierarchy of agriculture cannot afford the kind of living that is conducive to high social efficiency.

The general low level of farm income is the backdrop against which policies concerned with the instability of farm income must be projected.

CAUSES FOR THE INSTABILITY OF FARM INCOME

It is not easy to ascertain just how unstable the income of individual farm families actually is. The total farm income of a country as large and varied as the United States, with several hundred types of farming areas, hides most of the

[1] The FSA program appears to have thrown its weight in the opposite direction.

[2] Any program that increases the price per unit of products sold by farmers is open to this objection.

[3] The critical need for additional capital in large sections of Southern agriculture was discussed briefly, as it affected Piedmont farms, in Chap. III, pp. 78–79. See also D. Gale Johnson, "Contribution of Price Policy to the Income and Resource Problem in Agriculture," *Journal of Farm Economics*, Vol. 26, November, 1944.

income instability of regions and certainly of individual farms. A major region often suffers a crop failure while other regions have better than average crops, so that the income disturbance caused by the crop failure is not reflected in the total farm income of the country. No year passes without many farmers experiencing unexpected losses and others being the recipients of windfalls, which compensate each other in the national scene but fail to reveal what happens to the individual farmer over the years.

The main causes for the instability of farm income can be classified into two general groups—those originating in changes in demand and those arising out of agricultural production.

Income Instability Inherent in Farm Production

Few farmers can control their output with the certainty that characterizes most industrial firms. The manager of a cement plant, given the inputs of raw material and labor, can calculate his output with a nicety impossible in agriculture.[1] Agricultural production is subject to many risks and uncertainties that are a major factor in the income instability of the individual farmer. Frost, drought, floods, hail, wind, storms, animal and plant diseases of many types, and a whole array of insects and pests—all conspire to play fast and loose with the production of a given farm. They determine to no small degree whether yields are large or small, whether flocks and herds increase or are decimated, whether livestock is stunted by disease or if it gains well while on feed. Over these vagaries of Nature the individual farmer has relatively little control. The fortunes and failures of many farmers are determined by these production uncertainties, even in the better situated and more prosperous farming areas.

---

[1] There are a few minor exceptions to this generalization—for instance, certain dairy farms where all the variable inputs are purchased and all the farmer actually does is to "manufacture" milk, producing none of the feed and engaging in no other enterprises.

Policy to Lessen the Instability of Farm Income

In any given year there might be hundreds of thousands of farms thus affected, some having their output cut to zero, yet because of large yields in other sections the aggregate agricultural production of a country as varied and as large as the United States will not be affected. The unprecedented droughts of 1934 only reduced total agricultural production from an index of 96 in 1933 to 93 in 1934.[1]

There is another compensatory factor at work concealing the changes within the national farm income. The more closely the elasticity of demand approaches unity, the more stable is total farm income, with price changes serving to absorb the deviation between large and small crops. (But where the demand recedes from unity, either in being elastic or inelastic, a differing volume of output gives rise to instability in farm income.)[2] But this does not make for stability in the income of individual farmers. Whole regions may find themselves without crops or livestock to sell. This was the experience of many thousands of farmers in the plains states during years in the thirties, but even as they faced an income crisis, the better crops in other areas, and, what is more, the higher prices that came as a result of the somewhat reduced output due to the crop failure in the plains states[3] contributed to a steadiness in national farm-income figures.

---

[1] This small change in the index of agricultural production from one year to another understates, however, the effect of a drought on production. During a drought year livestock numbers are reduced and feed reserves are consumed, with the result that the production effect of the drought is spread over more than one year.

[2] This is obviously an elementary proposition: an inelastic demand causes large crops to fetch small incomes, and an elastic demand results in small incomes from small crops.

[3] Four principal corn belt states (Ohio, Indiana, Illinois, and Iowa) produced, in 1928–1930, a yearly average of 1,640 million feed units; by 1938–1940 this yearly output had risen to 1,916 million feed units, an increase of 17 per cent. Meanwhile, the production of feed in four drought-ridden states (South Dakota, Nebraska, Kansas, and Missouri) dropped from 1,433 million to 950 million feed units, a decrease of 33 per cent.

Income Instability Having Its Origin in Fluctuations in Demand

That the instability in farm income has its origin chiefly in business fluctuations was argued in Chap. VI. The cyclical rise and fall of the demand for farm products associated with business fluctuations has become the dominant factor causing a precipitous rise and fall of farm income. The resulting uncertainty of income has been far greater in the farm sector than in the nonfarm sector of our economy. The cyclical movements since 1910 of the income of farm people from farming and the fluctuations in income received by people not on farms are shown in Table XX, below. (The record is given on a per capita basis to take cognizance of the secular decline of employment in agriculture and the growth of employment in nonagricultural occupations.)

TABLE XX

CYCLICAL MOVEMENTS IN PER CAPITA FARM AND NONFARM INCOME

Per capita net income of persons on farms[a]		Per capita net income of persons not on farms[b]	
Period	Percentage change from first to last year of period	Period	Percentage change from first to last year of period
1911–1919	+160	1911–1920	+ 88
1919–1921	− 62	1920–1922	− 18
1921–1929	+ 87	1922–1929	+ 22
1929–1932	− 67	1929–1933	− 52
1932–1937	+153	1933–1937	+ 59
1937–1938	− 19	1937–1938	− 7
1938–1943	+213	1938–1943	+101

[a] Includes net income of farm operators from farming and wages of farm workers that live on farms; excludes government payments.

[b] Includes net income from nonagricultural sources and net income from agriculture accruing to nonfarm people.

SOURCE: *Net Farm Income and Parity Report: 1943, and Summary for 1910–42*, U.S. Department of Agriculture, Bureau of Agricultural Economics, Washington, D.C., July, 1944, Table 6, p. 12.

These figures make one realize how much more violent the movement of the farm income has been, compared to the nonfarm income. In its simplest terms it has meant: when

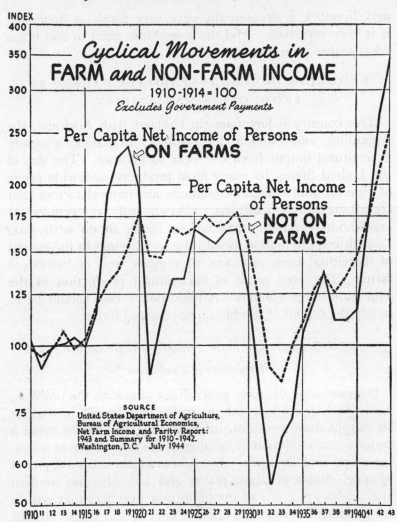

INDEX

Cyclical Movements in FARM and NON-FARM INCOME

1910-1914 = 100
Excludes Government Payments

Per Capita Net Income of Persons **ON FARMS**

Per Capita Net Income of Persons **NOT ON FARMS**

SOURCE
United States Department of Agriculture,
Bureau of Agricultural Economics,
Net Farm Income and Parity Report:
1943 and Summary for 1910-1942.
Washington, D.C.   July 1944

business became prosperous and boomed, farm income rose fully twice as fast as nonfarm income; when business slumped and became depressed, the income of farm people from farming fell more precipitously and decidedly further than the income of persons not on farms.   Between business fluctuations and wars, farm income derived from the sales of crops and livestock is occasionally very very good; as frequently it is very very bad. And the going from good to bad is not what makes farm life interesting.

REDUCING INCOME INSTABILITY CAUSED BY PRODUCTION VARIABILITY

This country is fortunate (in contrast with Australia, the Argentine, and Canada, for instance) in having a steady agricultural output from one year to another. The size of the United States, its many farm products, and wide range of climatic and cultural conditions are natural factors that contribute to this steadiness. Consequently, the problem of production variability has not so much to do with total agricultural production as with the wide swings in the output of individual farm products, or regions, and of individual farms. The even tenor of agricultural production in the aggregate is not enough. A basic policy goal should be to steady the output of products, regions, and farms.

Improvements in Farm Technology to Counteract
Fluctuations in Production

Here we have the most generalized attack on the problem. Better techniques will aid the individual farmer in making his output more constant, insofar as the techniques mean a better accommodation in farming to the natural forces affecting crops and livestock. Drought-resistant crops, dry-land farming, disease-resistant, plants and animals, and modern insecticides are a few of the important practices that reduce the incidence of weather, disease, insects, and pests. In the days when corn belt farmers were dependent upon horses for power, a season as wet as the spring of 1943 would have reduced the corn crop seriously. With tractor power, the field work was done on time and sufficiently well to produce, with favorable weather during the rest of the season, a bumper corn crop.

Advances in agricultural production control through farm technology come slowly. But we are moving ahead. A great part of the technical research of the state agricultural experiment stations and of the U.S. Department of Agriculture is directed to aspects of this production problem. There are, however, regions and areas where the climatic variations are beyond the limits of crop accommodations. Moreover, as farming areas become more specialized, plant and animal diseases and insects present new hazards to the individual farmer.

Crop Insurance for Areas of High Climatic Risk

Some form of crop insurance should be provided for farming areas dependent upon crops for most of their income and wherever, by nature of the area, yields fluctuate widely. Developing such an insurance program will not be easy. How to distinguish the fluctuations in yields caused by variations in weather from those stemming from bad management is no simple matter. But a first, though rough, approximation is possible and is already known for major crops in areas subject to these climatic hazards.

The main purpose of crop insurance should be twofold, namely:

1. To advance the interest of society by incorporating in the value of the land the risk and burden of the uncertainty inherent in the weather, which should be borne by the land and accordingly reflected in its value; and

2. To advance the interest of the individual farmer by minimizing the effects upon his income of year-to-year fluctuations in yields due to the weather.[1]

But the choice should not be between a crop-insurance program that attains the perfect goal or no crop insurance

[1] When the problem is thus formulated, the perfect solution would be a situation in which the value of each parcel of land measured and discounted accurately all the costs, over the long run, of all climatic hazards; and in which, at the same time, every farm family was able to order its affairs so that, in spite of erratic production, it would have a stable annual income.

program whatsoever. There has been too much stress on placing crop insurance on a wholly self-supporting basis, with "premiums" collected essentially equal to "benefits" paid plus cost of administration. This view that it is necessary to equalize cost and revenue at the outset is shortsighted. Data on yield fluctuations caused by weather are far from adequate, the long-run variations in weather are not known, and the task of administration will be complex. Much will have to be learned from trial and error. Any major progress made by a crop-insurance program in "embedding" the cost of climatic hazards into the parcel of land subject to the climate will be a real gain. Society has been called upon repeatedly to bear a much larger share of the cost through various farm-relief measures than it would have to bear in a crop-insurance program that did not entirely pay its own way.

Storage of Grain to Put Livestock on a More Stable Basis

Where crops are not sold for cash but are fed and thus converted into livestock and livestock products, the fluctuations in crop yields translate themselves into fluctuations in livestock production—unless the extra grain in years of better than average crops is carried forward and used as feed in years when crops are below average. Storage of feed on private account provides a solution to this problem, but it has been little used because many farmers do not have either sufficient capital to engage in such operations, or the experience and foresight to gauge crop variations.

Storage of feed grains (including wheat for feed) on public account is one of the more promising governmental techniques for bringing much-needed stability to the several hundred thousand farmers in areas where feed production fluctuates considerably from one year to another.[1] Most farming areas in the plains states have advantages in storage operations.

---

[1] Here, again, one must take cognizance of the limitations of public administration, caused by the existing state of political "irresponsibility" of pressure groups.

The cost of storage is usually low because feed grains (including wheat) keep well in the drier climate, and when it is necessary to move the feed, its movement is consistent with transportation cost-gradients. Storage is dealt with further under agricultural production adjustment in the next chapter.

DIMINISHING INCOME INSTABILITY CAUSED BY FLUCTUATION IN DEMAND

The problem here affects not only farmers but other producers, except that as the aggregate demand expands or contracts, the resulting rise or fall of the income from farming is greater than that of nonfarm income.

First Line of Defense: Stabilize the Industrial-urban Economy at High Production and Employment

If the total of nonagricultural production were to become as full and as regular as the over-all agricultural production has been, most of the instability in farm income associated with business fluctuations would be eliminated. How to achieve this goal falls outside the province of this inquiry. That does not imply that it is not an immediate concern of agriculture; farm people have an extraordinary stake in the performance of the rest of the economy—a point of view, based on fundamental economic interrelationships, to which this study has been devoted. But, patently, action in this direction cannot be taken by farmers or by those specifically responsible for the farm sector of the economy. The initiative lies elsewhere.

There is a growing consensus among economists that fiscal-monetary measures are the appropriate remedy for what we have referred to throughout this chapter as business fluctuations. Fiscal-monetary measures, broadly defined, are the actions of the government entailed in the issue and retirement of money, the spending as well as the raising of money, through taxation and public expenditures and through public borrowings and repayments, including government loans to individuals and corporations. Fiscal-monetary measures have this outstanding advantage: they are a means of attaining essential stability at a high level of employment and production within the framework of an enterprise economy. A system of compensatory payments to farmers, as herein proposed, should be viewed as a second-line defense, necessary to safeguard agriculture until we have developed a monetary-fiscal policy that is successful in maintaining our economy on keel with resources, labor, and land fully employed. Thus, until we have established a fiscal-monetary authority with the necessary power to remedy the disease of business fluctuations, a system of compensatory payments to farmers is a counter-cycle measure which, although restricted to the agricultural sector and thus certainly not comprehensive in scope, has the significant feature of not making a depression worse. It is likely, moreover, to open the way for agriculture to put aside its attempts to control production and support farm prices as alternative means for reducing the instability of farm income—a step to which farmers must be won if we are to move toward more desirable agricultural policies.

Second Line of Defense: Compensatory Payments to Farmers When Business Becomes Depressed and Unemployment Spreads

The prospect is that American farmers will find themselves, for a long time, confronted periodically by a drastic curtailment in the demand for farm products, even if our industrial-urban economy sets out at once to avoid or check business fluctuations. That accomplishment is no small affair, and it will unquestionably take time. Meanwhile, what is agriculture to do—sit tight and wait? Such advice will fall on deaf ears, even if it has merit, which is doubtful. Farm organizations are not likely to stand by, even if their leaders so choose, with farm income as sensitive to business fluctuations as appears to be the case. What measures can be taken that will moderate the impact of business fluctuations on agriculture and yet not make a general solution more difficult? Better still, is there any measure that will contribute toward counteracting business fluctuations?

To attempt to synchronize agricultural and industrial production, shrinking farm output when industrial demand falls and expanding farm output when business booms, is a policy that has little to recommend it—were it possible. Farming does not, in fact, permit rapid curtailment or even unduly rapid expansion, and consumers, certainly, prefer a stable and steady food supply regardless of the fortunes of business. What we want to achieve in the economy as a whole is precisely what we would destroy in agriculture were we to try making agricultural production a variable to synchronize it with demand. The steadiness of agricultural production must be seen as a significant national asset.

Efforts to vary agricultural production cyclically would at best only equalize the incidence of a depression between farming and industry. Farm income would still rise and fall with business fluctuations. Such a policy would in no wise be counter-cyclical in its effects.

To stabilize farm income by a system of price supports, or to endeavor to do so, interferes with internal and external trade and disregards the basic function of relative prices in guiding production and in directing products into consumption channels. Nevertheless, Federal statutes now in effect give it important weight, and it may easily come to dominate Federal farm programs during the early postwar period.

SYSTEM OF COMPENSATORY PAYMENTS

It is therefore here proposed that the government undertake a system of compensatory payments[1] to farmers that will accomplish the following:

[1] First presented in "Two Conditions Necessary for Economic Progress in Agriculture," *Canadian Journal of Economics and Political Science*, Vol. X, No. 3 (1944), by Theodore W. Schultz.

1. Reduce the instability of farm income caused by business fluctuations,[1]

2. Do this in a manner and at a time that will make the payments counter cyclical in their effect,

3. Make the payments to farmers in a way that will not disturb either agricultural production or the trade of farm products,

4. Stabilize farm income sufficiently by means of these payments to remove the incentive that has arisen in agriculture for alternative measures, such as controlling agricultural production and supporting farm prices, to offset the impact of business fluctuations on farm income.

There are two requisites to the use of compensatory payments, if they are to accomplish these primary purposes. They must be undertaken by the government only in the event of a business depression—if they are to be counter cyclical; and they must be so paid that they do not cause a disturbance in the trade and production of farm products.

Requisite 1: Counter Cycle

The requirement that compensatory payments be undertaken only during a business depression rests on two basic

[1] It should be obvious that this proposal is not advanced as a scheme to correct the instability of business or as a complete program for dealing with the adverse effects of business fluctuations on agriculture. However, compensatory payments to farmers as outlined in this section should be given a high priority among the depression measures taken in behalf of agriculture. They would reduce greatly the "income hazard" for that part of American agriculture that is largely dependent on the exchange system for its income through the sale of crops and livestock. They do not, however, bring equivalent benefits to that part of agriculture which is not largely dependent upon markets. Farm families in this less commercial group are affected adversely by the backing up of industrially unemployed into agriculture. Precisely this group has in the past been the main "shock absorber" as the rise and fall of the demand for industrial labor impinged upon agriculture. Accordingly, compensatory payments may be viewed as necessary but not sufficient. What is required is an extension of the benefits of social security to farm people, and federal grants for education, medical service, nutrition, housing, and for family allowance to aid especially low-income farm families who otherwise cannot afford this security and these services for themselves and their children.

ideas, namely, that business depressions are the main cause for the periodic drop in the general level of prices of farm products and in the income from farming, and that the maintenance of farm income is important, not only to check the deflation associated with a business depression, but to bring about recovery.

Plainly, this demands some way of ascertaining with reasonable accuracy when a depression is at hand and when it is over. Basically, what is needed is a measure of events affecting economic expectations in the urban industrial community. There are no indexes of this type at present. The next best thing is to measure changes in production and employment in secondary and tertiary industries. Whatever indicator is used should not include agricultural production, prices, or income. A sharp line of demarcation must be drawn between agricultural and other industries if a sound base for making compensatory payments to farmers is to be established.

If compensatory payments to farmers are to be strictly counter cyclical and related to business depressions, the level of unemployment might also be used as an automatic indicator of the need for such payments. For example, whenever unemployment exceeded 5 per cent of the total labor force, a depression would be deemed to exist. Unemployment records now available are, unfortunately, far from satisfactory for ascertaining the presence of a depression. Several alternative indicators easier to watch and perhaps more sensitive to business fluctuations are available. Changes in income payments to nonfarm people have much to recommend them. Factory pay rolls are better in one important respect, that they appear quick to reflect conditions in industry generally. Industrial production is another useful indicator. It may well be that a combination of these, always making allowance for secular developments, may prove best in devising an index of the performance of the urban-industrial sector of the economy for purposes of determining when compensatory payments should be made and when they should stop. One condition, however, must be met no matter what indicator is employed: The indicator should measure the state of economic activity of the nonagricultural sectors of the economy and not of agriculture itself. In no circumstances should compensatory payments to farmers intended to lessen the vulnerability of agriculture to business fluctuations be determined in accordance with parity prices based on a historical formula of the 1910–1914 type. To do so would be to destroy the counter-cyclical features of the income payments.

This attempt to earmark the characteristics of an approaching business depression and its departure also points to the need to distinguish between compensatory payments made to farmers and other income payments made to them. Income payments may be used for differing purposes: They may be employed as: (*a*) *Adjustment Payments* to aid a depressed sector of agriculture in making a difficult adjustment, affecting markedly the production, employment, and income of the area, such as now confronts the cotton South (the U.S. Department of Agriculture in its *Conversion Program for the Cotton South* recommends income assistance to farm families who enter the program planned to facilitate the conversion); (*b*) *Transition Payments* to discharge the government's commitment to support farm prices for two years after the war, by letting market prices channel farm products into trade and paying farmers the difference between the market price and the support-price commitment (this would afford an orderly way of making the transition from the war to the postwar demand-and-supply situation and at the same time carry out the obligations assumed by the government during the war in order to induce a very high level of agricultural production); (*c*) *Conservation Payments* to induce farmers to undertake farm practices and techniques that will contribute to the conservation of soil resources (policies appropriate to this end are set forth in Chap. XI); and (*d*) *Welfare Payments* to enhance the social efficiency of farm people, income payments intended to serve welfare criteria.

None of these income payments would necessarily be counter cyclical in their effects. Nor would they necessarily lessen the instability in income from farming caused by business fluctuations. They are, in fact, intended to serve other purposes. It is, therefore, very important not to confuse compensatory payments as here formulated with other types of income payments in agriculture. It is necessary to hold in mind the basic purpose of compensatory payments, which is first and foremost to counter the effects of business fluctuations upon income from farming.

Requisite 2: Nondisturbance of Trade and Production in Agriculture

If the introduction and withdrawal of compensatory payments are not to entail new disturbances in agriculture, they must be essentially neutral in their effect upon agricultural production and upon internal and external trade of farm products. In principle this requirement is met by making compensatory payments equal to the difference between the market price at the time a farmer sells his product and the predepression price, or such proportion of the latter as public policy deems appropriate. Putting aside for a moment the question of determining at what proportion of the predepression price compensatory payments should be inaugurated, the implications of this requisite deserve further elaboration. First, should compensatory payments be restricted to a few products, possibly to the "basic" crops? Should livestock products be included? What about fresh fruits and vegetables? Compensatory payments will fall short of their mark unless all farm products are included. There is no basis for exclusion. On the contrary, to the extent that some farm products are excluded it is very likely that disturbances in production will result since farmers would find it to their advantage to shift toward products covered by compensatory payments. Such shifts would give rise to malallocations of resources; some channels of trade would become overloaded with products while others would be in short supply.

A second question arises: Should the rate of the compensatory payment for each farm product be figured from its own predepression price or from some general index of prices received by farmers for all crops and livestock? The merit of the general index is its simplicity of administration; its use as a base would undoubtedly lessen appreciably the instability in income from farming. The shortcomings of a general index arise out of the fact that various farm-product prices do not fall or rise at the same rate as a consequence of business fluctuations. These differences in price behavior are sufficiently great to make it desirable to establish for each product its own predepression base. Otherwise, the compensatory payments during a depression would distort the effective relative prices in agriculture and, in addition, the income assurance from compensatory payments would differ widely from one sector of agriculture to another.

Ascertaining the predepression price for each farm product presents some difficult technical questions, although the data and some experience are at hand. The guiding principle is plain: The predepression price is that price for each farm product that reflects accurately both supply and demand conditions (just prior to the depression) when the economy was operating at high production and full employment. Allowances, of course, would have to be made for grades, quality, location, and the seasonality of many farm products. Based upon a set of predepression prices, the structure of relative prices within agriculture would not be distorted by the depression payments. On the contrary, this procedure would carry forward in effect the same relative prices until the depression was over. Accordingly, unlike a fixed historical base such as is specified in the parity formula, each depression would provide its own "historical base" since the structure of relative prices in agriculture prevailing at the time the depression occurred would govern throughout that depression. By the time the next depression occurred, all of the forces shaping the supply and the demand for farm products would have had their play in establishing a new set of relative prices for agriculture and presumably under conditions of high production and full employment.

Rate of Compensatory Payments

What proportion of the predepression price of a farm product should be covered by compensatory payments? This is a policy question for which there is no clear-cut, single answer; for, as is usual in policy, more than one purpose must be served.

Should the government make up all or a large or a small part of the difference between the predepression and the market price? The upper limit of a compensatory payment on any product at any time is, of course, determined by the size of the gap separating the predepression price and the market price. It obviously follows that the farther our farm prices fall during a depression, the wider the gap. During the mild decline in business that followed 1937, the index of farm prices receded 22 per cent; but from 1929 to 1932 it had dropped 54 per cent. The inference is plain. The better the performance of the urban-industrial sector of the economy, the narrower the gap between the market price of farm products during a depression and the predepression price.

But as long as we are afflicted with business fluctuations, whether mild or severe, the question does arise—how much of the difference between the predepression price and the market price should the government cover in compensatory payments? An answer may be sought along several lines. One procedure is to take past experience and improve upon it. In 1932 the per capita net income of persons on farms from farming was only one-third as large as it was in 1929. To have kept income even at one-half of the predepression level would certainly have been an improvement upon what actually occurred. Another approach is in terms of fiscal-monetary considerations, giving primary weight to checking a deflation through keeping the aggregate demand from being destroyed. This goal would stress the desirability of compensatory payments sufficiently large to cover all of the difference between the predepression price and the market price. Other values and purposes point to some middle ground. Equity requires that the people in each sector of the economy should bear their just share of the burden and that none should be wholly exempt. As matters now stand, agriculture has borne all too large a share of the burden of depression, but it is not fair to attempt the other extreme either. Still another consideration that should be given weight is the need for a margin of safety for the government in operating a system of compensatory payments, so that it is less likely to find itself overvaluing products during a business depression, because of changes in noncyclical factors. There is also the political factor. It is quite clear that farm people will not accept politically a policy that would do nothing about farm incomes until they had plunged to about the depths of 1932. On the other hand, they do not expect to achieve full-income assurance during a business depression. Farm organizations, their leaders, and the farm people they represent are willing to accept less than full coverage.

We have, therefore, a number of values, purposes, and considerations that bear upon the policy decision at hand, but it is plain that they are not additive. They are a mixture of forces and counterforces that public policy alone can reconcile. The general weight of the several views and values appears to fall somewhere within a range expressed in terms of 75 per cent and 95 per cent of the predepression price. A point midway in this range, namely, 85 per cent of the predepression price, has much to recommend it.

As an illustration, suppose the predepression price of hogs were $10 and compensatory payments were set at 85 per cent. If the price of hogs dropped to less than $8.50 the government would make a payment to farmers equal to the difference between $8.50 and the market price. To relate this to the concept of a depression defined in terms of unemployment, suppose that the labor force is 60 million persons and that five per cent or 3 million are unemployed. At that juncture, (by our definition) a depression would be deemed to exist. If hog prices, adjusted for seasonality, were $10 at that time, the $10 figure would be declared the predepression price for hogs. With compensatory payments set at 85 per cent of the predepression prices, should hog prices drop below $8.50, as we indicated above, payments equal to the difference between that figure and the market price would be made. Compensatory payments in this case would be discontinued either when unemployment declined to less than 3 million (even though the market price of hogs remained below $8.50) or when the market price reached or exceeded $8.50, regardless of the amount of unemployment.

Here we have introduced a modifying principle which can be stated thus: Compensatory payments should be discontinued *either* when the depression is over *or* when the market price of the farm product equals or exceeds the established percentage of the predepression price on which compensatory payments are based.

Advantages in Compensatory Payments

What are the advantages of a system of compensatory payments to farmers compared with alternative measures to correct the instability of farm income caused by business fluctuations—such as acreage allotments to control agricultural production, or support prices for farm products?

1. Compensatory payments of the type proposed would definitely be counter cyclical in their effect, which is not necessarily true of the alternative measures listed. Compensatory payments would mean governmental expenditures only during a depression, the amount increasing as the depression deepened, namely, as the aggregate demand declined and farm prices fell.

2. Compensatory payments would leave market prices free to clear whatever supplies are marketed. They would not (as do support prices) interfere with either internal or external trade. This advantage of compensatory payments can hardly be overemphasized in view of the growing inconsistency between American agricultural policy and American trade policy, and the likelihood that after the war the program of price supports now authorized by federal legislation will further reduce the sales of American farm products.[1]

3. Compensatory payments would not disturb agricultural production. They would keep the effective relative prices of farm products (market price plus the compensatory payment) from becoming distorted as a result of a business depression. They would offer no inducements to farmers to curtail or shift production when business output recedes and the aggregate demand for farm products drops. On the contrary, the payments may bring about a slight increase in output of some farm products during a depression. To the extent that this occurs it is an advantage in the short run, in that more resources are put into employment than would otherwise be the case; it is a disadvantage in the long run if the effect is to induce more unemployed industrial workers to return to farms than would have done so without such payments. In any case, the production effort in agriculture would be maintained, in contrast to measures designed to curtail agricultural production in the event of a depression.

4. Compensatory payments would permit the prices of farm products, and accordingly the price of food, to decline during a depression. A program of support prices presumably would not allow this decline, nor would production control, if the control were effective.[2] Business and labor

---

[1] The drift of present policy is strongly in the direction of pricing many important farm products out of the market, an exceedingly shortsighted policy, to say the least.

[2] Several attitudes are current with regard to food policy in the pricing of farm products during a depression:

1. *Food disposalists* would for the most part support farm prices (not neces-

may be inclined to the view that a system of compensatory payments would give those farmers who sell crops and livestock a protection from the adverse effects of depression out of proportion to the protection now enjoyed by any other group. While there is some validity in this view, it should not be overlooked that both business and labor stand to gain markedly from the cheaper food prices during depression[1] (compared to what would occur if agriculture were to reduce its output or if market prices of farm products were maintained at some predepression level).

5. Compensatory payments would benefit business and labor insofar as the payments maintained the demand of farm people for industrial and other products during a depression.

---

sarily involving any production control, however) and use food-disposal programs of various types to move that part of the supply that could not be sold through trade channels at the support-price levels. The disposal programs would seek to improve diets.

2. *Nutritionists* would base public food programs strictly on nutritional requirements of the population, regardless of business fluctuations or farm surpluses.

3. *Price-minded agriculturalists* would let the mechanism of relative prices carry the main burden of disposing of farm products, whether the supply is small or large and regardless of business fluctuations.

Each of these views has limitations, but their relative merits may be noted. The nutritionists, in my judgment, present a strong case against the tendency of making food policy serve (a) to keep farm prices steady, (b) to dispose of particular agricultural surpluses by means of school lunches, in-plant feeding, food-stamp plans, and similar programs, and (c) to counteract the adverse effects of business fluctuations on farm incomes. The food disposalists are on weak ground with this exception: even if food prices are sufficiently low during a depression to move food supplies into consumption channels, they may still be high enough to restrict the diets of some segments of the population, which should then be protected by special food programs. Nutrition goals, however, should prevail over the years regardless of business fluctuations; likewise, relative prices should be free to channel food supplies to consumers regardless of business fluctuations; these two objectives, thus stated, are essentially complementary. They afford certain necessary conditions, but they are not likely to be sufficient.

[1] If these payments should induce farmers to expand production somewhat during a depression, to that extent they would contribute to lower prices. There is also the possibility that farmers may withhold less produce than they otherwise would during some stage of a depression, and this, too, would make food somewhat cheaper during that phase of the depression.

The gain here would come chiefly in the purchases of durables: constructing buildings, putting in permanent fences, improving watering systems, installing electric power, retooling with modern farm machinery and equipment, replacing obsolete trucks and automobiles, and obtaining for the home the many semi-durables that are becoming a part of the standard of living of farms.[1]

Difficulties in Compensatory Payments

First, they would tend to maintain within agriculture the relative prices that happened to prevail during the pre-depression period. The incentives to produce a particular product would be the market price plus the compensatory payment. Insofar as they relate to the allocation of resources, the relative prices at the beginning of a depression would become less applicable during a long depression to the extent that major forces playing on cost and utility alter the over-all picture of supply and demand. On the other hand, it needs to be recognized that it is the nature of a depression to breed distortions and economic maladjustments, and that for the most part compensatory payments would spare agriculture more serious dislocations (for example, the depletion of soil resources in order to stay solvent, postponement of the purchases of necessary durables, the curtailment of investments in education, etc.). Each new depression would in any event bring its own predepression base. The system of compensatory payments recommended would not freeze the relative prices within agriculture to something historic, such as the

[1] In this study, as already indicated, no attempt has been made to analyze the effects of agriculture on the business economy, although farm people represent a major market for American business. The farm market, relative to the income received by farm people, is weighted heavily toward semi-durables and durables, compared to the markets provided by other major segments of the population. The importance of stabilizing the expenditures by farmers for these durables in order to lessen business fluctuations is an interrelationship that has received scant attention. It deserves careful examination in any analysis of business fluctuations.

1910–1914 base employed in the parity price formula. Automatically, a new base would be established for each depression.

Administering a system of compensatory price payments offers a second difficulty. In the early postwar period, farm prices will be badly out of line with other prices. A year's, or even two years', production will be required to meet relief needs and to build normal carry-overs. The transitional adjustments necessary to make both industrial and agricultural production consistent with postwar requirements will take considerable time. Until this occurs it may be premature, or at least it will be exceedingly difficult, to ascertain and isolate business (or cyclical) fluctuations from structural adjustments necessary in going from a war to a peace economy.

Then there is always the question whether in our democratic form of government such a proposal can be put to good account. Will not pressure groups use compensatory payments to raid the public treasury? There is no "yes" or "no" answer to such a question. The best that one can do is to compare the policy with alternatives. Are appropriations for AAA payments, for price supports, and for subsidizing farm products for export and domestic uses less vulnerable on this score? Probably not. Are the governing principles more or less exacting than those laid down for alternative measures? On this count we have shown that the proposal has net advantages.

What about the many farm families who do not produce farm products primarily for sale and thus would not receive compensatory payments for falling prices, since they do not enter the market? In the 1940 census nearly a third of all farmers cited household use of their own products as the major source of income. The bulk (about 90 per cent) of the farm products sold by farmers are produced by about half our farms; the rest are only loosely connected to the markets and prices of farm products. The pattern of distribution of benefits of compensatory payments would be determined by the per cent of its output sold or traded by the farm. (Table XXI gives some indication how compensatory payments would have been distributed if a business depression had occurred in 1940.)

The plain fact is that price policy and compensatory payments related to prices can be of no material aid to fully half the families in agriculture, families who produce relatively little for sale and who, with few exceptions, receive exceedingly low incomes. Although business fluctuations do not affect the well-being of the less commercial farmers so immediately and directly as they do farmers who produce chiefly for sale, the fact remains that compensatory payments do not bring either short-run or long-run assistance to the bulk

TABLE XXI

CLASSIFICATION OF FARMS BY YEARLY VALUE OF PRODUCT, BY FARM PRODUCTS SOLD, TRADED, OR USED FOR HOUSEHOLD, AND BY FARM PRODUCTS SOLD AND TRADED, IN 1939

Yearly product value, per farm[a]	*Per cent of all farms (classified farms)*	*Per cent of total value of all farm products sold, traded, or used for household, by farms*	*Per cent of total value of all farm products sold and traded, by farms*
$ 1– 99	5.4	0.2	0.08
100– 249	13.3	1.8	0.85
250– 399	13.5	3.4	2.03
400– 599	14.3	5.5	3.95
600– 749	7.9	4.1	3.32
750– 999	9.4	6.4	5.55
1,000–1,499	11.6	11.1	10.54
1,500–1,999	6.8	9.2	9.24
2,000–2,499	4.3	7.5	7.81
2,500–3,999	6.2	15.0	16.02
4,000–5,999	2.7	10.2	11.23
6,000–9,999	1.5	8.5	9.60
10,000 and over	1.0	17.2	19.78
	97.9	100.1	100.00

[a] 1940 Census Classification includes farm products sold, traded, or used by farm households.

SOURCES: *Sixteenth Census of the United States, 1940, Agriculture*, Vol. III, General Report, pp. 979, 992, 1005. *Analysis of Specified Farm Characteristics for Farms Classified by Total Value of Product*, U.S. Department of Commerce and U.S. Department of Agriculture, Cooperative Study, Washington. D.C., 1943, p. 30.

of the low-income farm families. Other measures are required in the less commercial sector of agriculture. One of these is an expanding economy maintaining full employment. The pent-up underemployment in agriculture presses heavily on the farm families with the lowest incomes. Another measure called for is the extension of social security to farm people and, beyond that, the protection of the youth of the nation by a system of family allowances.

XI. TOWARD POLICY IN PRODUCTION ADJUSTMENTS

THE keystone of agricultural policy in the later interwar years was the "adjustment" of agricultural production. Adjusting agricultural production is, however, a big umbrella. Many things were done in the name of agricultural adjustment. The following is a rough classification of the main purposes of these measures:

1. To curtail production of specific farm products, adjusting output to the decline in demand in export markets and to the drop in domestic industrial production and employment.

2. To conserve the productivity of the soil.

3. To prevent the accumulation of further stocks when the holdings of the CCC became excessively large.

4. To induce shifts among crops, expanding those with better demand prospects and curtailing those with a less favorable outlook.

5. To encourage better farming practices.

This listing does not, in fact, exhaust the aims featured by those who pursued "agricultural adjustment."

Adjusting agricultural production has indeed become a kind of catchall. Much of what was done was simply farm relief—relief from the disastrous decline in farm prices in the early thirties, from the droughts of 1934 and 1936, and from other emergencies. The farm-relief features of agricultural adjustment, important as they have been, are not considered here.[1] The long-run production adjustments needed in a developing economy have, for the most part, been covered in the preceding section. To keep in balance the allocation of

[1] We have already indicated why a comprehensive treatment of relief and social security for agriculture will not be undertaken in this study.

resources between agriculture and other industries requires, as we have repeated, a constant movement of labor resources out of agriculture and (an aspect that is stressed less) a movement of more capital into agriculture; that is, the use of more machinery, equipment, fertilizer, livestock, carry-overs of feed, and capital to build up land resources. Except for some Federal expenditures in behalf of soil conservation, agricultural-adjustment programs developed during the thirties were not directed toward this long-run problem of allocative efficiency. The curtailment activities of the AAA did displace a large number of farm workers, chiefly in cotton, but this was both inadvertent and unfortunate. Agricultural adjustment, in practice, has attempted to deal mostly with short-run problems and, for the most part, with problems that have their origin, so it was assumed, within agriculture.

PURPOSES TO WHICH AGRICULTURAL PRODUCTION ADJUSTMENTS ARE INAPPROPRIATE

In formulating policy for agricultural production adjustment, let us begin by pointing out some of the purposes to which it is not suited.

Adjusting Agricultural Production to Business Fluctuations

Should agricultural production be adjusted upward and downward so that it synchronizes more closely with business booms and depressions? In our judgment the answer to this question must be in the negative, though a negative answer may seem to contribute nothing to what is one of the basic unsettled issues in policy, namely, what to do to protect farm people, in some measure, from the adverse effects that mass unemployment and a low level of industrial production have on farm prices.

The goal should be to improve the performance of the nonagricultural sectors, and it should not entail a retreat on the agricultural side. We are not warranted in assuming that the past behavior of business is normal, or that it cannot be corrected. A policy of restricted agricultural output during a depression might bring a small measure of relief to farm people, but it would in all probability worsen the over-all situation of the economy. The steadiness of agricultural production is an asset in the development and attainment of the larger goal of full employment and high production. Compensatory payments and the extension of the benefits of social security to farm people (including unemployment insurance for hired farm laborers) are available for lessening the burden of the wide fluctuations of farm prices, and, in our judgment, they have much to recommend them over adjustments in agricultural production. These alternatives should be employed until such time as the business economy reaches a stage in its development where it too will stay at its job at high production year after year.[1]

Adjusting Production When Farm Products Fail to Move into Export Channels

This is one of the reasons frequently advanced for production control, particularly for cotton and tobacco and only to a lesser extent for wheat, corn, and rice. Export markets accepted a much smaller volume of American farm products from 1930 to 1940 than they did before the depression, but to assume that these markets are permanently reduced ignores the relationship of prices to trade. With CCC loans tied to a 1910–1914 parity formula, such products as cotton and wheat have been substantially overvalued. The loan rates have become the effective prices because they have been higher than the market prices (both international and domestic) would otherwise have been. The consequence has been limited buying from the United States and encouragement to other countries to expand their production. Meanwhile, the

[1] This argument should not be construed as a tacit approval of letting agriculture continue to act as a depression "shock absorber" for the industrial sector of the economy—a place to which unemployed people can return and somehow live, largely at the expense of farm people, until the depression is over.

United States, to prevent further stocks of these products from accumulating, has tried to curtail output. Cotton has been a noble experiment in this wise. Formerly half the cotton crops entered export channels; yet American cotton is now divorced from the structure of world prices by the loan rates. If the loan rates are maintained at the levels now prevailing, they may put this country into the curious position of importing cotton for domestic use.[1]

This experience of *adjusting* and *pricing* ourselves out of the markets that still stand ready to buy American cotton, wheat, and rice points to the inadvisability of using acreage allotments of the AAA type to shrink domestic output when the foreign demand drops. The loss of markets abroad is serious, but these methods are not the best ways of adapting our economy to the loss.

Adjusting Production to Offset an Assumed Liability in a Large Agricultural Output

It is easy to become "overproduction"-minded, to take the view that low prices are unnecessary, and to approach both production and prices in terms of the short-run interest of producers. There has been altogether too much of this procedure in our economy. Industry has directly translated this thinking into restrictionist production and price policies, while farmers have turned to government and have used public means to restrict output and maintain prices. Both industrialists and farmers have been given much-needed perspective on this point by the war economy, and have learned what can be effected by expansion. The primary importance of high production, of expansion as more resources become available, and of full use of all resources has impressed itself on the minds of all groups.

Many farmers have been uneasy about curtailing output, but this uneasiness has been based not so much on economic

[1] Unless a two-price market is established along with a tariff on cotton to keep the cotton from reentering.

or political principle as on moral convictions. We are concerned, however, with the economic consequences of large-volume agricultural production. Is it a liability to the national economy as a whole? The answer depends upon the governing conditions.

a. When the large output is the result of too many resources in agriculture—measured in terms of their marginal productivity—then part of the large output represents a loss, in the sense that some of the resources used in agriculture would produce more in other fields. This is a main element in the underemployment in agriculture that confronts the United States or any like country as its economy develops. Programs to curtail agricultural production have not, however, been directed to this basic maladjustment.

b. When the large agricultural output comes during, and partly as a consequence of, a business depression (that is, results in part from greater effort by farmers to stay solvent in the face of falling farm prices, and in part from the return of unemployed industrial workers to farms), it may be a gain to the national economy to have agriculture stay on the job, keeping employed the resources normally in agriculture and, in addition, putting to use some of those left unemployed by industry. Here a policy is required that will reduce the income vulnerability of agriculture during such periods, but one that will not curtail agricultural output.

c. When the large production can be traced to uneconomic exploitation of soil resources, with an important divergence between the private and social cost of maintaining the soil, the additional production achieved actually reduces the total social product, and the national economy suffers a loss. Measures to meet this problem are offered later in this chapter.

d. When the large production is the result of high yields, the national economy stands to lose unless farmers are in a sufficiently strong financial position to carry forward enough of the bumper crop (especially in the case of feed grains) to equalize, at least in part, the results of subsequent poor yields.

Patently, the problem here is not one of output but of finance. Policy in this regard is considered later in this chapter.

e. When the overlarge production of a particular farm product results from a government supported price or a commodity loan higher than is necessary to induce farmers to produce an amount consistent with the demand (not merely in a depression period but over the years), the national economy sustains a loss in the extra production thus induced. In this point we focus not so much on agriculture as a whole as on particular farm products.[1] Appropriate policy, which one might suppose to be self-evident when a large production occurs as a consequence of this overvaluation, asks for pricing closer to the realities of costs and demand.

Subsidizing Less Production or More Consumption

When an apparent surplus of farm products again puts in its appearance, we can choose between curtailing output or enlarging consumption. The choice will have far-reaching economic and social implications. In the thirties, the main effort went to curtailing the production of so-called "basic crops" and (for a brief period) of hogs, not to expanding consumption. Not until the later thirties was any emphasis given to measures to increase farm-product consumption.

Many persons in the United States have been unable to afford adequate diets, even during the war when people have been unusually prosperous and rationing has facilitated a more equal distribution of food. Even with the relatively cheap food that is in prospect after the war, this situation will continue because of extraordinarily low incomes among certain segments of the population. There certainly are good grounds for public action to improve the diets of such persons.

---

[1] Support prices and CCC commodity loans, determined according to the existing parity formula, will induce too large a production of certain products. Some farm products are overvalued by the parity formula—decidedly overvalued as a result of changes that have occurred since 1910–1914 in both costs and demand, as is the case for such important products as cotton and wheat.

The case for public measures—school lunches, in-plant feeding, a food-stamp plan, and others—is given added support by the new knowledge of nutrition.

The possibility of subsidizing the sale of particular farm products under the guise of better nutrition is apparent, and needs to be guarded against. Public expenditures for school lunches, a food-stamp plan, and other measures to improve diets are not likely to add so much to the income of farmers (per dollar of public expenditures) as do AAA parity payments which are made directly to farmers. However, the difference in gains to society as a whole is great enough to throw the balance decidedly in favor of enlarging consumption (by public expenditures) rather than curtailing production.[1]

POSITIVE MEASURES IN ADJUSTING
AGRICULTURAL PRODUCTION

To bring about the best use of agricultural resources—best in terms of the necessary marginal shifts among and between crops and livestock, best in terms of investment and disinvestment of capital (including soil productivity), and best in terms of time of sales, location of production, and adaptation to the kinds, qualities, and amounts of products demanded— *we must make prices, namely, the relative prices of both factors and products, the keystone of agricultural policy.*

Farm prices admittedly have serious limitations for guiding agricultural production. They have led to undesirable results, such as the misuse of soils and the inadequate storage of feed stuffs. By all odds the most important proviso to the efficacy of price policy in agriculture is the fact that very little can be done through prices to improve the economic pro-

---

[1] We are here viewing AAA parity payments as a means for inducing farmers to curtail production and not as payments to increase the incomes of farm families. When used as income payments, which are needed in some parts of agriculture, they should be granted in accordance with welfare criteria and not according to size of farms, acreages in certain crops, production per acre, or other production criteria.

ductivity of the two, or perhaps even three, million farm families with the lowest incomes in agriculture.[1]

Nevertheless, the main shortcoming of the agricultural programs of the decade prior to the war was the lack of a comprehensive price policy. What we had was an era of particular farm programs with prices as goals to be achieved rather than programs with prices as means for directing the allocation of resources. As one might expect, the particular programs were not integrated into a consistent whole as would have been the case if price had been given a central position in policy. Where firms are small and where there are millions of them, as in agriculture, prices received by producers can be a powerful control in adjusting production. The problem of pricing farm products is therefore given separate and detailed consideration in the following chapter.

Putting prices aside temporarily, let us consider measures for soil conservation, storages, improvement of farm practices, improvement of tenure, and aids to depressed areas. Each of these offers methods for adjustments in agricultural production that cannot be accomplished adequately by means of price alone.

Conserving Soil Productivity

The economics of soil conservation is difficult by virtue of its complexity. It involves problems of investment and disinvestment, intricate technical considerations, the lack of a means of accounting for divergence between private and social cost in soil maintenance, the considerable lack of both technical and economic knowledge on the part of farmers, much capital rationing, and the role of expectations and uncertainty.[2] There obviously can be no definitive reply to the question of appropriate means for bringing about a more

[1] D. Gale Johnson, "Contribution of Price Policy to the Resource and Income Problems in Agriculture," *Journal of Farm Economics*, November, 1944.

[2] The best study that has been made of this subject is that of Dr. A. C. Bunce, *Economics of Soil Conservation*, Iowa State College Press, Ames, Iowa, 1942.

rational (in an economic sense) use of soil resources, but there are measures that move toward this goal.

In the United States the misuse of soil is for the most part simply delay in adopting farming practices suited to the characteristics of the soil and to a continental climate. Farming practices already known and not greatly different in many cases from those now followed would go far in conserving the productivity of many of our best soils if their adoption could be brought about. Recent agricultural programs, especially those of the AAA and the Soil Conservation Service, have made large contributions to better use of soils, chiefly by increasing farmers' awareness of the seriousness of soil erosion and depletion, of the shortcomings of certain farm practices, the liability that certain crops represent for the soil, and ways and means for reducing soil losses.

It is not possible to outline here all the elements of a comprehensive policy to conserve our soils. However, the more important measures that should be pursued are:

a. Farmers should be induced to adopt better farming practices. Education should be used to the fullest possible extent. But it can be anticipated that educational programs by the Agricultural Extension Services, Smith-Hughes teachers, and others will not be enough. Some technical assistance and probably some financial aid will continue to be necessary. The technical assistance needed is chiefly advice and help in farm husbandry, farm engineering, and farm economics.

b. The customs and laws responsible for the sharp divergence between private and public costs and returns should be overhauled. To lessen this divergence, farm-tenure arrangements need to be improved and the causes of the prevalent capital rationing removed, especially in the poorer parts of agriculture.

c. Not all soil-conservation programs should be put in the category of public works, to be expanded and contracted to meet the requirements of fiscal-monetary policy. Better results will be obtained by classifying soil-conservation programs into two groups: those of a continuing type and those that may be administered on a variable basis and can be synchronized with public works to counteract depressions.

d. Soil-conservation programs are likely to be most effective if administered in practice on a decentralized pattern, along the lines authorized in the soil-conservation districts of most states.

e. Soil conservation should not be made the "rider" to acreage allotments that seek to curtail production for other reasons. Though such crops as cotton, corn, and tobacco— the major row crops—cause much soil erosion, larger returns per unit of public expenditure will be obtained when the two objectives are not mixed.

f. Finally, there is always the danger that particular soil-conservation projects will entail expenditures disproportionate to the future value productivity of the restored land. Much care needs to be exercised in borderline undertakings.

A clear distinction between soil depletion and soil erosion is important. Depletion is that disinvestment in soil productivity that does not harm appreciably the basic structure of the soil; therefore, the process can be reversed, that is, the soil can be restored when costs fall or product prices rise. Erosion is a disinvestment in soil productivity that causes the structure of the soil to deteriorate in a manner that makes the reverse process exceedingly costly, often, in fact, impossible. Where soil depletion is in question, use of the land can, in the main, be guided by entrepreneurial decisions. Such a guide is unreliable where erosion is involved, because of the burden that may be thrown on society if and when it is necessary to restore the soil.

Storages of the More Durable Farm Products

Like the economics of soil conservation, the economics of farm storage is in its infancy. The programs sponsored under the ever-normal granary provide several lessons, but there can be no final judgment yet about the elements necessary in a storage policy.[1] Certainly, the price effects of storages must be considered, price effects related to geographical locations, to qualities of a commodity, and to periods of time. Changes in the flow of products into domestic consumption and into foreign trade are also involved. Further, storage is related to the variations in yields caused by weather, to the cyclical shifts in demand caused by fluctuations in business, to price uncertainty, and to cost of production.

While no conclusive answers are at hand, some tentative judgments may be formulated with regard to storages as a means of bringing about adjustments in agricultural production.

a. Storages of feed to counteract the fluctuations in yield caused by weather have a more important contribution to make than is generally supposed. The carry-overs of corn, for example, which prior to 1933 ranged from less than 100 million bushels to 275 million, were wholly inadequate to compensate for year-to-year variations in feed output. Five hundred million to a billion bushels may be closer to the mark, and experience may show that even larger carry-overs are necessary to maximize the steadiness of the corn belt feed-livestock economy. Where to store such feed, the type of storage that is most appropriate, and particularly its timing are questions far from solved.

b. Storage of wheat is on a different footing from storage of feed, for several reasons. Wheat, in the main, is not used as a raw material in agriculture; more significant, it is tied into international markets, a short crop in one country often being offset by large crops elsewhere. The level of wheat storages in central markets of the world has in recent years been excessively large.

To the extent that wheat enters feeding channels, however, it can be related to the livestock economy by becoming subject

[1] One of the major difficulties lies in the political sphere, the fact that interested pressure groups have not yet attained a full sense of national responsibility.

to the storage policy developed for feed. If wheat is stored at a loan rate about 10 per cent higher than that of corn, it would be essentially on a feed basis since at that price it substitutes for corn. A large measure of stability might be introduced into the economy of the plains states after the war by using wheat as feed. This would serve not only to expand livestock production in that region, but also to maintain a feed supply large enough to keep the over-all livestock economy on an even keel, in spite of the erratic climate and its effects upon crop production.

c. What storage can do for cotton is far from clear. The experiences of the cotton-storage program since 1937 are not instructive because it has been primarily a price-raising device which has kept much cotton out of domestic as well as export channels. Like wheat, cotton is an international commodity with large stocks at various centers. It differs from wheat in that demand is closely correlated with business cycles.

d. No storage program in which the loan rates are tied to a 1910–1914 parity formula can possibly give satisfactory results. Bound by this legislative tie to parity, the Commodity Credit Corporation was forced into making the same mistakes that ruined the Federal Farm Board, and the CCC is with us only by virtue of the war. The 1933–1939 experience should have proved that loan rates tied to parity will not support the objectives of a storage policy.

Enlarge Small Family Farms

Many thousands of family farms in the United States are too small as operating units to make efficient use of modern farm technology and to earn a return for labor and capital inputs that are at all comparable to returns in other fields. This is one of the manifestations of an overcrowded agriculture—a ratio of people to land too high to permit an equilibrium distribution of the nation's labor force. When high employment in other parts of the economy creates jobs, many more farm people will leave farming, as they did during the war, and such migration will make possible the enlargement of farms. The war set the stage for an orderly program of this type. In sections of the Piedmont, for example, the typical farms have ranged from 80 to 100 acres, have been dependent on cotton and corn, have suffered much erosion, and have produced very small incomes; as a consequence of war jobs, many people moved out, farm homes stand empty, and some of the land is no longer in cultivation.

Farmers are already taking advantage of this opportunity to change their holdings. But in too many instances it is not the small family farm that is being enlarged through migration. The main deterrents are lack of knowledge about modern farm technology and its requirements, price uncertainty, and, most serious, the vise of capital rationing which squeezes the small farmer. Credit institutions, private and public, are geared too much to an outmoded farm technology and are not prepared to serve many farm families in enlarging their units, especially in the South where the need for this adjustment is greatest.

Better Farming Practices

Under the impetus of competition and with the help of the educational programs of the agricultural extension services, rapid progress has been made in adopting new and better farming practices. Notwithstanding this advance, the experiences of the AAA, FSA, and SCS indicate that additional gains may be had from more direct measures to advise, assist, and induce farmers to improve their farming practices.

Managerial advice often needed could be supplied by farm-management associations organized by farmers and the agricultural college, by home and farm plans provided by FSA, and by private farm-management services. Small grants and aids are a very strong incentive in bringing about changes associated with better practices, and are especially germane to soil-conservation programs. Some major adjustments involve loss in income in the first year or two or even longer after the practices are adopted. In those circumstances a more substantial public grant, to enable a farmer to forego current income, may be the price for the better long-run practices— better chiefly in terms of the lower social costs achieved by preventing deterioration of the structure of the soil.

Improving Farm Tenure

There has been little or no emphasis upon farm tenure in the agricultural adjustment programs, yet this is a sphere in which an important additional contribution can and must be made.

Farm-tenure arrangements in the United States are primitive when compared with the progress that has been made in the countries of western Europe and in Great Britain. The informal and common laws governing our landlord-tenant relationships are out of step with the modern agriculture that we have evolved. Nor will improvements in farm tenure be obtained by the kind of legislation that has had our attention in recent years. The Federal government, in fact, can do little to improve the situation. The adjustments that are required are primarily institutional in character, and the remedy lies primarily with the states and localities.

Much of the misuse of our soil and the consequent divergence between private and social cost has its origin in the inadequacy of our farm-tenure institutions. The insufficiency of feed and grain storages is also partly caused by our farm tenure. The effects of our farm tenure on the farm community, on the social facilities that the community develops, upon education, and upon the standard of living of farm people are many—and they are mostly unfavorable. A separate monograph would be required to discuss the elements needed to improve farm-tenure arrangements in the United States and to make them consistent with the goal of the family-type farm. We merely call attention to the importance of the problem in the formation of agricultural policy.

Adjustment Aids for Depressed Areas

The forces reshaping the supply and demand for farm products are likely to bring an acute, long depression to some parts of American agriculture. These areas will be in trouble even if the general situation with respect to employment, prices, and trade is a healthy one.

A special problem of surpluses is likely in fats and oils, adversely affecting lard and butter and the soybeans, cottonseed, peanuts, and flaxseed used for oil. This surplus, however, will be spread over enough of agriculture to lessen somewhat the burden it will place on any particular area. Wheat will also be in trouble, especially if CCC wheat loans hold to 1910–1914 price relationships. The wheat-producing areas, however, are in a decidedly better competitive position than they were following World War I. Wheat for feed can offer a substantial part of the solution for the prewar wheat problem of this country.

The principal depressed area after the war will be the agriculture of the South. The conversion of the cotton South presents many difficulties. High employment in the urban-industrial sectors of our economy is obviously a prerequisite to the conversion of Southern agriculture, since much of the excess supply of labor in agriculture is concentrated in that region. But a rapidly expanding nonagricultural economy will not be enough to see Southern agriculture through. The mechanism of relative prices is not sufficient to do a satisfactory job if any consideration is to be given to the incomes and welfare of many thousands of farm families.

The South must face the growing competition for cotton from synthetic fibers and from lower-cost cotton-producing areas in other parts of the world, and new competition for the protein feed and oil made from cottonseed, from the expanded production of soybeans and other protein- and oil-bearing crops. Barriers to foreign trade continue to place cotton at a disadvantage. The introduction of new farm machinery and equipment adapted to the needs of Southern agriculture will add to the competitive strength of farms in many areas in the South, but this advance in farm technology will also make necessary additional major adjustments—relocation of crops, enlargement of farms, new forms of capital and credit to serve these capital needs, and new skills to handle a more varied and complex pattern of agricultural production.

Every indication points to the need of developing a comprehensive adjustment program for the cotton South, a program planned to achieve for the South an economy of high production and high per capita incomes. Its focus must take in more than cotton alone, for cotton is not the main problem. It is simply a convenient symbol. It is safe to say that if the excess supply of labor in the agriculture of the South were to find employment opportunities comparable to those commonly available to people in other regions, the so-called "cotton problem" would no longer exist. Both the cotton and the soil-conservation problems are caused largely by the cheapness of labor in the South; that is, by an overcrowded agriculture with altogether too many people trying to earn a living at farming. Even though reductions in the excess supply of labor are effected, it still will be necessary to shift resources away from cotton to other crops in many areas in the South, although in some sections with special advantages in growing cotton under more mechanized conditions, cotton production should be expanded. Cotton loans and prices based on 1910–1914 price relationships have patently become a liability; cotton prices at or near parity will not permit the required shifts and adjustments in production. Nor will acreage allotments to control cotton production, based on either prewar or wartime production history, provide an efficient index of the proper distribution of the cotton crop. What is required is a cotton price that reflects accurately the competitive value of cotton by grade, quality, and location. Farmers must be permitted to adjust their acreage to such a price if the land-use pattern devoted to cotton is to be consistent with its value and cost.

These moves would pave the way for more direct measures that will be needed in an adjustment program for the cotton South, namely: (*a*) measures to help farmers recombine their resources, including the enlargement of many farms, shifting into crops and livestock best suited to each farm, and introducing improved techniques and practices in farming; (*b*) measures to help maintain farm-family incomes while farmers make the necessary production adjustments, or (for those who want to leave agriculture) while they find a job in another occupation and make arrangements to move; and (*c*) measures to enhance the productivity, in the long pull, of people and of soil resources. To do this, public investments will be necessary to maintain and build up the land, and through improved education, improved health, and like measures to enhance the social efficiency of the individual.

XII. ELEMENTS OF A PRICE POLICY
FOR AGRICULTURE

Two of the primary problems in agricultural policy have to do with prices; one relates to the general level of prices, the other to the structure of prices.

Farmers are much concerned about both. As debtors, they are exceedingly vulnerable to wide movements in the level of prices; as producers, in a highly competitive field, they have been burdened by the great uncertainty that has characterized specific farm-product prices and the relationships between them.

The general level of prices is identified with the value of money. The ever-changing value of money has brought many difficulties to American farmers. The history of our agrarian movements expresses the concern of farm people about money values, a concern that has become imbedded in farm folklore. They believe that somehow the value of money can be managed by government in a way that will serve the interest of creditors and debtors alike. Farm people are outspoken in protest when the general level of prices drops and they as debtors are hard pressed. To counteract the declining price level after the Civil War, the agrarian movements turned to greenbacks, to monetization of silver, and to many variants of a commodity dollar.

In modern terminology, this concern about the value of money would be expressed as concern about fiscal-monetary policy. The appropriate aim of fiscal-monetary policy is *a stable price level at full employment*. The appropriate measures to this end pertain to money—to the issue and retirement of money, to the raising and also the spending of money by government, to taxation, public borrowing and repayments, and government loans to individuals and corporations. Farmers do not put fiscal-monetary policy in these sophisticated terms. But the fact remains (and it is an important fact, as we move toward a more adequate fiscal-monetary policy) that they have a deep-rooted, traditional concern about money. They have been victims of the caprice of the general price level too often to favor anything but a stable price level at full employment.

In recent years, however, farm leaders have abandoned their grand march for managed money and a stable price level. Fiscal-monetary aims have been put aside as too theoretical, remote, and all-inclusive. Farm leaders today seek more immediate gains and believe they have become more "practical." By turning to specific farm-product prices they can count "benefits." Thus, instead of using the influence of farm organizations to attain much-needed fiscal-monetary reforms, they have broken ranks and turned to lesser objectives in the pricing of farm products.

Behind this shift of emphasis by farm organizations is the belief that they have gained a stronger bargaining position. They can better influence government to make tangible "contributions" to agriculture; they can better demonstrate to their membership the benefits that the organization obtains for them. It is, of course, much more difficult to procure legislation to deal adequately with fiscal-monetary issues, or to demonstrate that the more comprehensive measures are directly beneficial. Parity prices are a peculiarly valuable device for farm leaders—first, for bargaining with Congress and with administrative agencies for specific price advantages, and second, as tangible evidence of the achievements of the farm organization. Parity prices possessing these characteristics, it is extraordinarily difficult to substitute a more defensible price objective; it is extremely hard even to modify the formula appreciably to make it somewhat more workable. In spite of these developments, *there remains among the rank and file of farm people a belief that it is money, and the value thereof, that*

*should be managed by the Government, and not the price of eggs, cattle,
butter, or of any particular farm product.* This view may again
express itself after the war when farm prices fall and fluctuate.
It is a view that has much merit, for it recognizes a significant
element in the pricing problem.

AIMS NOT APPROPRIATE IN PRICING
FARM PRODUCTS

If price policies were single-purposed, the task of analysis
and appraisal would be simplified greatly. Almost always,
however, the goal is multipurposed, and some of the purposes
are incompatible. This is notably true of price policy in
agriculture.

Back of the efforts to price farm products lie these general
objectives: (*a*) to give farmers some element of monopoly
gain; (*b*) to improve the personal distribution of income within
agriculture and between farm and nonfarm persons; (*c*) to
help maintain the aggregate demand for goods and services
at a level sufficiently high to induce full employment and high
production; and (*d*) to effect a better allocation of resources.

The first of these aims, which contains elements of monopolistic competition through pricing, is inconsistent with the
general interest. Since, by common agreement, the government is vested with the general interest, this is hardly an
appropriate price-policy purpose. The government's task is
to keep monopoly from becoming established or by control
to reduce to a minimum effects adverse to the general interest.
A number of farm programs need scrutiny on this score
because they serve as instruments for the establishment of
some monopolistic competition in behalf of farm groups.

The second set of aims is probably also inappropriate in
pricing farm products. To improve income distribution it is
necessary to be guided by welfare criteria, while in the allocation of resources to maximize production it is necessary to be
guided by the principle of marginal production. It is therefore essential to distinguish, both in analysis and in policy,

between the personal-*income distribution problem* and the *resources allocation problem* and to treat each separately.[1] If the pricing of farm products is employed as a means to bring about a more equal distribution of incomes among persons, it is likely to cause inefficiencies in the use of resources, confusion, and waste.[2] Price policy is not an effective or even a suitable technique to improve the personal distribution of income.

What role agricultural price policy can play in helping a fiscal-monetary authority maintain in the economy as a whole a level of demand that will sustain a high level of production is still to be explored. For this final set of aims, however, there is general agreement that, in the main, the mechanism of relative prices can be both efficient and effective (especially with the type of competition that prevails in agriculture) in inducing farmers to allocate resources so as to maximize output.[3]

In the brief observations that follow, no further comment is made about the first and second categories of aims since they are not appropriate for price policy. As to the other two categories, there are several mistakes obvious in the experiences of recent years that clearly should be avoided.

Prices Are Not Goals

The entire weight of economic analysis supports the use of prices as a means to facilitate and guide economic activity, not as goals. Nevertheless, much of the basic agricultural

[1] This is not to deny that the two are interdependent, since the solution of the "resource problem" would affect the "income problem," some of the effects being favorable.

[2] The present writer has developed more fully the basis for the distinction between the income and the resource problems in agriculture. See *Redirecting Farm Policy*, The Macmillan Company, New York, 1943. Also, D. Gale Johnson, "Contribution of Price Policy to the Income and Resources Problems in Agriculture," *Journal of Farm Economics*, November, 1944.

[3] Other institutional considerations, such as capital rationing, the immobility of labor, etc., qualify this statement, but in itself the mechanism of relative prices is appropriate to this end.

legislation now in force was formulated on the assumption that prices are, in substance, goals to be achieved. This is the real import of parity prices. Congress has made it mandatory that crop control, loan rates, support prices, and other measures be used to achieve parity prices.

Prices Do Not Necessarily Equilibrate Labor Supplies

The mechanism of relative prices has not been effective in distributing the labor force between agriculture and other occupations. During the interwar years the movement of workers to and from farms was, for the most part, wholly contrary to the changes in the relative prices of farm and other products. Migration from farms increased even as farm prices rose, and vice versa. The availability or nonavailability of jobs in industry was the real determinant in the labor flow. The gap in absolute earnings between farm and industrial workers had become so wide that improvement in farm-product prices would not alone correct the imbalance. The situation is not likely to be greatly different in the early years after the war. It is a mistake to expect that either an increase or decrease in farm prices will of itself equilibrate labor supplies, until the present oversupply of labor in agriculture has been corrected by a long period of high employment.

Obsolete Price Relationships Burden Agriculture

It would be wholly accidental if the relative prices of any past period, whether the years are 1910–1914 or a more recent period, proved to be appropriate for later years. We begin in error when we try to establish, as is done under the parity-price formula, a relationship among the prices of farm products, and a relationship between farm and nonfarm prices, that happened to prevail during a particular past period. *To guide farmers in their production, prices of farm products must be forward, not backward, in their orientation. They should be based on current and expected supply and demand, not upon some historical situation.*

Farm Prices Are Least Effective When Industrial Output Falls or Rises Rapidly

The capacity of farm prices to bring about the best use of agricultural resources is at a maximum when income payments and, consequently, aggregate demand in the country are fairly stable. They lose some of their capacity to shift the use of resources when industrial output is either dropping or rising rapidly, and when the nation's pay roll is likewise decreasing or increasing at a rapid rate. Since farm prices keep company with these abrupt up-and-down swings, farmers respond less to the changes among farm prices, and the mechanism of relative prices can do less to bring about desirable shifts in production.[1]

PRICE POLICY FOR AGRICULTURE AFTER THE WAR

Attention of policy makers in the United States during the interwar years, and especially after 1932, centered upon the collapse of farm prices and income. Most of the measures taken were of a relief nature.

[1] This point is well expressed in a more general context by T. de Scitovsky, "Capital Accumulation, Employment and Price Rigidity," *Review of Economic Studies*, Vol. 8 (1940–1941), p. 73: "It may be objected at this stage that we are too much concerned about the stability of prices, for—one might say—what does it matter if prices fluctuate, as long as production remains undisturbed and there is no unemployment? Up to a certain point this objection is justified. I do think that economists often take it too much for granted that a stable price-level is the only thing that matters. But the kind of instability described above would rob the pricing system of its function: the allocation of economic resources among different uses. For a short time after instability has set in this would not matter since production would continue in its accustomed grooves. But after a time tastes may change—owing perhaps to the redistribution of income caused by rapidly changing prices, or to any other cause—and then production will fail properly to adjust itself to changed demand conditions, because relative prices are a very poor index of the relative urgency of wants when the price-level as a whole is galloping up or down."

What stands out is that price policy as such was subordinated and kept in a secondary role; programs affecting production and income were given the right of way. We did not, in fact, have a comprehensive price policy for agriculture. Farm prices were not utilized to induce shifts in the use of resources within agriculture or to bring about a better economic equilibrium generally. This is understandable because of the general collapse; the problem confronting the nation, as far as agriculture was concerned, was not a breakdown in agricultural production but a crisis in farm income. Agricultural production remained large, and its composition was not altered substantially by the price and income collapse. The disparity between farm prices and other product prices became so great, however, that steps had to be taken to remedy the resulting distressed conditions in large numbers of farm families. Thus, out of the depression came the parity prescription. This heritage of the depression, putting prices in the role of goals, meant that the historic function of prices as guides was, in part, set aside.

Although the parity formula continued in the forefront of the conflicts that arose in shaping wartime policy for agricultural production and for checking food prices and the cost of living, mobilization for war placed prices once more in a strategic position. The income problem in agriculture receded as the mobilization for war got under way, and less emphasis was placed upon measures to achieve more income. More reliance was given to relative prices of farm products to induce the kind and amounts of production necessary to wartime requirements.

The price technique that has gained ascendancy during the war is a system of support prices,[1] put into operation to induce farmers to expand the production of certain farm products. It is important to note that most of the support prices were announced by the government in advance of the

[1] Support prices are price floors announced by the government and administered by the Department of Agriculture and War Food Administration.

time when farmers made their production plans. They were also, for the most part, sufficiently specific as to time, place, and type of product to permit farmers to treat them as *given data* in making their crop and livestock plans. These earlier support prices, therefore, were in effect minimum forward prices. They were reasonably successful in inducing additional production and also in bringing about shifts in production. Congress has made it mandatory that these support prices be maintained for at least two years after the war at levels specified in terms of parity.

In view of existing legislation and their fairly adequate performance during the war, support prices are likely to dominate price policy in agriculture after the war. How satisfactory will the program of support prices now in effect be in peacetime? First, what should a positive price policy for agriculture include?

Stabilize the General Level of Prices

Any price policy for agriculture worthy of consideration must start with the general level of prices. It is the movement of the price level that either makes or breaks farmers. There isn't much point in laboring for an enlightened policy covering the relationships among farm prices when the center of gravity of all prices is constantly moving either up or down. These broader movements submerge the important gains that otherwise could be attained from a better distribution of resources within agriculture. They distort the claims and counterclaims of debtors and creditors.

As a group, farmers are in the debtor category; they hold title to commodities and to land. When the level of prices falls, they stand to lose much—many of them are liquidated, including many of the most efficient farmers who have extended their debts to obtain modern machinery and equipment and an effective combination of resources. Contrariwise, when the level of prices rises, farmers are the recipients of unusually large windfalls—the kind of prosperity that breeds land booms and seriously distorts values.

Stability in the general level of prices should therefore stand first among objectives in a nation's price policy. Agriculture may have a larger stake in this goal than any other major group in our society, since farmers are peculiarly vulnerable to price movements. The techniques appropriate to this objective call for major fiscal-monetary reforms.[1]

Close the Gap Separating Internal and External Prices

A second important aim in pricing farm products should be to lessen the divergencies between domestic and foreign prices. The United States has much to gain from foreign trade in food, feed, and fiber. Nevertheless, we are embarked on an agricultural policy that is driving a wedge between the internal and external prices of several important farm products. These resulting price divergencies soon acquire vested interest, and conflicts arise as the inconsistencies between trade policy and agricultural policy grow.[2]

Cotton developments in the past decade illustrate how serious the consequences can be when a major product is divorced from the structure of world prices. In cotton we are in effect pricing ourselves out of the world market. To span the gap in prices between the domestic and foreign markets, we resort to exports, subsidies, and other devices for maintaining a two-price or even a multiprice system. Since the main cause for the gap is the nature of our support prices, the remedy lies in overhauling that system.[3]

---

[1] This is so comprehensive and complex a field that it requires special treatment.

[2] See Theodore W. Schultz, "Which Way Will Farmers Turn?" *Foreign Affairs*, July, 1945. It should be noted, also, that on May 26, 1945, when the House of Representatives debated and passed The Extension of Reciprocal Trade Agreements Program, Congressman Pace from the cotton South (Georgia) offered a restricting amendment to protect farm products that have support prices.

[3] Policy with regard to support prices will be considered below.

Forward Prices Are Required in Agriculture

We have already stressed the fact that farmers are very vulnerable to any fall (or rise) of the general level of prices because they are debtors, short of capital, and unable for the most part to hedge against the contingency of a general price deflation. (An inflation, of course, brings with it windfalls.) Farmers as a class are also subject to a great deal of price uncertainty from unexpected changes within the agricultural price structure. Nearly all production in agriculture requires long-range planning and commitments since it takes months, even years, to complete a production period. Most crops require at least a year, livestock from one to three years. Fruit-bearing trees take a decade and longer, and farm wood-lots and other forestry undertakings even more time.

The process of transferring resources into or out of agriculture is very sluggish; in contrast, however, the shifting of some resources from one crop to another or the producing of less of one kind of livestock or more of another takes place relatively quickly. The structure of farm prices affects significantly the use to which agricultural resources are put. The price of wheat relative to that of corn affects the use to which the cropland in the overlapping areas of these two crops is put; the price of corn compared to that of hogs, cattle, poultry, and milk affects the amount of corn stored or fed and the choice of animals to which it is fed. Yet the structure of prices on which farmers must rely in making their production decisions has always been highly uncertain, even for one production period ahead.

What we have in agriculture, therefore, is a system of relative prices on which farmers cannot depend as they proceed with their production operations. Farm prices, unlike the prices of industrial products, are always in motion, constantly shifting. Inaccurate price expectations are the rule in agriculture, and the production consequences are plain. There is much misdirection in the uses to which farm land, capital, and labor engaged in farming are put.

The malallocations of resources in farming have been many: the wide periodic swings (often called cycles) in hog, beef, and poultry production; the sharp changes in acreages planted in flaxseed, rye, barley, and potatoes, to cite only a few of the products thus affected; and the failure of farmers to store enough of their crops when yields are large to counteract the adverse effects of subsequent low yields on their livestock operations. Price uncertainty has enlarged very considerably the compass of capital rationing, checking the enlargement of many farms that are inefficient because they are too small, and inducing farmers to keep their resources too flexible both contractually and technically. Because of the large measure of price uncertainty that burdens agriculture (both as to the level of farm prices generally and the structure of farm prices) and the attendant capital rationing (both external and internal for many farms), most farmers are either unable or unwilling to commit themselves to contractual payments, even though the additional resources would improve substantially the efficiency of the farm they operate. Labor inputs on most farms, including that of the family and operator, provide flexibility and thus a kind of "safety" in dealing with price uncertainty, for labor becomes a residual claimant. As a consequence, throughout most of American agriculture farmers tend to employ too much labor (family labor, the operator, and hired labor) and too few nonhuman resources (machinery, equipment, land, fertilizer, buildings, livestock, feed inventories). This adjustment to uncertainty and the capital rationing associated with it holds down the per capita earnings of farm people and pushes up the rate of returns on capital, with the marginal-value productivity of capital much higher than its money cost.

Price uncertainty affecting farming therefore has its cost, for it reduces the efficiency of agriculture. Can this cost, this inefficiency and waste, be lessened? In a very real sense, yes, because many of the farm product price changes constantly occurring within a given production period can be eliminated without disturbing trade. There are certain kinds of price changes affecting farmers that are not essential to attain a moving equilibrium, to reconcile the forces affecting supply and demand of farm products. More price certainty for farmers is possible for at least one production period ahead. The additional price certainty that would be gained by eliminating these unnecessary price fluctuations would substantially better the capacity of relative prices of farm products to perform their primary economic function of guiding production. To achieve this greater certainty in prices received by farmers, we have proposed elsewhere[1] a system of forward prices for agriculture.

Forward Prices Defined

Four major characteristics distinguish forward prices from the prewar price policies of the government and from indeterminate market prices:[2]

1. The prices would be announced far enough in advance to enable farmers to develop their next production program in harmony with the announced prices.

2. The prices would cover a sufficient period of time to permit farmers to complete at least one production period.

3. The price announcements would be sufficiently precise for each farmer readily to interpret the implications of the announced prices for his farming operations.

[1] "Economic Effects of Agricultural Programs," *American Economic Review*, XXX (1941), pp. 127–154; and Theodore W. Schultz, *Redirecting Farm Policy*, pp. 43–44, and Geoffrey Shepherd, "Stabilization Operations of the Commodity Credit Corporation," *Journal of Farm Economics*, Vol. 24 (1942), pp. 589–610.

[2] This formulation of the major characteristics is essentially the same as that first presented by D. Gale Johnson and Theodore W. Schultz in "Elements of a Price Policy for Agriculture," Memo. 5 (mimeo.), Iowa Agricultural Experiment Station, Ames, Iowa, 1942.

4. The prices announced should be those prices which will achieve the desired output.

The fundamental principle that should guide the formulation and administration of forward prices in agriculture is this: Price changes *that keep farm production in line with demand* should be maximized; price changes *that do not contribute to production adjustments* (price changes that occur within a given production period) *but contribute to price uncertainty in farming* should be minimized. It is becoming increasingly clear both from analytical work and the experience we have had during the war that it is possible to go a long way in separating these two types of price changes that affect farmers. A price change that is expected and known at the time production plans are made does not necessarily give rise to uncertainty. Price changes that cannot be anticipated by farmers when they plan their operations breed uncertainty. It is these latter price changes that continue to disturb farmers, cause waste and inefficiency, and burden agriculture. These price uncertainties should be lessened as may be done through a system of forward prices for agriculture.[1]

CONVERT SUPPORT PRICES INTO FORWARD PRICES

We now have an elaborate system of support prices. When they were initiated they were in substance minimum forward prices, certainly for the products that the Government wanted expanded to meet wartime demands. Can these support prices be converted into a workable system of forward prices?

Postwar Setting

As the demand for farm products begins to slacken, farm prices—instead of exerting pressure against OPA ceil-

[1] This is not the place to elaborate the theoretical foundations for forward pricing, its implication for markets, storage stocks, and international trade, and the problems that it presents in public administration. D. Gale Johnson of the University of Chicago has completed a comprehensive study of the theory of forward prices as applied to agriculture. This study will be published shortly by the University of Chicago Press.

ings—will fall, and as they fall, the Department of Agriculture support prices will come into play. Some of the support prices became effective even before the war ended as some farm prices dropped to or below the support levels. Hogs, eggs, and potatoes put support prices to a test during the winter and spring of 1944, and it became apparent that the government was ill prepared to make its announced support prices effective even while extraordinary wartime demands for food still prevailed. But the main test of the economic effects and workability of support prices will come after relief needs have been met and our empty granaries have been refilled. The support prices authorized by Congress are of a type likely to place the government in serious difficulties in making effective the prices it is now obligated to maintain.

What Is the Existing Support-price Program?

The laws dealing with support-price operations separate agricultural commodities into three groups: (*a*) the old basic commodities, (*b*) the new "Steagall" commodities, and (*c*) other commodities. At the end of 1944, 166 agricultural commodities were included.[1]

The so-called "basic-commodities list" is well known: cotton, wheat, and corn—the big three of American agriculture —and tobacco, rice, and peanuts. Congress has made mandatory the support of the farm prices of these commodities by producer loans at 90 per cent of parity,[2] except for the price of cotton, which has been fixed at 92.5 per cent of

---

[1] Robert H. Shields, Solicitor, WFA and U.S. Department of Agriculture, in a paper released Aug. 16, 1944, "Federal Statutory Provisions Relating to Price Supports for Agricultural Products," gives a most useful and clear review of the many Federal statutes bearing on support prices. His statement has been drawn upon heavily in the preparation of this section.

[2] To prevent feed costs from rising, an 85 per cent minimum loan rate was authorized.

parity. The loans must be continued for at least two years after the war.[1]

The "Steagall" commodities are hogs, eggs, chickens and turkeys, milk and butterfat, certain dry peas and beans; soybeans, peanuts, and flaxseed used for oil; American-Egyptian cotton, potatoes, and cured sweet potatoes. Whenever the Secretary of Agriculture found it necessary to encourage the expansion of production and announced this fact, a support price became mandatory under the Steagall Amendment. For these commodities, also, price supports at not less than 90 per cent of parity for at least two years after the war are stipulated.

The third group of commodities to which support prices apply has come to include wool, naval stores, American hemp, sugar beets, sugar cane, blackeye peas and beans, certain fruits and vegetables for processing, barley, grain, soybeans, rye, Sea Island cotton, and certain vegetable, hay, and pasture seeds. Congress has declared that the lending and purchasing operations of the U.S. Department of Agriculture shall be so carried out that they will bring the prices and incomes of producers of nonbasic, non-Steagall commodities into a fair parity relationship—insofar as funds available to the U.S. Department of Agriculture permit. Continuance of the support prices for this group of commodities after the war is not required.[2]

Purpose of Support Prices

Two goals have been stressed by the government: protecting farm income and getting produced the crops and livestock that have been most needed. The emphasis was on the latter objective during the war. Accordingly, support prices were used as a guide for farm production. Floors

[1] Namely, for two years from Jan. 1 following the date on which the President or the Congress proclaims hostility to have ended.

[2] *Ibid.*, pp. 15–16.

under prices lessen the risk of farmers, and by so doing they have encouraged the production of urgently needed crops.

Many different activities have been employed to maintain particular farm prices, including commodity loans for the durable crops, contracts with processors and handlers, government purchases of farm products (both in their natural and processed states), special payments on certain products, and consumer subsidies. Storage operations, diversion programs, and market agreements have also come in.

Postwar Support-price Commitments Very Defective

This brief description of support prices[1] does not reveal their effects upon the allocation of resources in agriculture and upon the movement of farm products through markets. The current support prices have been devised within the parity formula,[2] and not necessarily with an eye to the forces reshaping supply and demand for the particular farm product. Since they are set by law for two years after the war, they have an inflexibility that will make it difficult if not impossible to adjust agricultural prices to a changing structure of values as we convert from a wartime to a peacetime economy.

[1] A ninety-six-page bulletin issued by the War Food Administration, *Food Program for 1944*, contains a nine-page appendix giving the 1944 schedule of support prices as announced by the Food Administrator on March 4, 1944. This list includes hogs, corn, wheat, cotton, rice, tobacco, peas, blackeye peas, blackeye beans, dry edible beans, potatoes, eggs, chickens, milk and butterfat, butter, American Cheddar cheese, skim milk powder, other manufactured dairy products, fruits for processing, vegetables for canning (followed by two pages listing prices for nine vegetables), fresh vegetables, cured sweet potatoes, barley, grain sorghums, rye, vegetable seeds, winter cover-crop seeds, hay and pasture seeds (list includes thirty-nine different seeds), American, Egyptian, and Sea Island cotton, American hemp, wool, and naval stores.

[2] The Steagall Amendment contains the provision that, for the so-called "Steagall commodities," the price should be supported at comparable prices or parity prices, whichever are applicable with respect to the particular commodity. Comparable prices have been established for soybeans, peanuts for oil, and dried peas; and support-price operations based on comparable prices are in effect with respect to these commodities. These recalculations, however, are all in one direction, namely, making the support price higher than it would be if the parity formula were employed.

The long-period commitment, of course, in no way synchronizes with the different production periods characteristic of agriculture. For most farm products, the effort is to keep the market price from going below the support level, the consequence being a clogging of both internal and external trade whenever the price that would clear the market is less than the support price.

When the wartime demands for farm products have receded, it should be obvious that the present program of support prices will find itself in serious difficulty. Instead of inducing the shifts in production that the postwar period will call for, it is likely to perpetuate much of the production that was consistent with the war effort. Agriculture will not be confronted with a schedule of relative prices that reflects expected changes in both demand and supply. The schedule of support prices will then be historical commitments, essentially backward in their orientation. They can be a considerable factor in delaying adjustments in the use of agricultural resources after the war, and they are likely to disrupt trade.

The principal defects of the support prices to which the government is committed for at least two peacetime years may be summarized as follows: The *purpose* underlying their development was to expand production to meet wartime needs. The general level of the commitments is therefore high relative to nonfarm commodity prices, but what is more serious still, the specific support prices for major farm products are altogether too high for a nonwar economy. During the war, for example, we were very short of fats and oils. We turned to soybeans, flaxseed, and peanuts (among the crops) and paid prices for these products much higher, relative to many other farm commodities, than are necessary to produce an adequate supply to satisfy peacetime demands. The *rules* that were established for the administration of support prices are governed by parity, which means that all the maladjustments in relative prices implicit in the parity formula are perpetuated. It means that the old "basic" crops, certainly wheat and cotton, will be substantially overvalued after the war. The *administrative techniques* for making support prices effective will include commodity loans, not to serve the objectives of a well-conceived storage policy, but to keep "basic" farm commodity prices at the support level. In the case of perishable farm products, the technique may become that of purchases by the government in sufficient amount to keep the market price at the support level, to be followed by dumping or disposing of the government purchases at home and abroad outside of regular market channels. Trade will be seriously disrupted by the use of techniques that seek to hold market prices at the support level. Finally, there is the *question of costs*, which are likely to be exceedingly high in terms of the appropriations required to carry out the support-price commitments, if the approach is to keep the *market price* from dropping below the support levels.

The program of support prices for farm products should be remodeled and made into a system that permits forward pricing in agriculture. To accomplish this, a number of fundamental changes would be required in the Federal statutes on which support prices are based. Since the support prices to which the government is now committed will be substantially higher for many farm products than the proposed forward prices needed to induce the kind and amount of farm production required for our peacetime economy, there will be an obligation on the government to cover the difference between these two prices. The simplest way of making good on this obligation is by means of special payments direct to farmers, in order not to disturb trade. Safeguards will be needed to prevent even these special payments from having undesirable production effects.

Thus we can attain the third of the major objectives of a price policy for agriculture; namely, the lessening of the price uncertainty confronting farmers. It is possible and highly desirable that we leave behind the support price program that emerged during the war and go over to a system of forward prices in agriculture. Such forward prices should present each farmer, as he proceeds with his production operations, with a schedule of relative prices for at least one production period ahead, considerably more dependable than heretofore. As this is accomplished, it would increase the ability of farmers to allocate and use the resources at their disposal much more efficiently. It would also reduce very appreciably the price uncertainty burdening American farmers.[1]

* * * *

The immediate postwar years offer a real opportunity to establish effective, necessary, forward-looking policies for agriculture. The bleak years of the depression and the disturbances of World War II have made many willing to reexamine their plans and their purposes. The problems confronting American agriculture will not be resolved quickly. They are too intimately a part of the unstable

[1] Finally, two observations on procedure in administering forward prices. It would be prudent in practice to announce not the true expected price, but a price somewhat below that figure, namely, a minimum forward price that would be some major fraction of the true expected price. The advantage of this procedure to the government—in protecting its operations from errors in its estimates with regard to prospective supply-and-demand forces—is, of course, apparent. But the other side of this coin also needs to be read: The lower the announced minimum forward prices relative to true expected prices, the less significance the whole system of such forward prices will have in reducing the price uncertainty confronting farmers.

The other observation pertains to the handling of various classes of farm products. Products that can be stored appear to offer a ready operational procedure for making a minimum forward price effective, but this is not the case. Storability is in itself not a sufficient criterion for determining whether or not the government should add to stocks in order to make an announced forward price effective, since storage operations are not appropriate when the demand falls off. The test must rest on other grounds. For example, in the case of feed grain (primarily corn) the basic question would be: Will storage operations, at such a juncture, contribute to a steadier output of animal products over the years? In case this criterion is not met, and for perishables whose storage is impractical, the market price should be permitted to seek levels below the minimum forward prices. The farmer will have the assurance, however, that if the market price goes below, he will receive a compensation equal to the difference. Thus there would be no clogging of trade.

industrial-urban sector of the economy and, in a larger sense, a part of the evolution of modern society. Much will be gained, however, if we know more clearly what the forces are, what we want to do, and what in fact we are doing.

Certainly the interwoven pattern of city and country should at long last be apparent to us all. The need is great for policies serving American agriculture that are consistent and integrated with our other national policies. But agriculture cannot be expected simply to continue to bear the load placed upon it by our unstable economy. Positive measures are required.

A NOTE ON
THE COMMITTEE FOR ECONOMIC DEVELOPMENT
AND ITS RESEARCH PROGRAM

The Committee for Economic Development was organized in August, 1942, by a group of business leaders who were convinced that the attainment and maintenance of high employment after the war dare not be left to chance. To seize the opportunities for unprecedented peacetime prosperity in the postwar era and to avoid the real perils of mass unemployment or mass government employment, they believed that individual employers, while in no degree relaxing their efforts toward military victory, must begin to plan promptly, realistically, and boldly for rapid reconversion and vigorous expansion after the war.

There is widespread agreement among economists that American prosperity after the war calls for the sustained employment of 7 to 10 million more workers than in 1940, our banner peacetime year hitherto. The only sound road to such increased employment is the enlargement of production and sales of goods and services to a level some 30 to 45 per cent higher than that of 1940. This meant that business men had to plan for postwar business on a greatly expanded basis as compared to any known peacetime year.

To help them to make their maximum contribution toward this goal, the Committee for Economic Development—through its Field Development Division—has been working locally in more than 2,900 counties and communities in all states of the union. More than 65,000 businessmen have been serving as members of these committees, aiding as many as possible of the nation's 2 million private employers in the planning of their postwar production and employment.

No pattern or over-all program has been imposed on these local committees. Each is autonomous, since each understands the peculiar problems of its community better than can any outsider. Yet the problems they had to meet and the tools they needed were in basic respects the same.

Therefore, tested procedures for making both postwar production and employment plans have been supplied to them by the national C.E.D. office. In addition, the country's outstanding specialists in industrial management, in product design, in advertising and selling, and in training of sales personnel have placed their skills freely at the service of all cooperating business men, through handbooks, films, training courses, business clinics, and forums for the local committees.

To plan for the future, the businessman needs particularly some measure for estimating postwar demand for his individual product. Another important service of C.E.D. was its postwar market analysis, conducted with the cooperation of many trade associations and leading industrial firms and covering more than 500 finished-goods products. The findings of this two-year study were made available to business and to the public in a report, *American Industry Looks Ahead*, issued in August of 1945.

Even with the best of tools the businessman knows he cannot be wholly successful in carrying out plans for postwar expansion unless national policies prevail that make business expansion possible. To define what these national policies of government, business, and labor should be to encourage higher production and more jobs is the special task of the C.E.D. Research Division. This is the purpose of the research reports, of which this volume is the sixth.

To the long-range economic questions involved in this undertaking have been added the particular economic problems arising out of the war. Both areas have been studied. It is hoped that the reports, as a group, will provide the information that many have been seeking concerning problems intimately related to the life of each of us, as well as to the future of our society.

The authors of these reports have already won distinction in their own fields. Perhaps more important is the fact that their previous work has demonstrated not only the competence but the vigor of thought which these complex problems demand. Knowing, however, that the problems that would be scrutinized—demobilization of the war economy, taxation, monetary policy, international trade, agriculture, and the like—are not separate ones, but are integrated and must be studied in relationship one to the other, the C.E.D. sought to make possible an exchange of information and views by the experts and, equally important, between the scholars and businessmen.

What may be a unique scheme of conferences was established, the objective being to blend the practical experience and judgment of the business world with the scholars' knowledge of the action of economic forces. A Research Committee consisting of representative successful businessmen was set up; to this group was added a Research Advisory Board whose members are recognized as among our leading social scientists; and finally, the persons who would be responsible for the individual reports were named, to comprise the Research Staff.

The subject matter of each report is discussed by the members of these three groups meeting together. "Discussed" in an inadequate term. "Earnestly argued, and for long hours" does more justice to the work. The author of the report therefore has the benefit of criticism and suggestion by many other competent minds. He is able to follow closely the development of the reports on other economic matters that affect his own study.

No effort is made to arrive at absolute agreement. There is no single answer to the problems that are being studied. What is gained is agreement as to the determinative factors in each problem, and the possible results to be achieved by

differing methods of handling the problem. The author
of the report has full responsibility, and complete freedom,
for proposing whatever action or solution seems advisable to
him. There is only one rule—the approach must be from
the standpoint of the general welfare and not from that of
any special economic or political group; the objective must
be high production and high employment in a democratic
society.

Since the author is free to present his own conclusions and
does not speak for the Research Committee or for the Research
Advisory Board, the Research Committee will issue for each
study, where desirable, a separate C.E.D. *policy statement.*
This may endorse all of the recommendations arrived at by
the author, or it may disagree with some.

The research studies already under way divide roughly
into two parts:

A. *The transition from war to peace:* the problems involved in
   the early *attainment* of high levels of employment and
   production;
B. *The longer-term fundamental problems* involved in the
   maintenance of high levels of productive employment
   after the transition period has passed.

The subjects to be covered by the individual monographs
in the two series are:

A. *The Transition from War to Peace:*

1. *The Liquidation of War Production,* by A. D. H. Kaplan,
   The Brookings Institution (already published). The
   problems involved in the cancellation of war contracts and the disposal of government-owned surplus
   supplies, plants, and capital equipment are weighed
   quantitatively as well as qualitatively. How much
   war plant has the government financed, and what part
   of it could be put into civilian production? What

criteria should prevail in selecting the producers to be released first from war manufactures, as the war production program is curtailed? How and when should surplus goods be sold? Rapid resumption of peacetime production, with conditions favorable to high levels of employment, is the gauge by which the recommendations are measured.

2. *Demobilization of Wartime Economic Controls*, by John Maurice Clark, Professor of Economics, Columbia University (already published). When and how should the wartime controls be removed? The interdependency of the wartime controls of production, man power, prices, wages, rationing, credit policies, and others is made clear. How relaxation of each control may affect the peacetime economy —in terms of demand and supply, and therefore in terms of job and production levels—is weighed. The conditions that can be expected to prevail at different stages of the transition from a wartime to a peacetime economy are outlined, with emphasis on the variables with which we must be prepared to deal. Professor Clark does not overlook the significance of attitudes and objectives.

3. *Manpower Demobilization and Reemployment*, by Robert R. Nathan, Consulting Economist, and Emmett H. Welch, Chief, Economic Statistics Unit, Bureau of the Census. The relationship of demobilization policy to reemployment. Recommendations are made for a program that would avoid long-period joblessness among returning servicemen as well as war workers.

4. *Providing for Unemployed Workers in the Transition*, by Richard A. Lester, Associate Professor of Economics, Duke University (already published). An estimate of the size and the duration of transition unemployment. The efficacy of public works employment,

relief employment, the adequacy of unemployment compensation, wartime savings, dismissal pay, and the like are appraised. A program is developed to provide for the maintenance of workers who will be out of jobs in the transition from war to peace.

5. *Financing Industry during the Transition*, by Charles C. Abbott, Associate Professor of Business Economics, Harvard University. The sources upon which business has relied for its capital are examined, along with the current financial condition of large and small corporations. These two are weighed against the likely needs of financing by industry for reconversion and expansion in the transition years following the war.

6. *Monetary and Banking Policies in the Postwar Transition Period*, by John K. Langum, Vice-president, Federal Reserve Bank of Chicago. What monetary and banking policies can do to encourage production and employment. Federal fiscal policy is analyzed in its relationship to the financial requirements of business in reconversion and expansion. The significance of monetary policies prior to the war and the money and banking conditions that will stem from war financing are reviewed. The relationship of business spending to other money flows and the resultant production pattern is discussed.

B. *The Longer-term Fundamental Problems:*

1. *Production, Jobs and Taxes*, by Harold M. Groves, Professor of Economics, University of Wisconsin (already published). A study of the Federal tax structure as it affects the creation of jobs. This is to be followed by a comprehensive report, now in press, on the development of a constructive tax

policy. The larger report inquires into the problems of state and local, as well as Federal, taxation.

2. *Agriculture in an Unstable Economy*, by Theodore W. Schultz, Professor of Agricultural Economics, The University of Chicago (the present volume). An investigation going to the roots of the "farm problem." The significance of excess labor resources on farms, the failure of price mechanisms to induce shifts of resources out of agriculture, the differences between the farm and industrial sectors in responding to reduced demand. The importance to farmers of continued prosperity in business. A solution to the farm problem without resort to price floors or restrictions on output.

3. *International Trade and Domestic Employment*, by Calvin B. Hoover, Dean of the Graduate School of Arts and Sciences, Duke University (already published). An examination of the kind of foreign-trade policies and mechanisms we can adopt that will increase our gains from international trade and also contribute to world peace. A statement of the requirements in terms of the economies of other countries as well as our own.

4. *Business Arrangements in Foreign Trade*, by Edward S. Mason, Professor of Economics, Harvard University. A study of cartels and other forms of international business organizations.

5. *Minimizing Business Fluctuations and Unemployment*, a major series of studies which will be undertaken during the coming year, by John Maurice Clark, K. E. Boulding, M. de Chazeau, Albert G. Hart, Gardiner C. Means, Howard B. Myers, Theodore O. Yntema, and others to be appointed.

6. *The Special Problems of Small Business*, by A. D. H. Kaplan, The Brookings Institution, assisted by J. K. Wexman. An inquiry into the competitive position and the needs of small business.

7. *Providing Adequate Incentives for Enterprise,* by C. E. Griffin, Professor of Business Economics, University of Michigan.
8. *The "Billion Dollar Questions."* By Theodore O. Yntema, Gardiner C. Means, and Howard B. Myers. An economic primer posing the basic economic problems to be faced in a free-enterprise system.

C. *Supplementary Papers:*

1. *The Economics of a Free Society,* by William Benton, Chairman of the Board, Encyclopaedia Britannica, Inc. (published in *Fortune,* October, 1944).
2. *Personnel Problems of the Postwar Transition Period,* by Charles A. Myers, Assistant Professor of Industrial Relations, Massachusetts Institute of Technology (already published). An examination of the problems that will confront employers in connection with the rehiring of servicemen and war workers, and issues that will arise in the shift of the work force from wartime to peacetime production.
3. *Federal Tax Reform,* by Henry C. Simons, Associate Professor of Economics, The University of Chicago. The development of a basic philosophy of taxation to simplify the Federal tax structure and distribute the tax burden among individuals in relation to their incomes.
4. *Incidence of Taxation,* by William Vickrey, formerly Tax Research Division, Treasury Department.
5. *World Politics, Employment and Free Private Enterprise,* by Harold Lasswell, Director of War Communications Research, Library of Congress.
6. *Changes in Substantive Law, Legal Processes and Government Organization to Maintain Conditions Favorable to Competition,* by Corwin Edwards, Professor of Economics, Northwestern University.

These are the subjects so far authorized by the Research Committee of C.E.D. Others may be undertaken at a later date. These subject titles will not necessarily be the same as the book titles when finally published.

EXCERPTS FROM BY-LAWS OF THE COMMITTEE FOR ECONOMIC DEVELOPMENT CONCERNING THE RESEARCH PROGRAM

Section 3. Research Committee.

It shall be the responsibility of the Research Committee to initiate studies into the principles of business policy and of public policy which will foster the full contribution by industry and commerce in the postwar period to the attainment of high and secure standards of living for people in all walks of life through maximum employment and high productivity in the domestic economy. All research is to be thoroughly objective in character, and the approach in each instance is to be from the standpoint of the general welfare and not from that of any special political or economic group.

Publication

The determination of whether or not a study shall be published shall rest solely with the Research Director and the Research Advisory Board. . . . A copy of any manuscript reported for publication shall be submitted to each member of the Research Advisory Board, of the Research Committee, of the Board of Trustees, and to the Chairman and Vice-chairmen of the Field Development Committee. For each subject to be so submitted the Research Director, after consulting with the Chairman of the Research Advisory Board, shall appoint a Reading Committee of three members of the Board. Thereupon, as a special assignment each member of the Reading Committee shall read the manuscript and within fifteen days from its assignment to him shall signify his approval or disapproval for publication. If two out of the three Reading Committee members signify their approval, the manuscript shall be published at the expense of the Corporation. . . . In no case shall publication necessarily constitute endorsement by the Committee for Economic Development, the Board of Trustees, the Research Committee or by the Research Advisory Board of the manuscript's conclusions. Upon approval for publication, the Research Director shall notify all members of the Research Advisory Board and no manuscript may be published until fifteen days following such notification. The interval is allowed for the receipt of any memorandum of comment, reservation, or dissent that any member of the Research Advisory Board may wish to express. Should a member of the Research Advisory Board so request, his memorandum of comment, reservation, or dissent, which must be signed, shall be published with the manuscript. Any signed comment, reservation, or dissent which the Research Director may wish to express or have expressed by others shall at his request be published with the manuscript. . . . In the event the manuscript is not approved for publication at the Corporation's expense as above provided, the individual or group making the research shall nevertheless have the right to publish the manuscript.

Supplementary Papers

The Research Director may recommend to the Editorial Board for publication as a Supplementary Paper any manuscript (other than a regular research report) . . . which in his opinion should be made publicly available because it constitutes an important contribution to the understanding of a problem on which research has been initiated by the Research Committee.

An Editorial Board for Supplementary Papers shall be established consisting of five members: The Research Director, two members from the Research Committee, and two members from the Research Advisory Board. The members from the Research Committee and the members from the Research

Advisory Board shall be appointed by the respective chairmen of those bodies. The Research Director shall be the chairman of the Editorial Board and shall act as Editor of the Supplementary Papers. . . . If a majority of the members of the Editorial Board vote for publication, the manuscript shall be published as one of a series of Supplementary Papers, separate and distinct from the regular research reports. . . . Publication does not constitute endorsement of the author's statements by the Committee for Economic Development, by the Board of Trustees, by the Research Committee, or by the Research Advisory Board.

RESEARCH COMMITTEE

RESEARCH ADVISORY BOARD

INDEX

Index

Index

Income(s), of family workers, 108
  fluctuations in, 1922–39, 65n
  of hired farm worker and industrial
    worker, United States, 1910–
    1943, graph for, 106
  instability of, 5, 9, 47, 70n, 130n,
    209, 211–216
  level of, 2
  per capita, 57, 63, 65n, 70
  per head of working population in
    various countries, table for,
    58n
  rise in, 50
Income elasticity, 44, 51–55, 60–62,
  65–70
Income and expenditure, on farm
  products, table for, 63
Income instability, cause of, 216–219
  diminishing, 219–221
  inherent in farm production, 212–
    214
  origin of, 214
"Index Numbers of Wholesale Prices" in
  the U.S., 1786–1931, by W. F.
  Warren and F. A. Pearson, 63n
India, 46, 48n, 54
Indiana, 213n
"Industrial," 9n
Industrial output, fluctuations in rate
  of, 113–127
  subnormal, negative effects of, 145n
Industrial production, 115, 120, 121,
  122, 125
"Industrialization," 9n
Industrial-urban economy, stabiliza-
  tion of, 219–220
Industries, secondary, 113n, 125–126,
  202–203
Industries, tertiary, 113n, 125–126,
  202–203
"Industry," 9n
Industry, effect of, on agriculture,
  113–127
Inflation, 120, 181
In-plant feeding, 242
Insecticides, 216

Installment payments, 93
Insurance, crop, 41, 169, 217–218
International trade, 83
Iowa, 78, 213n
"Iowa Corn Granary and How It Has
  Affected Hogs in the Corn Belt,
  Our U.S.," by T. W. Schultz and
  O. H. Brownlee, 178n
Iowa study, 173
Iron, 72

J

Jamaica, workers from, 184
Johnson, Albert R., 32n
Johnson, D. G., 78n, 211n, 243n, 256n,
  264n, 265n
Johnson, Sherman E., 77n
Jones, Lawrence A., 32n
Jute, 50n

K

Kaplan, A. D. H., 66, 66n
Kansas, 213n
King, W. I., 63n
Kirk, Dudley, 56n
Kiser, L. K., 56n
Kneeland, H., 67n
Kuznets, Simon, 57, 58, 59

L

Labor, cheap Southern, 251
  distribution of, 85, 88, 128, 129–130
  equilibrium of, 88
  excess of, 9, 82, 91–98, 111, 191
  facilitating movement of, 183–185
  migration of, 82
  redistribution of, 82, 86
  self-employed, 89n
  shortage of, 25
  supply of, 77, 84, 85, 205, 257
  transferable, 85
Lambs, 20

Index

Index